MASSACHUSETTS INSTITUTE OF TECHNOLOGY
RADIATION LABORATORY SERIES
LOUIS N. RIDENOUR, *Editor-in-Chief*

THRESHOLD SIGNALS

THRESHOLD SIGNALS

Edited by

JAMES L. LAWSON
RESEARCH ASSISTANT, GENERAL ELECTRIC RESEARCH LABORATORY
SCHENECTADY, NEW YORK

GEORGE E. UHLENBECK
PROFESSOR OF PHYSICS, UNIVERSITY OF MICHIGAN

OFFICE OF SCIENTIFIC RESEARCH AND DEVELOPMENT
NATIONAL DEFENSE RESEARCH COMMITTEE

PUBLISHED & DISTRIBUTED BY

BOSTON TECHNICAL PUBLISHERS, INC.

5 Bryant Road, Lexington, Massachusetts 02173, U. S. A.

1964

Foreword

THE tremendous research and development effort that went into the development of radar and related techniques during World War II resulted not only in hundreds of radar sets for military (and some for possible peacetime) use but also in a great body of information and new techniques in the electronics and high-frequency fields. Because this basic material may be of great value to science and engineering, it seemed most important to publish it as soon as security permitted.

The Radiation Laboratory of MIT, which operated under the supervision of the National Defense Research Committee, undertook the great task of preparing these volumes. The work described herein, however, is the collective result of work done at many laboratories, Army, Navy, university, and industrial, both in this country and in England, Canada, and other Dominions.

The Radiation Laboratory, once its proposals were approved and finances provided by the Office of Scientific Research and Development, chose Louis N. Ridenour as Editor-in-Chief to lead and direct the entire project. An editorial staff was then selected of those best qualified for this type of task. Finally the authors for the various volumes or chapters or sections were chosen from among those experts who were intimately familiar with the various fields, and who were able and willing to write the summaries of them. This entire staff agreed to remain at work at MIT for six months or more after the work of the Radiation Laboratory was complete. These volumes stand as a monument to this group.

These volumes serve as a memorial to the unnamed hundreds and thousands of other scientists, engineers, and others who actually carried on the research, development, and engineering work the results of which are herein described. There were so many involved in this work and they worked so closely together even though often in widely separated laboratories that it is impossible to name or even to know those who contributed to a particular idea or development. Only certain ones who wrote reports or articles have even been mentioned. But to all those who contributed in any way to this great cooperative development enterprise, both in this country and in England, these volumes are dedicted.

L. A. DuBridge.

Preface

WHEN the plan for this book was made the authors hoped that it would be possible to present a more or less complete account of the experiments and the theoretical ideas pertaining to the problem of the detectability of a signal in noise. However, because it became clear that the literature on the subject was so large and that we had no convenient access to the results of a great deal of work in progress at other institutions, it soon appeared that we would be unable to realize our original plan of giving a critical account of the whole subject. Accordingly we decided to limit ourselves to describing as completely as possible the work done at the Radiation Laboratory during the war, with sufficient introductory material to make the account intelligible. The authors regret that this decision has necessitated the omission of many interesting investigations and calculations.

Another aim of the authors was always to confront the theoretical ideas with the experimental investigations and in this way achieve some kind of unification of theory and experiment, which the authors felt was so often lacking in the existing literature. We feel that we have done so with some success, particularly in Chaps. 8 and 10, though elsewhere we may have fallen short of this aim.

This book is the result of the cooperative effort of many people. On the experimental side many of the investigations were performed by R. Meijer, S. G. Sydoriak, V. Josephson, and especially by R. H. Ashby, L. B. Linford, and A. M. Stone. The latter two have also helped considerably with the editing of the material in this book. On the theoretical side the authors wish to acknowledge the help given by H. Goldstein, A. J. F. Siegert, and Ming Chen Wang. The first two were responsible for most of the work described in Chap. 6 and helped with the writing of that chapter. The theory of the ideal observer described in Chap. 7 was initiated by Dr. Siegert. The authors are especially grateful to Dr. Ming Chen Wang who performed the work described in Chap. 13 and who also helped with the calculations and the writing of nearly all the other theoretical chapters.

Cambridge, Mass.
November, 1949

JAMES L. LAWSON
GEORGE E. UHLENBECK

Contents

CHAPTER 1

INTRODUCTION

The fundamental process in the reception of electromagnetic signals is to make perceptible to the human observer certain features of the incoming electromagnetic radiation. Since perception is the acquisition of information, these features may be called "intelligence" or "information." The electromagnetic wave may contain this information in many ways; the particular method used to abstract it and make it perceptible depends upon the structure of the original radiation.

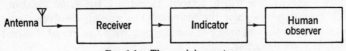

FIG. 1·1.—The receiving system.

A book of this length does not permit adequate discussion of all types of radiation. It is hoped, however, that most of the common types now widely used—principally in the fields of radio, television, communications, and radar—and the process of reception applicable to each can be presented.

To change the characteristics of the signal into a form suitable for human perception, several events must usually take place. The complete system in which this train of events occurs can be conveniently referred to as the receiving system and can be subdivided into four fundamental functional parts as shown in Fig. 1·1.

The Antenna.—The function of the antenna is to convert the electromagnetic energy falling upon it to electric voltages or currents, which appear on the input terminals of the receiver. In some cases it is desirable to consider the antenna as a part of the receiver, since some of the receiver properties are determined by certain properties of the antenna (radiation resistance, etc.).

The Receiver.—The function of the receiver is to select the incoming signal and to change its electrical form in such a way that the output of the receiver contains only the desired parts of the signal. In general, these parts are only those frequencies suitable for human perception. The frequencies perceptible to the ear have become known as audio frequencies, and those visually perceptible as video frequencies. Perhaps 20 kc/sec represents the upper limit of audio frequencies, but video frequencies may be as high as 10 or even 100 Mc/sec, depending upon the indicator.

1

In addition to frequency selection and frequency changing, the receiver must also provide amplification. The incoming radiation is ordinarily feeble and must be greatly amplified in order to actuate the indicator. The total required power amplification in the receiver may for some applications be as high as 10^{15}. Noise and interference limitations prevent its being made as high as one pleases.

The main purpose of this book is to discuss these fundamental limitations and to determine the effect of the various parameters in the receiving system on the detectability of signals.

The incoming signal may be of several types. It therefore follows that the characteristics of the receiver itself must be specialized and are determined by the type of information required from the incoming signal. Because of the general complexity of receivers, furthermore, there are usually several types which perform essentially the same function but which may differ in their limitations. The various receiver types are most conveniently discussed in conjunction with the kinds of signal for which they are designed.

The Indicator.—The output of the receiver consists of voltages or currents containing those desired frequencies in the signal that are suitable for human perception. The function of the indicator is to convert these voltages or currents into audio sound waves or perhaps light patterns that the human observer can perceive. Common forms of indicators are the loudspeaker for radio reception and the cathode-ray oscilloscope for the reception of video signals. There are obviously many ways in which this indication can be presented to the observer. Several alternative methods of indication are mentioned in Sec. 2·6.

The Human Observer.—Human perception of certain signal properties depends not only on what is presented to the observer on the indicator but also on what use he makes of that information. Perception sensitivity will therefore depend on characteristics of the human observer that are not always flexible. The ear, eye, and brain are subject to certain limitations that in many cases restrict the assimilation of useful information. The signal information may, for example, be spread out over a time so long that the human observer cannot integrate the information. His memory is limited; hence he can effectively use information only within a limited time. The human observer must therefore be considered as part of the receiving system. It is even sometimes convenient to express human limitations in terms of certain indicator or receiver parameters. In the example just mentioned the human memory time can be related to an equivalent time constant or bandwidth in the receiver. Similarly, properties of the ear, such as its bandwidth or frequency sensitivity, will be similar to the electrical properties of equivalent filters in the receiver.

CHAPTER 2

TYPES OF SIGNALS AND METHODS FOR THEIR RECEPTION

CONTINUOUS-WAVE SIGNALS

2·1. Unmodulated Continuous-wave Signal.—The simplest form of signal is the so-called unmodulated continuous wave. This is the name given an electromagnetic wave in which the magnitude of the alternating electric field strength is constant in time; for example,

$$\mathcal{E} = \mathcal{E}_0 \cos 2\pi(f_0 t + \alpha_0). \tag{1}$$

Both $\mathcal{E}_0$ and the frequency f_0 are constant. The constant α_0 defines the zero of the time scale, so that

$$\mathcal{E} = \mathcal{E}_0 \cos 2\pi\alpha_0 \qquad \text{at time } t = 0.$$

The characteristics of a c-w signal are therefore constant amplitude, constant frequency, and particular phase at $t = 0$. These conditions cannot be met by any known electromagnetic radiation, since in such a case $\mathcal{E}_0$ must have existed throughout all time. Likewise, if $\mathcal{E}_0$ is not constant, there will be more than a single frequency associated with the wave. This will be shown in Sec. 2·2. Therefore there is no such thing as a monochromatic c-w signal. If $\mathcal{E}_0$ is only slowly varying with time, however, $\mathcal{E}$ will be very nearly monochromatic in frequency. It is convenient to refer to $\mathcal{E}_0$ as the signal-carrier amplitude. The carrier frequency is essentially monochromatic or, more specifically, will contain a frequency band small with respect to the lowest desired audio or video frequency.

The information that can be abstracted from this c-w carrier is very meager. One can only inquire, does the carrier exist or not? And to obtain the answer even to this question may take a long time. To improve the rate at which information can be transmitted, some parameter of the original c-w signal is varied with time or *modulated*. In the usual modulation of a c-w carrier, either a variation of the amplitude (amplitude modulation), a variation of the frequency (frequency modulation), or a variation of the phase of f_0 (phase modulation) may be made. These will be discussed in the next section. The modulating frequencies are, for convenience, those which ultimately become the indicator frequencies, that is, audio or video frequencies, since the human observer most easily abstracts information from them.

The modulating function may be represented by $F(t)$. For audio

3

modulations one wishes to make $F(t)$ correspond to the instantaneous pressure of the modulating sound wave. Since this pressure is normally 1 atm in the absence of sound, it is necessary that $F(t)$ be a constant different from zero in the absence of modulation. The sound pressure may vary upward or downward with audio modulation. For a single audio tone, therefore, $F(t)$ may be represented by

$$1 + \epsilon \cos 2\pi(pt + \beta),$$

where $\epsilon < 1$.

For a complex audio sound, $F(t)$ may be represented by

$$1 + \sum_n \epsilon_n \cos 2\pi(p_n t + \beta_n),$$

where the values of the ϵ's are such that $F(t)$ never becomes negative. If the original sound wave is feeble, the fluctuating part of $F(t)$ may be amplified but must not be made so great that $F(t)$ becomes negative.[1] This amplification is always desirable in practice, since one wishes to make the part of $F(t)$ that contains the intelligence as large as possible with respect to the constant part or carrier that contains essentially no information. For a single audio tone where

$$F(t) = 1 + \epsilon \cos 2\pi(pt + \beta), \tag{2}$$

it is convenient to refer to ϵ as the *fractional modulation* or to 100ϵ as the *modulation percentage*.

If the modulating wave is to represent some other desired characteristic, such as light intensity for television transmission, a constant carrier amplitude may not be necessary. Unlike the sound-wave case, where within the wave itself the pressure can be less than that with no sound, the light intensities reproduced by currents in a photoelectric cell are never less than those produced with no light. In other words, it is never necessary to modulate *downward* from the zero intensity case. Thus $F(t)$ can represent directly the light-intensity values when the photoelectric cell is scanned over the televised scene. A carrier is no longer required to ensure that the complete modulating function be positive. In this case the terms "fractional modulation" and "modulation percentage" are meaningless. The function $F(t)$ can be made as large as one pleases by amplification, until the peak values exceed that which can be supplied in transmission.

---

[1] This restriction is necessary because, as will be shown later in the text, devices designed for reproducing $F(t)$ actually give the *absolute value* of $F(t)$; therefore, in order to reproduce $F(t)$ without distortion, its sign must never reverse.

2·2. Amplitude Modulation.—The incoming wave may be represented by the equation

$$\varepsilon = \varepsilon_0 F(t) \cos 2\pi(f_0 t + \alpha_0), \tag{3}$$

where the carrier field strength ε_0 and the frequency f_0 are constants. The function $F(t)$ represents the modulating function, and α_0 is a phase constant. The *amplitude* of the r-f wave is observed to be modulated by $F(t)$. In general, ε contains none of the frequencies in $F(t)$ but consists of a band of frequencies in the neighborhood of f_0. This band of

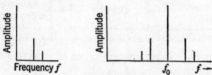

(a) Modulating function   (b) Radio-frequency spectrum
FIG. 2·1.—Sidebands produced by amplitude modulation.

frequencies will be spread over a frequency range just twice as large as the modulating frequencies in $F(t)$. This can be easily shown in the following way. Let

$$F(t) = \left[1 + \sum_n \epsilon_n \cos 2\pi(p_n t + \beta_n) \right]; \tag{4}$$

then

$$\varepsilon = \varepsilon_0 \left\{ 1 + \sum_n \epsilon_n \cos 2\pi(p_n t + \beta_n) \right] \cos 2\pi(f_0 t + \alpha_0) \right\} \tag{5}$$

and

$$\varepsilon = \varepsilon_0 \cos 2\pi(f_0 t + \alpha_0) + \frac{\varepsilon_0}{2} \sum_n \epsilon_n \cos 2\pi \left[(f_0 t + p_n)t + \alpha_0 + \beta_n \right]$$

$$+ \frac{\varepsilon_0}{2} \sum_n \epsilon_n \cos 2\pi[(f_0 t - p_n)t + \alpha_0 - \beta_n]. \tag{6}$$

The carrier term, it should be noted, remains unchanged at frequency f_0 and amplitude ε_0. There are no terms at the modulating frequencies Σp_n, but for each modulating frequency p_n there are two terms in ϵ whose frequencies are $(f_0 \pm p_n)$, respectively. These are commonly referred to as sidebands about the carrier of frequency f_0. The amplitude of each sideband is $\frac{1}{2}\varepsilon_0 \epsilon_n$.

This condition is illustrated in Fig. 2·1, where a modulating function containing two frequencies is assumed. The sideband spectrum is similar to the spectrum of $F(t)$. For a single tone of 100 per cent modulation the sideband amplitude is $\frac{1}{2}\varepsilon_0$. The two sidebands for a single tone, therefore, for any fractional modulation ϵ contain a total power equal to $\epsilon^2/2$ times the carrier power.

A common example of the a-m wave is that used in ordinary broadcast radio transmission. In this case $F(t)$ is simply the audio or speech wave. The input to the receiver from the antenna is essentially an electric voltage $\mathcal{E}_{in}$ that is linearly proportional to the radio-wave field strength $\mathcal{E}$. The function of the receiver is to reproduce the modulating audio function $F(t)$ from the input voltage $\mathcal{E}_{in}$. The reproduction can be accomplished

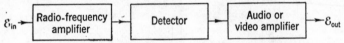

FIG. 2·2.—Elements of a single-detection receiver.

in a variety of ways. Three general types of receivers are used for this purpose.

Single-detection Receiver.—In this type the frequency changing is accomplished by means of a *detector*. The essential parts of the receiver are shown in Fig. 2·2.

The r-f amplifier is used to provide sufficient r-f signal to the detector for the latter to operate properly. The purpose of the detector is to reproduce the audio–modulation function. It will, in general, provide other frequencies that are not wanted. The purpose of the audio or

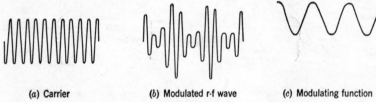

(a) Carrier   (b) Modulated r-f wave   (c) Modulating function

FIG. 2·3.—Amplitude-modulated wave.

video amplifier is to reject all unwanted frequencies and to amplify the desired frequencies until they are of sufficient size to actuate the indicator.

A detector must be a nonlinear device; but as will be shown, nonlinearity is not a sufficient condition for detection. A representation of the a-m r-f wave is shown in Fig. 2·3, where for simplicity the modulating function $F(t)$ is assumed to be composed of a carrier plus a single a-f tone.

It has been shown that the analysis of an r-f wave of this type contains only three frequencies: the carrier radio frequency and two sidebands separated from the carrier frequency by the modulating frequency. It does not, in general, contain the modulating frequency itself; this can be seen by noticing that the average value of the wave, averaged over times corresponding to the modulating function, is essentially zero. If, however, the negative r-f voltages are suppressed without altering the positive voltages, then the average value of the wave will vary according to the modulating function, and detection will occur. Detection will therefore result from a nonlinear device that amplifies negative voltages differently from positive voltages. If the input and output voltages of this nonlinear device are represented by the general power series

$$\mathcal{E}_{\text{out}} = \sum_n g_n \mathcal{E}_{\text{in}}^n, \tag{7}$$

detection takes place only because of the presence of the even terms; that is, $n = 2, 4, \cdots$. The odd terms do not contribute to detection, since for these terms negative or positive input voltages produce negative or positive output voltages, respectively. Thus a pure cubic-law nonlinear device will not be a detector.

Perhaps the simplest detector is the so-called square-law device in which the output voltage is proportional to the square of the input voltage;

$$\mathcal{E}_{\text{out}} = g\mathcal{E}_{\text{in}}^2. \tag{8}$$

As shown previously, $\mathcal{E}_{\text{in}}$ and $F(t)$ may be generally represented by the equations

$$\mathcal{E}_{\text{in}} = \mathcal{E}_0 F(t) \cos 2\pi(f_0 t + \alpha_0), \tag{9}$$

$$F(t) = \left[1 + \sum_n \epsilon_n \cos 2\pi(p_n t + \beta_n) \right], \tag{10}$$

so that

$$\mathcal{E}_{\text{out}} = g\mathcal{E}_0^2 F^2(t) \cos^2 2\pi(f_0 t + \alpha_0), \tag{11}$$

or

$$\mathcal{E}_{\text{out}} = g\mathcal{E}_0^2 \left[1 + \sum_n \epsilon_n \cos 2\pi(p_n t + \beta_n) \right]^2 \left[\frac{1 + \cos 4\pi(f_0 t + \alpha_0)}{2} \right], \tag{12}$$

from which

$$\mathcal{E}_{\text{out}} = g\mathcal{E}_0^2 \left[1 + 2 \sum_n \epsilon_n \cos 2\pi(p_n t + \beta_n) \right.$$
$$\left. + \sum_n \sum_l \epsilon_n \epsilon_l \cos 2\pi(p_n t + \beta_n) \cos 2\pi(p_l t + \beta_l) \right]$$
$$\left[\frac{1 + \cos 4\pi(f_0 t + \alpha_0)}{2} \right]. \tag{13}$$

The frequencies present in $\mathcal{E}_{\text{out}}$ are, therefore, zero (d-c term), p_n, $2p_n$, $p_n + p_l$, $p_n - p_l$, $2f_0$, $2f_0 \pm p_n$, $2f_0 \pm 2p_n$, $2f_0 \pm (p_n + p_l)$, and $2f_0 \pm (p_n - p_l)$. The only terms of interest are the p_n terms and, incidentally, the terms $2p_n$, $p_n + p_l$, and $p_n - p_l$. These four general terms (apart from the d-c term) are the only ones that will fall in the pass band of the audio or video amplifier.   They have amplitude functions at the output of the square-law detector given by $g\mathcal{E}_0^2\epsilon_n$, $g\mathcal{E}_0^2(\epsilon_n^2/4)$, $g\mathcal{E}_0^2(\epsilon_n\epsilon_l/4)$, and $g\mathcal{E}_0^2(\epsilon_n\epsilon_l/4)$, respectively.   Of these four terms the first is the desired one, the second represents second harmonic distortion, and the third and fourth represent *cross-modulation* products.   In general, detection produces cross-modulation terms and harmonic distortion, but it will be noticed in the preceding example that the amplitudes of these undesired terms relative to the desired one are usually quite small.   If the coefficients are small (small modulation percentage), these terms may be neglected in comparison with the desired p_n terms.

In principle the a-m wave can be detected without producing distortions in the modulating function even when the fractional modulation is high.   This is accomplished by means of the so-called linear detector, which passes or amplifies all voltages of one polarity linearly but shows no output at all for input voltages of the opposite polarity.   The average output voltage is therefore linearly proportional to the *envelope* of the r-f wave, which, of course, is related to the modulating function $F(t)$ itself.   The envelope of the modulated wave is not strictly $F(t)$ but represents $F(t)$ only if a sufficient carrier exists to ensure that $F(t)$ is always a positive function.   The envelope, in general, represents the *absolute value* of $F(t)$.   The significance of this will be brought out more clearly in later chapters, but this fact ultimately leads to possibilities of cross modulation even with the envelope detector.

Even though this linear, or envelope, detector reproduces $F(t)$ properly, its characteristic curve is extremely nonlinear at zero voltage.   At this point the curvature is infinite.   Practical detectors are limited in this curvature; therefore the region of small voltages is not similar to that of an ideal linear detector.   For this reason practical linear detectors always operate at high voltage levels and must therefore be preceded by considerable r-f amplification.   Examples of such detectors are diode detectors, infinite-impedance triodes, and high-level anode-bend detectors.

Because of limited curvature in characteristics, low-level detectors are almost invariably square law; examples are crystal detectors, low-level diodes, etc.   If desired, high-level detectors can be made square law, but ordinarily linear detectors are preferred.

Few receivers in common use are of the simple type shown in Fig. 2·3. The difficulties with the single-detection receiver are usually associated with the r-f amplification.   The r-f amplifier must generally be tuned to the desired r-f signal and have considerable over-all gain.   It is usually difficult to construct a tuned r-f amplifier of several stages with proper stability, selectivity, and tuning range.   In widespread use is a type of receiver, the superheterodyne, that overcomes these difficulties.

Superheterodyne Receiver.—The essential elements of a superheterodyne receiver are shown in Fig. 2·4. The r-f signal is fed through an r-f amplifier, whose function will be shortly discussed, to a *mixer, converter,* or "first detector" as it is sometimes called. Into this mixer is also injected the unmodulated output of a local r-f oscillator, whose amplitude at the mixer is made very large compared with that of the incoming r-f signal. The mixer is a detector of one of the two varieties just described, in whose output will be found many frequencies. Besides the incoming

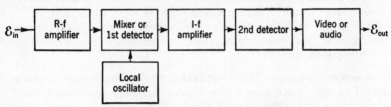

FIG. 2·4.—Elements of a superheterodyne receiver.

frequencies f_0, the modulation sidebands, and the local-oscillator frequency ω, harmonics of these frequencies will be found and, most important, cross terms between the signal frequencies and ω. Either the frequency $f_0 + \omega$ or $|f_0 - \omega|$ can be set to a particular value by tuning the local-oscillator frequency ω. Thus any incoming r-f signal with its modulation sidebands can be converted to a particular *intermediate* frequency with similar modulation sidebands. This i-f signal is then amplified as shown in Fig. 2·4 to a suitable level for proper detection; then the audio or video frequencies are extracted as in the case of the simpler receiver of Fig. 2·3.

Because the amplitude of the local oscillations is large compared with the signal oscillations at the mixer, the amplitude conversion from radio frequencies to intermediate frequencies is essentially linear. The signal oscillations may be regarded as small perturbations on the strong local oscillations. Modulation sidebands are thus exactly the same at the intermediate frequency as they are at the radio frequency, since the system is essentially linear. Furthermore, the so-called *conversion efficiency* of the mixer from radio frequency to intermediate frequency can be very good because of the strong local oscillator. A detailed discussion of the superheterodyne converter appears in the literature.[1]

For a given local-oscillator frequency ω, there are two possible radio frequencies that will combine with ω to form the intermediate frequency. To suppress one of these possible r-f channels, it is customary to place in front of the mixer a simple r-f amplifier tuned to the desired radio fre-

[1] See, for example, K. R. Sturley, *Radio Receiver Design,* Part 1, Chap. 5, Chapman & Hall, London, 1943.

quency (see Fig. 2·4). This process is called *radio-frequency preselection*. For some applications, however, this precaution is not essential.

The principal advantages of a superheterodyne receiver over the simple type shown in Fig. 2·3 are the following:

1. Since most of the gain may be situated in the fixed i-f amplifier, the selectivity and gain of the receiver are essentially independent of the radio frequency.
2. The tuning control (essentially by the local-oscillator frequency) is much simpler than for a gang-tuned series of r-f amplifiers.
3. For the reception of very-high-frequency waves, high receiver gain is much easier to obtain at the relatively low intermediate frequency.

It is possible to extend the treatment to receiver systems that contain several mixers. Each process of *heterodyne* detection or *conversion*, that is, one involving the mixing of r-f signal with a local oscillator, will yield a new i-f signal whose amplitude function is linearly proportional to the amplitude function of the original r-f signal. Many superheterodyne receivers have been built involving two heterodyne detectors. The r-f signal is first converted by means of the first local oscillator to a relatively high first intermediate frequency, which is later converted to a second lower intermediate frequency by a second fixed-tuned local oscillator before final detection takes place. The advantages claimed for the double-superheterodyne receiver are twofold. (1) The first intermediate frequency can be made high with the result that the r-f preselection (preceding the first mixing) becomes much more effective. (2) The high over-all gain in the receiver can be divided between the two intermediate frequencies; hence at no time is it necessary to construct an amplifier at one frequency of extreme over-all gain. This process minimizes the danger of feedback and instability in the amplifier. The principal disadvantage of the double-heterodyne receiver is, of course, its relative complexity.

No matter how many heterodyne detectors are used in a receiver, however, the over-all conversion from r-f voltage to final i-f voltage is linear; if the pass band of the receiver is great enough, the signal amplification will be independent of the modulating frequency. In other words, if the original r-f signal voltage at the input of the receiver is represented by

$$\mathcal{E}_{in} = \mathcal{E}_0 F(t) \cos 2\pi (f_0 t + \alpha_0), \tag{14}$$

where, as before, $F(t)$ is the modulating function and f_0 is the radio frequency, the voltage in the last i-f amplifier will be given by the expression

$$\mathcal{E}_{i-f} \propto \mathcal{E}_{0i-f} F(t) \cos 2\pi (h_0 t + \gamma), \tag{15}$$

where h_0 is the last intermediate frequency and γ is a phase constant determined by α_0 and the phases of the local oscillators. Because of this completely linear relationship, all problems encountered in a superheterodyne receiver can usually be treated in terms of the i-f amplifier and some simple conversion quantity representative of the mixer itself. For example, in problems of noise this quantity, as will be shown in Chap. 5, has to do essentially with the conversion efficiency of the mixer and the noise figure of the i-f amplifier.

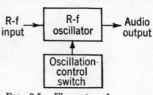

FIG. 2·5.—Elements of a superregenerative receiver.

Superregenerative Receiver.—A superregenerative receiver is one in which the process of great amplification and the process of detection are accomplished within one vacuum tube. The main purpose, therefore, is to provide a high-gain sensitive receiver by the use of a minimum number of tubes. The chief drawbacks of such a receiver are (1) the difficulty of making and maintaining proper adjustment and (2) nonlinear reproduction or distortion.

The method by which high gain and detection are accomplished is shown in its essential form in Fig. 2·5. The r-f input is connected to a tube whose circuits are tuned to the desired signal frequency. An oscillation control switch is used to put this tube into an oscillating condition. As soon as this switch makes a connection, the *condition* for oscillation is established, but the oscillations themselves are not created. They begin to build up, however, from the initial voltage found at the oscillator input (signal voltage in general) and if allowed to proceed would build up to a steady value determined by the power-output capabilities of the oscillator tube. If the gain of the oscillator is constant during the buildup (which implies linear amplification), the oscillation buildup will follow a rising exponential curve that will eventually flatten off at the saturation output value.

In the superregenerative receiver, however, the oscillation control switch is usually turned off before the oscillator reaches a steady value. The final oscillating voltage at the output of the tube depends, therefore, on the value of input voltage (signal) and on the length of time the oscillation control switch is left connected. It is also clear that it depends upon the regenerative gain of the oscillator tube, that is, the regenerative feedback.

As soon as the oscillator control switch is turned off, the oscillations in the r-f input to the oscillator die out exponentially until they reach the value of voltage supplied by the signal. At this point it is possible to start the entire operation again. In practice the oscillation control switch is turned on and off successively at a high rate called the "quench" or "interruption" frequency.   The control switch is in actual practice a quench oscillator that controls the feedback in the r-f oscillator.   The quenching rate must be high, since the sampling of the signal voltage at the start of oscillation buildup must be rapid compared with the modulation frequency.   The input and output voltages in the super-regenerative r-f oscillator are shown diagrammatically in Fig. 2·6.

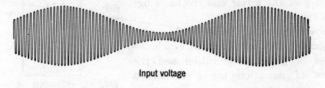

Input voltage

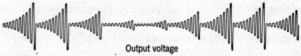

Output voltage

Fig. 2·6.—Input and output voltages in a superregenerative receiver.

In the preceding description of the superregenerative receiver oscillator linearity has been assumed, and under these conditions no detection takes place.   If the oscillator tube is operated in a nonlinear region, however, the average plate current being therefore dependent upon the oscillation, amplitude detection will occur.   The amplification possible from the single tube can, in principle, be increased without limit, since it depends only on how far the oscillations are allowed to increase.   It is for this reason, however, that when the tube is operated at high amplification, the over-all gain is extremely sensitive to the circuit conditions, such as r-f oscillator feedback or interruption frequency.   If these circuit conditions are held constant, however, the output signal will be linearly proportional to the input signal.   For this reason it is common to refer to this method of superregenerative operation as the linear mode of operation.   In this case the buildup curve is a *pure* exponential.   In general, however, linearity is not obtained, since the r-f feedback usually varies during the buildup process.

The r-f oscillator may be operated in a slightly different fashion to alleviate the critical gain adjustment.   This is done by quenching the oscillator *after* it has reached a saturated value.   The time necessary to reach saturation clearly depends on signal size, hence the output voltage will still contain signal intelligence.   The operation is illustrated in Fig. 2·7.   Operation of the tube in a nonlinear region will result in detection, yielding currents containing signal intelligence.   The properties of this method of superregenerative operation and those of the previously described method are somewhat different, particularly with regard to the question of nonlinearity. In the type shown in Fig. 2·6 the output voltage increases essentially linearly with input signal, whereas in the type shown in Fig. 2·7 the output voltage is essentially proportional to the logarithm of the input voltage.

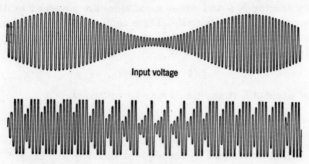

Input voltage

Output voltage

FIG. 2·7.—Input and output voltages of a superregenerative receiver.

2·3. Frequency-modulated C-w Signals.—In the transmission of an f-m r-f signal the amplitude of the r-f signal is held constant, the radio frequency itself being varied in accordance with some desired modulating function $F(t)$. Such a signal may be represented by

$$\mathcal{E} = \mathcal{E}_0 \cos 2\pi \int_{t_0}^{t} [1 + F(t)]f_0 \, dt. \tag{16}$$

There are two important parameters of frequency modulation, namely, the frequencies contained in $F(t)$ itself and the total frequency excursion or deviation, $f_{max} - f_{min}$.

It should be noted that if $F(t) = 0$, the wave is represented by

$$\mathcal{E} = \mathcal{E}_0 \cos 2\pi(f_0 t + \alpha_0) \tag{17}$$

as before, but this is a correct representation only when the frequency is constant. In general, the phase angle of $\mathcal{E}$ will be proportional to the time integral of the frequency, whether or not the frequency itself is constant. The unit constant put under the integral with $F(t)$ plays the same role as that of the carrier with amplitude modulation; that is, it permits "downward" as well as "upward" modulation. It is still necessary to make the quantity $1 + F(t)$ positive at all times. For interference-suppression purposes the frequency excursion, as will be shown in Chap. 13, should be large. The excursion must be small, however, compared with the center frequency f_0, so that several **channels** may be available. For these reasons f_0 is usually made as high as is practicable.

As in the case of amplitude modulation, a modulating frequency p in $F(t)$ produces a carrier and sidebands. The relative numbers and amplitudes of these sidebands are, however, quite different. A single modulating frequency p actually produces an infinite number of sidebands whose frequency spacing is p and whose amplitudes are governed by the frequency excursion and by p itself. These amplitudes are given by Bessel functions J_n of ascending order. If the instantaneous frequency of the modulated wave is represented by

$$f_0(1 + k \cos 2\pi pt),$$

the phase angle of $\mathcal{E}$ at any time t may be written as

$$2\pi \int_0^t f_0(1 + k \cos 2\pi pt)\, dt = 2\pi f_0 t + \frac{kf_0}{p} \sin 2\pi pt,$$

plus a constant determined by the angle at time $t = 0$. Thus

$$\mathcal{E} = \mathcal{E}_0 \cos\left(2\pi f_0 t + \frac{kf_0}{p} \sin 2\pi pt + \alpha_0\right), \tag{18}$$

which may be written in the form[1]

$$
\begin{aligned}
\mathcal{E} = \mathcal{E}_0 \bigg\{ & J_0\left(\frac{kf_0}{p}\right) \cos 2\pi f_0 t \\
& + J_1\left(\frac{kf_0}{p}\right) [\cos 2\pi(f_0 + p) - \cos 2\pi(f_0 - p)] \\
& - J_2\left(\frac{kf_0}{p}\right) [\cos 2\pi(f_0 + 2p) - \cos 2\pi(f_0 - 2p)] \\
& + J_3\left(\frac{kf_0}{p}\right) [\cos 2\pi(f_0 + 3p) - \cos 2\pi(f_0 - 3p)] \\
& - J_4\left(\frac{kf_0}{p}\right) [\cos 2\pi(f_0 + 4p) - \cos 2\pi(f_0 - 4p)] \\
& + \cdots \bigg\}.
\end{aligned}
\tag{19}
$$

The factor kf_0/p is often called the modulation index and represents the ratio of frequency excursion or deviation (from the carrier frequency f_0) to the modulating frequency. In f-m radio practice the modulation index is usually higher than 10.

Equation (19) shows that for each modulating frequency p an infinite number of sidebands exist, separated from the carrier frequency f_0 by

[1] See, for example, B. van der Pol, "Frequency Modulation," *Proc. IRE*, **18**, 1194, July, 1930.

harmonics of p.   For a large index of modulation the important sidebands are those lying within the frequency excursion interval; the Bessel functions of order higher than the argument (modulation index) approach zero rapidly as the order becomes high.   On the other hand, for a low index of modulation few sidebands have an appreciable amplitude; the first (J_1 term) is, apart from the carrier (J_0 term), the only one of appreciable amplitude.   These qualitative effects are illustrated in Fig. 2·8,

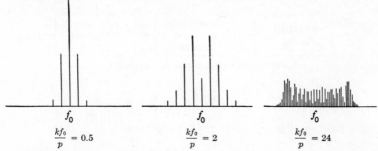

$$\frac{kf_0}{p} = 0.5 \qquad \frac{kf_0}{p} = 2 \qquad \frac{kf_0}{p} = 24$$

(a) Amplitude spectra for f-m waves.   The vertical lines represent the relative amplitudes of the carrier and sideband components.

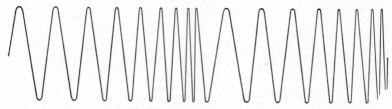

(b) Frequency-modulated wave.
Fig. 2·8.—Frequency modulation; typical waveform and spectra.

which shows amplitude spectra for three typical cases.   In addition to the effects just mentioned it can be seen that for large index of modulation, the density of sidebands is nearly uniform within the excursion interval.   Furthermore the carrier, which varies with $J_0(kf_0/p)$, can vanish for certain values of the modulation index; this situation is quite different from the a-m case.   In Fig. 2·8 the sideband amplitudes are all shown with positive coefficients; the diagrams indicate therefore the absolute values of sideband amplitudes.   This is, of course, the quantity that would be measured by a linear receiver of bandwidth sufficiently narrow to contain only one sideband.

The function of the receiver is to convert the f-m signal into an a-m signal, where it may be converted in the usual manner to an audio or video signal.   In addition to the frequency-to-amplitude converter there is an amplitude *limiter* that removes amplitude fading from the incoming signal; it is also helpful in reducing certain kinds of external interference such as ignition or spark-generated interference.

The frequency-to-amplitude converter ordinarily consists of a discriminator circuit whose output voltage changes linearly not only with the amplitude of the incoming signal but also with its frequency. Since amplitude variations, which may occur in the incoming signal because of fading, are essentially removed by the initial amplitude limiter, the only

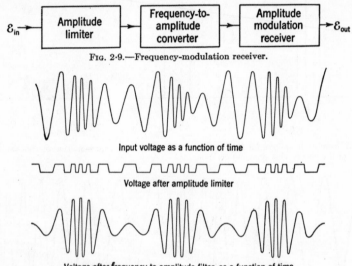

Fig. 2·9.—Frequency-modulation receiver.

Input voltage as a function of time

Voltage after amplitude limiter

Voltage after frequency-to-amplitude filter, as a function of time

Fig. 2·10.—Voltage waveforms in f-m receiver.

thing that can produce amplitude variation of the output signal is the frequency variation of the incoming wave. Once the a-m wave is produced, it is rectified or detected in the usual fashion. A block diagram of an f-m receiver is shown in Fig. 2·9. Typical voltage waveforms occurring at various places in the receiver are shown in Fig. 2·10. It will be noticed that incidental signal fading in amplitude is virtually eliminated. Production of the a-m wave will of course involve changes in radio frequency that will occupy a large frequency band. The a-m receiver must therefore be able to amplify this large band of frequencies before detection takes place; otherwise distortion will occur. The linearity of over-all response is governed almost completely by the linearity of the frequency-to-amplitude converter. This converter, or *slope filter* as it is sometimes called, can be made very nearly linear.

An ideal f-m receiver is therefore essentially insensitive to an incoming

a-m signal.   Likewise an a-m receiver is insensitive to an f-m wave, except
where the bandwidth of the a-m receiver is smaller than the frequency
excursion of the f-m signal.   In this case, because of the slope of the
response curve, the frequency function is converted to an amplitude
function, usually in a nonlinear fashion, and the receiver will not be
insensitive to the f-m signal.

2·4. Phase-modulated C-w Signals.—Phase modulation is in one
sense merely a type of frequency modulation.   The total phase angle of
$\mathcal{E}$ is made to vary in accordance with the modulating wave $F(t)$.   A p-m
wave can therefore be represented by

$$\mathcal{E} = \mathcal{E}_0 \cos 2\pi[f_0 t + \alpha_0 + mF(t)], \tag{20}$$

where m is a constant representing the change in phase angle accompanying a unit change in $F(t)$.   If $F(t)$ is expressible in a Fourier series,

$$F(t) = \sum_n a_n \cos 2\pi p_n t, \tag{21}$$

comparable p-m and f-m representations can be written

$$\mathcal{E} = \mathcal{E}_0 \cos \left[2\pi(f_0 t + \alpha_0) + m \sum_n a_n \cos 2\pi p_n t \right],$$

$$\text{phase modulation;} \quad (22)$$

$$\mathcal{E} = \mathcal{E}_0 \cos \left[2\pi(f_0 t + \beta_0) + kf_0 \sum_n \frac{a_n}{p_n} \sin 2\pi p_n t \right],$$

$$\text{frequency modulation.} \quad (23)$$

These expressions are similar, but they differ in one important respect.
The coefficients of the p_n terms are independent of p_n for phase modulation but are inversely proportional to p_n for frequency modulation.
Phase modulation may therefore be converted to frequency modulation
by placing in the modulator a filter whose gain is inversely proportional
to frequency.   Similarly, frequency modulation may be converted to
phase modulation by placing in its modulator a filter whose gain is proportional to the modulating frequency.   Thus the essential difference
between frequency and phase modulation lies in the characteristic of the filter in the modulator.   The relative advantage of one system over the other
depends on the modulating function $F(t)$ and on the frequency spectrum
of undesired interference.   In actual practice it is customary to use
neither pure phase modulation nor pure frequency modulation.   The
lower audio frequencies are usually frequency modulated, and the higher
frequencies are phase modulated.   Appropriate filters in the receiver
straighten out the frequency characteristic.

PULSED SIGNALS

2·5. Infinite Pulse Trains.—Systems have been developed in which the reception of a series or train of r-f pulses is of primary interest. The fields of radar and pulsed communication utilize such pulse trains. In principle the pulsed function could be amplitude, frequency, or phase, and methods for reception would follow lines suggested in the preceding sections. Because of the great use made of amplitude pulsing, however, and the insignificant use made at present of frequency or phase pulsing,

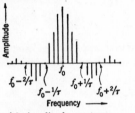

(*a*) Amplitude spectrum

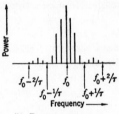

(*b*) Power spectrum

FIG. 2·11.—Frequency spectrum of infinite pulse train.

this book will treat only the case of amplitude pulsing. The phase relations of the amplitude pulses may be important, of course, and this relationship will be considered where necessary, but the essential feature is one of amplitude pulsing.

The amplitude pulses, it is assumed, are repeated at a rate denoted here by the pulse repetition frequency, or PRF. If the pulse train is infinite in extent, the frequency spectrum can be computed by conventional methods in Fourier analysis. Denote the pulse train by $F(t)$; then

$$F(t) = \sin 2\pi f_0 t \sum_{k=0}^{\infty} \Delta_k(t), \qquad (24)$$

where

$$\Delta_k(t) \begin{cases} = 1 & \text{for } \left(\dfrac{k}{f_r} - \dfrac{\tau}{2}\right) < t < \left(\dfrac{k}{f_r} + \dfrac{\tau}{2}\right), \\ = 0 & \text{otherwise.} \end{cases}$$

In this expression, f_r denotes the PRF, and τ the pulse length. A Fourier development of Eq. (24) shows that

$$F(t) = \sin 2\pi f_0 t \left(f_r \tau + \frac{2}{\pi} \sum_{n=1}^{\infty} \frac{\sin \pi n f_r \tau}{n} \cos 2\pi n f_r t \right) \qquad (25)$$

or

$$F(t) = \sum_{n=0}^{\infty} \frac{(2 - \delta_{n,0})}{2} \frac{\sin \pi n f_r \tau}{\pi n} [\sin 2\pi (f_0 + n f_r) t + \sin 2\pi (f_0 - n f_r) t], \qquad (26)$$

where the symbol $\delta_{n,0}$ is equal to unity when $n = 0$; otherwise it equals zero.

This equation is illustrated in Fig. 2·11 for a situation in which $f_0 \gg f_r$. It can be seen that apart from the carrier frequency f_0, there are a host of sideband frequencies separated from f_0 by multiples of f_r; these are the only frequencies present and have amplitudes determined by Eq. (26).[1]

A good deal of information is contained in such a train of pulses. The PRF, phase of pulses, etc., could be ascertained if required. If the quantity to be determined is merely the *existence* of the pulse train, however, a complete analogy can be drawn to the c-w case of Sec. 2·1. The amplitude pulse train is a kind of carrier, which in itself contains little information. It may, however, be modulated to increase the information that can be transmitted and, as in previous cases, may be modulated in amplitude, radio frequency, or phase. In addition, it is possible to modulate it by varying the PRF or by varying the pulse length or width. These methods of modulation as well as methods for detection will be discussed in later sections.

2·6. Finite Pulse Trains.—In radar applications a transmitter is made to send out r-f energy in a succession of pulses. The frequency of the radio wave itself may be extremely high, and the duration of a single pulse may be only a few microseconds. Occasionally a system is made where the pulse duration, or length, is as small as 0.1 μsec. The pulses are repeated at an audio rate, that is, from perhaps 50 to 10,000 pps. The pulses of r-f energy are sent out into space perhaps omnidirectionally but more usually concentrated or focused in certain regions by a directional antenna system. Objects in these regions will reflect or scatter the radiation. Some of this scattered energy is picked up by a receiving system usually located near the transmitter. The receiver must be capable of passing to the indicator the video pulses, that is, the detected r-f pulses that correspond to the scattered or reflected pulses of r-f energy. One of the major difficulties in the radar problem is to make the receiving system sufficiently sensitive to detect the scattered r-f energy of objects several miles away. The limitation in sensitivity is generally imposed by noise of some sort generated within the receiver (see Chap. 5), or governed by external interference (see Chap. 6).

The fundamental purpose of the radar set is to provide information

---

[1] This development requires that the successive pulses have a defined r-f phase, as though they were determined from a master c-w oscillator of frequency f_0. The subsequent chapters of this book deal only with pulse trains in which the phase from pulse to pulse may or may not be random; it makes no difference in the reception process for amplitude pulses, since the output of any detector is insensitive to r-f phase. The mathematical specification for a train of r-f pulses having random phases is different from Eq. (24), however; the sine term will contain, in addition, a random phase angle dependent upon the index k.

that permits the human observer to locate objects of particular interest. With a directional antenna system the azimuth and elevation of search are known; and by the system of pulses, the range of or distance to a reflecting object can be found.   This range is measured by the time difference between the transmitted pulse and the received echo pulse.   Since the angular location of the reflecting object requires a directional radiator, a general search of the entire region requires some sort of *scanning*.   The scanning or searching motion of the antenna system is usually reproduced in some form within the indicator, so that easy correlation of the presence of a particular echo with a particular azimuth or elevation can be made by the observer.   Because of the scanning action, the return signal reflected from an object consists of a *finite* train of r-f pulses.   This train of pulses is, of course, repeated at the next scan.

The scanning can be accomplished in many ways, and the pulse video information at the output of the receiver can be presented on the indicator in many ways.   The method of scanning is dictated by both the function of the radar set and mechanical considerations for moving the antenna assembly.[1]   The method of indication is usually one that makes the radar information most intelligible to the observer.   Some of the more common indicators used are listed below for reference.

The Type A or Linear Time-base Oscilloscope.—This indicator[2] consists of a cathode-ray oscilloscope in which the video signals from the receiver are impressed upon the vertical deflection plates and a linear sawtooth sweep voltage is applied to the horizontal deflection plates.   This horizontal sweep is usually started by the initial impulse from the radar transmitter and is made to move across the oscilloscope at a rate convenient for radar range measurements.   The next transmitted impulse starts the sweep over again.   Thus, near-by objects that scatter the r-f energy will cause a visual vertical deflection, or "pip" (also called "blip"), near the starting edge of the sweep; a reflecting object at a distance will produce a pip at a horizontal position corresponding to the range of the object.   Thus the linear time base provides a range measurement of objects scattering the r-f pulses.   The amplitude of the video deflection, or pip, is a measure of the effective scattering cross section of the object in question.   It is also a function of the range of the object, because of geometrical factors, and a function of the over-all sensitivity of the radar set.   The type A oscilloscope thus essentially provides information about the range of an object and some information as to its "radar" size.   It does not give azimuth or elevation information, but this can always be obtained from separate dials geared to represent the antenna coordinates.   Because of the time necessary for the observer to

[1] See *Radar Scanners and Radomes*, Vol. 26, Radiation Laboratory Series.
[2] See *Cathode Ray Tube Displays*, Vol. 22, Radiation Laboratory Series.

coordinate the A-scope range with elevation and azimuth, the system is not well suited to rapid scanning or search. It is most useful in the measurement of radar range on systems that have a broad antenna-radiation pattern and either do not scan at all or scan relatively slowly. This type of indication, however, is sensitive in the detection of weak echoes.

In addition to other obvious advantages, a radar can give far more precise range information than an optical range finder. The radar range error can, unlike the optical, be independent of the range itself and can be made as small as a tenth of the equivalent range represented by the pulse length. For high precision the sweep on the A-scope would have to be extremely linear and well calibrated or some other marking device provided. It is customary to provide *range* marks, or a series of sharp timing "pips," to mark the sweep at convenient intervals. If extreme precision is required, a movable delayed-timing pip is provided whose time delay is calibrated and accurately known. It may be generated from a crystal-controlled oscillator. This timing pip can be made to coincide with the desired radar echo, whose accurate range can thus be determined. Where the sweep length is very long in comparison with the pulse length as presented, it is difficult to see the relative positions of the echo pip and timing pip. For this purpose an especially fast horizontal sweep may be provided. Such an oscilloscope is known as an *R-scope* (range). It is merely an A-scope in which the start of the sweep may be accurately delayed and the sweep speed made sufficiently great to delineate the desired echo and timing pip. The R-scope is also useful in examining the character of the returned echo pulse or pulses and is generally more sensitive than the A-scope in the detection of extremely feeble echoes.

The Type B Oscilloscope.—This indicator was initially developed to add azimuth information to what was presented on the A-scope; this was done by impressing the video signals from the receiver on the control grid of the cathode-ray oscilloscope. The video signals therefore modulate the beam current in the oscilloscope and consequently the intensity of light output. Under these conditions the vertical plates of the oscilloscope are left free. It is necessary only to impress on these plates a voltage that corresponds to the azimuth of the radar antenna. As the antenna is made to scan in azimuth, the trace of the time-base sweep is made to move up and down in synchronism with the antenna position. This type B oscilloscope therefore produces on its screen a bright spot whose position in range and azimuth on the oscilloscope face corresponds to the actual range and azimuth of a reflecting object. It is therefore a radar map, differing from the usual map by a distortion caused only by the particular coordinates chosen. Like the "deflection-modulated" type A oscilloscopes, "intensity-modulated" oscilloscopes such as type B are very sensitive in the detection of weak echoes; but the intensity-modulated oscilloscopes are much better adapted for scanning systems. Because it is convenient to view the oscilloscope face like a map, and because the radar-scanning frequencies are generally below the flicker frequency for the human eye, it is customary to use for the screen of the cathode-ray tube a special material whose light output decays relatively slowly with time.

The Plan-position Indicator, or PPI.—This is the name given an intensity-modulated oscilloscope in which the time-base sweep is made to start at the center of the tube and move radially outward. The azimuth of this radial sweep on the oscilloscope is made to correspond to the azimuth of the radar antenna. This type of sweep is usually provided by a magnetic deflection yoke placed around the neck of the cathode-ray tube. As the antenna is scanned in azimuth, the magnetic yoke is synchronously rotated about the axis of the tube. This synchronization is easily accomplished by driving the yoke by a synchro motor or some other remote mechanical synchro-transmission device. Thus the PPI provides a map of all radar echoes, where the map scale factor is merely the ratio of twice the velocity of the radio wave to the sweep speed. Because of the ease with which a true map can be interpreted, the PPI is an ideal indicator for use with radar sets searching continuously in azimuth. Intensity-modulated range marks are generally provided for calibration purposes. They appear as concentric brightened rings at regularly spaced radial intervals.

The Range-height, or RH, Indicator.—Neither the type B oscilloscope nor the PPI can present elevation information, and for radar sets whose function is height-finding some other indicator is desirable. Without recourse to a three-dimensional intensity-modulated indicator, which has not yet been devised, the presentation of elevation information requires the omission of either azimuth or range information. If the azimuth information is suppressed, an indicator presenting range and height, or RH oscilloscope, can be provided. The radar antenna is made to nod or oscillate in elevation angle. The angle of the deflection yoke in an oscilloscope of the PPI variety is made to follow the antenna elevation angle in such a way that the indicator presents a true radar map of a particular vertical section of space. Thus the RH indicator will present true range and height of radar targets, neglecting, of course, the curvature of the earth's surface. The range and height scales can, if necessary, be expanded or contracted to provide convenient values.

The Type C Indicator.—If the range information is suppressed, an indicator presenting azimuth and elevation information, or type C indicator, can be provided. Because the range information is suppressed, the indicator will show a bright spot on its screen at an elevation and azimuth where a radar-reflecting object exists at any range. This is the radar presentation which most closely approximates a visual picture of the surroundings. It is probably one of the least useful radar presentations, however, since it does not utilize the one parameter, that is, range, given best by the radar set. There are usually a tremendous number of radar-reflecting objects at any prescribed azimuth and elevation, and it is useful to select preferentially particular ones for presentation of the type C indicator. This selecting is made possible by a variable range "gate," or "strobe," which sensitizes the indicator only for echoes occurring within a defined range interval. The gate may be set at any range, and its length adjusted to correspond to any required range interval. Gating not only is useful for type C indicators but is often widely used where the video impulse from a single target is to be selected and used to control other circuits, perhaps even the coordinates of the radar antenna itself. The type C indicator is less sensitive to the detection of weak echoes than the PPI or type A or B oscilloscopes.

Aural Perception.—The presence of the video pulses at the output of the receiver may be indicated aurally to the human observer. One way of accomplishing this is to put the video signals into an audio loudspeaker, then listen for the audio tone produced by the PRF. When this method of detection is used, all radar range information is lost unless the incoming signals are gated in order to pass to the loudspeaker only those signals which occur within a desired range interval. This aural detection of the PRF component is surprisingly sensitive and very useful in recognizing signals from a particular radar set, since the PRF's of various installations may differ markedly. The ear appears to be very sensitive to changes in pitch or tone.

Meter Detection.—By still another method of perception, the aural signals are rectified and impressed on an ordinary d-c meter and the presence of a signal determined by the meter deflection. If this method is adopted, both radar range information and information about the PRF are lost but, as in the case of aural detection, the video signals may be gated. It might be argued that meter and aural detection methods are equivalent, but this equivalence is not easy to show. The use of the rectifier or detector in producing the meter deflection gives rise to possible cross modulation. This will be discussed in Chap. 9.

Types of Receivers Used.—The function of the radar receiver is to provide pulsed video signals from the incoming series of r-f pulses. In principle the three types of receivers mentioned in Sec. 2·2 may be used, but some remarks on the usefulness of each type can be made. The simple single-detection receiver is useful principally where the receiver is to be made sensitive to a large r-f band. In this case no r-f amplification is used; detection is accomplished at low level and is thus necessarily square law. Because of the low detection sensitivity of the square-law detector, most of the signal energy is lost, the remainder being forced to compete with noise produced after detection. For this reason this type of receiver is not so sensitive as the superheterodyne for weak signals, perhaps by a factor of 10^4 in power. However, the r-f bandwidth can be made several hundred megacycles per second in extent.

The superheterodyne receiver is almost universally used in radar applications, because it has better sensitivity than the single-detection receiver and better stability than the superregenerative receiver. At the very high frequencies the r-f amplification, because of its limitations and difficulties, is not customarily used, but the r-f signal is usually immediately converted into an i-f signal. The i-f amplifier therefore has a relatively great voltage gain, perhaps as much as 10^6, weak signals being, as a result, made suitably large for linear detection or rectification. This amplification must be of such a nature that it has a satisfactory response to the desired pulses. From Fig. 2·11 it can be seen that most of the energy in the pulses is concentrated in a band of frequencies roughly equal to the reciprocal of the pulse length. Therefore the r-f and i-f bandwidths must each be of the order of magnitude of the reciprocal of pulse length. Since the pulse lengths in use vary from 10^{-7} to 10^{-5} sec, the bandwidths must be of the order of 10^5 to 10^7 cps. This is the chief difference between receivers made for radar pulses and those made for radio transmission, the latter being designed to pass only audio frequencies.

Some superregenerative receivers have been constructed for pulse reception. The quench frequency must be high compared with the reciprocal of the pulse length to make sampling sufficiently frequent. For pulse lengths of less than 1 μsec, this has been found difficult to do. Furthermore the criticalness of adjustment has greatly restricted the usefulness of such receivers. Nevertheless, certain of their properties, such as high gain over satisfactory bandwidths, necessitate taking them into consideration.

In all these methods of reception the main object of perception is to become aware of the existence of the incoming r-f signal. The question is not one involving the detailed analysis of the signal characteristics but simply whether or not the signal exists. As pointed out in Sec. 2·5, it is often useful to consider the detection of a series of pulses that are modulated in some manner at a slow rate. The information one wishes to abstract from this type of signal is the relatively slow modulation function appearing in the pulse train, in much the same way that one wishes to abstract the modulating function from an a-m or f-m c-w signal.

2·7. Amplitude-modulated Pulse Trains.—There are two reasons why it is useful to consider the perception of the modulation function of a modulated pulse train. First of all, the echoes obtained in radar reception are indeed modulated by changes in the characteristics of the target under surveillance. The effective scattering cross section of the target may vary with time because of changes in the target aspect or position; it may also vary in a way characteristic of the particular target itself. For example, propeller rotation on an aircraft will give rise to a periodic change in its effective radar scattering cross section. Information concerning the modulation of received pulsed echo trains may therefore be helpful in deriving information concerning the nature of the target. As another example, one can see that the phase of the returned radar echo depends upon the total path length taken up by the radio wave and therefore changes markedly with target movement. By a phase-detection scheme a modulating function that depends on target speed can thus be derived. The phase changes brought about by target movement can be conveniently measured by one of two general methods. The coherent-pulse system mixes the incoming echoes with a strong local c-w generator whose phase is reset to the phase of the transmitted pulse each time it is produced. The resulting echo amplitude will be constant from pulse to pulse unless the target in question moves during this time interval by an amount that is appreciable with respect to the wavelength of the r-f signal. As the target moves, the echo will be seen to beat up and down with a frequency given by the Doppler shift. By analyzing the phase modulation of the return pulses, therefore, information concerning radial target speed can be derived.

A second method of phase detection is possible. Instead of utilizing the local source of phased c-w oscillations, the echo from the moving target is mixed with other strong echoes from fixed targets. Again beats in the echo amplitude are obtained in the same way as for the coherent-pulse system. The presence of these beats depends, however, upon the presence of local fixed echoes at the same range as the target. Since this condition is not under the observer's control, the system has a limited area of usefulness. It is, however, much simpler than the coherent-pulse system.

One of the main uses for modulated pulse trains, however, lies in their application to specialized communication systems. Such systems have the advantage of highly directional propagation characteristics and a high degree of security. In these systems a continuous succession of pulses modulated at speech frequencies is sent out. As pointed out in Sec. 2·5, the modulation itself may be applied to the pulses in several different ways. Amplitude modulation will be discussed in this section, and other types of modulation in Sec. 2·8.

The amplitudes of the continuously recurring pulses are assumed to vary in accordance with the modulating function. If the modulating function is one that can take on both positive and negative values with respect to its normal or quiescent value, there must be provided, as in previous examples, a carrier term large enough to prevent the entire amplitude function from reversing sign. The function of the receiver is to obtain the modulation function from the relatively complicated train of incoming pulses. The first step in the chain of events is the detection of the r-f signal to provide video pulses, just as in the case of normal radar echo detection. Since distortion of the modulating function is undesirable, linear detection is greatly preferred; and for the sake of sensitivity, a superheterodyne receiver should be used. The amplitudes of the video pulses are still slowly modulated by the modulating function. The possibility of gating the pulses at this point makes this type of communication system much more secure than the ordinary a-m c-w signal. The proper video pulses can be selected by a gate whose PRF is the same as that of the desired signal and whose timing is made to coincide with the pulses either by a special timing pulse or by automatic locking voltages derived from the incoming pulses themselves. The sensitivity of the receiver to weak signals in noise is affected by gating and by the gate length itself. This point will be discussed in Chap. 10.

The spectrum of the pulses can be derived in a straightforward fashion. Let us represent the modulating wave $F(t)$ by the function

$$F(t) = 1 + \epsilon \sin 2\pi p(t + \delta), \tag{27}$$

where ϵ is the fractional modulation and p is the modulating frequency. This function is now to represent the amplitude of the pulse train, which has a PRF denoted here by f_r and pulse lengths indicated by τ. For the sake of simplicity it is supposed that the pulse amplitude at the start of the pulse will assume the value of $F(t)$ and that the pulse amplitude is maintained constant throughout each pulse. That is, the signal function will be given by

$$F_s(t) = \sum_k F\left(\frac{k}{f_r}\right) \Delta_k(t). \tag{28}$$

where

$$\Delta_k(t) = \begin{cases} 1 & \text{for } \dfrac{k}{f_r} < t < \dfrac{k}{f_r} + \tau, \\ 0 & \text{otherwise.} \end{cases}$$

The Fourier development of $F_s(t)$ becomes

$$F_s(t) = \tau f_r + \epsilon \frac{f_r}{\pi p} \sin \pi\tau p \sin (2\pi pt - \pi\tau p + 2\pi p\delta)$$

$$+ \frac{1}{\pi} \sum_{l=1}^{\infty} \left\{ \frac{2 \sin \pi l \tau f_r}{l} \cos 2\pi l \left(f_r t - f_r \frac{\tau}{2}\right) \right.$$

$$+ \frac{\epsilon f_o}{l f_r + p} \sin \pi\tau(l f_r + p) \sin [2\pi(l f_r + p)t - \pi\tau p + 2\pi p\delta]$$

$$+ \left. \frac{\epsilon f_o}{l f_r - p} \sin \pi\tau(l f_r - p) \sin [2\pi(l f_r - p)t + \pi\tau p - 2\pi p\delta] \right\}. \tag{29}$$

It can be seen that, in general, many frequencies are present in $F_s(t)$, namely, all the harmonics of the PRF f_r and cross terms between these harmonics and the modulating frequency p. The amplitude of any term of frequency f is modified by the familiar $(\sin \pi \tau f)/\pi \tau f$ because of the pulse length τ. A convenient chart for reading off all frequencies present is shown in Fig. 2·12. Output frequencies are given on the abscissa scale for any input modulating frequency chosen on the ordinate scale. The

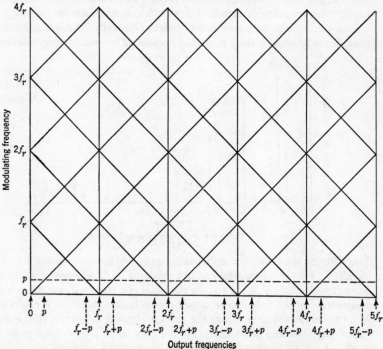

FIG. 2·12.—Output frequencies for a given modulating frequency.

output frequencies present are those which appear at the intersections of a horizontal line, whose ordinate is the modulating frequency p, with the array of diagonal lines and vertical lines shown in the diagram. An example is shown by the dotted line drawn for $p = f_r/4$; the output frequencies are shown to be $\Sigma \, lf_r$ and $\Sigma \, (lf_r \pm f_r/4)$.

The diagram shown in Fig. 2·12 is not suitable for indicating the intensities of the various components. A simple rule to remember is to consider that all intersections with diagonal lines yield amplitudes which are ϵ times those of the vertical lines. Furthermore, *all* intersections are modified according to the individual pulse spectrum $(\sin \pi \tau f)/\pi \tau f$ and therefore fall off with increasing frequency. A typical spectrum is shown in Fig. 2·13, where $f_r\tau = 0.2$ and $p = f_r/4$ as shown in Fig. 2·12. The frequencies shown with dotted lines are those caused by the modulation itself.

It would be possible to put the video pulses directly into a loud-speaker and derive sound that contains the modulating function (see Fig. 2·13). It would also contain many undesired and extremely annoy-ing frequencies. These undesired frequencies are all higher than the modulating frequencies provided $p < f_r/2$ and can thus be filtered out before going into the loudspeaker itself. Generally, the desired audio component must be greatly amplified because of its small energy content.

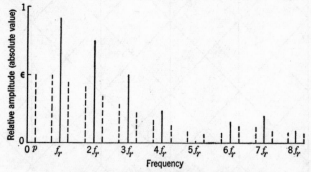

Fig. 2·13.—Video spectrum of modulated pulse train.

The filtering and audio amplification may be greatly helped by the so-called "boxcar" generator, or demodulator. This device consists of an electrical circuit that clamps the potential of a storage element, such as a capacitor, to the video pulse amplitude each time the pulse is received. At all times between the pulses the storage element maintains the poten-tial of the preceding pulse and is altered only when a new video pulse is produced whose amplitude differs from that of the previous one. The name "boxcar generator" is derived from the flat steplike segments of the voltage wave.

The output of the boxcar generator is given by Eq. (29) (by putting $\tau = 1/f_r$) and can also be obtained from Fig. 2·13. It can be seen that *none* of the lf_r terms remain except the d-c term. The output frequency present at the modulating frequency p is also incidentally much amplified because of the increased pulse length. The output voltage, however, still does contain at reduced amplitude the cross-modulation terms. Nevertheless, the main body of interfering audio frequencies has been removed, and therefore the problem of additional filtering is greatly simplified. The boxcar generator can be used only on gated systems, unfortunately, or at least on systems from which an accurately timed clamping pulse is available.

If cross-modulation terms in the output must be avoided, the highest modulation frequency must be substantially less than one-half of the PRF f_r. If a filter is used to separate the output frequencies, it will have a cutoff or attenuation curve that is not infinitely sharp; therefore the maximum value of p must be further restricted. If p is limited to $f_r/3$, then one octave exists for the filter to achieve its cutoff value. This is considered to be an acceptable value. It will be noticed that this restriction will apply to *all* of the pulsed communication schemes, since it follows directly from the effect of sampling the signal voltage at discrete times.

Before proceeding to other forms of modulation, the part played by various detection processes should be considered. The first detection process (actually the so-called "second detection" in a superheterodyne receiver) reduces the r-f voltage to a video voltage. This provides a measure of the intensity of the r-f wave without regard to its exact r-f structure. This video voltage still varies at a fairly high rate and may contain *modulation* intelligence. An additional detection process, that is, boxcars with audio filtering, will bring out the modulation frequencies. Still another, or fourth, detection can be provided. This one measures the average intensity of these audio voltages; that is, it measures the fractional modulation ϵ. Thus the detection process is one that principally provides a measure of the average intensity of a function. Because of this averaging process, the frequencies present in successive detections become progressively lower.

One more point regarding the demodulated signal should be noted. The video output is a measure of the signal size and can therefore be used as a signal-actuated control voltage. It is sometimes convenient to use this voltage to control the gain of the receiver. This control must clearly be made of such a sign that an increase in video signal will reduce the receiver gain; otherwise the system will be regenerative. With this degenerative system, the receiver gain tends to maintain the average output signal constant in size regardless of input signal size. The action of this type of automatic gain control, or AGC, will be described in Chap. 11.

When the AGC does not need to be rapid, an ideal arrangement is to use the output of the boxcar generator as the feedback control voltage. This arrangement is shown in block form in Fig. 2·14, where all the parts are self-explanatory with the exception of the filter between the third detector and gain-control lead. The function of this filter is essentially to pass only the d-c component to the gain control lead, thus effectively removing the desired modulation frequencies. In this fashion these modulating frequencies themselves are not degenerated in the receiver.

If the filter passes the modulating frequencies, they will be degenerated and greatly reduced in amplitude at the receiver output. They are not, in general, completely degenerated because of the finite change in output signal required to cause a change in receiver gain. For some applications this finite degeneration is not serious, since audio amplification will restore the amplitude of the modulation signal. In addition, because of the rapid feedback, the speed of AGC is greatly increased. The filter, however, must considerably attenuate the PRF, or oscillation will develop because of the cross terms of Fig. 2·12.

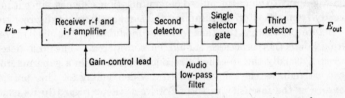

Fig. 2·14.—Audio-modulation receiver with automatic gain control.

2·8. Other Types of Modulation. *Pulse-length or Pulse-width Modulation.*—In this case the modulation is accomplished by variations in pulse length. The PRF and the pulse amplitude are held constant. Reception consists of detecting the r-f pulses, then converting the length variations to amplitude variations. As pointed out in Sec. 2·7, the PRF must be at least three times that of the highest modulating frequency, and a low-pass filter must be used to exclude undesired cross terms.

The conversion from pulse length to amplitude is most easily accomplished by passing the signal through a filter of limited pass band. Through such a filter, if its bandwidth is considerably less than the reciprocal of the maximum pulse length, the output response will have an amplitude proportional to the product of input pulse length and amplitude. This operation can be accomplished in the r-f and i-f sections of the receiver before detection takes place. It is most convenient, however, to *limit* the incoming signals (usually done most easily after detection) before converting the pulses to amplitude-modulated signals. The limiter plays the same role as the limiter for f-m radio (see Sec. 2·3); that is, it eliminates amplitude variations in received signals produced by fading and reduces interference of a type in which peak voltages are very high. The bandwidth of the receiver in front of the limiter should be adequate to pass the shortest pulse properly. From Fig. 2·11 it can be seen that the bandwidth should exceed the reciprocal of the shortest pulse length.

In addition to peak limiting, it is usually desirable to provide a lower limit below which no output signal occurs. If the input signals fall below some defined minimum level, noise or interference in the receiver renders them useless. Therefore a lower limit, which excludes this noise, is beneficial. The presence of both a lower and upper limiter constitutes a "slicer," so named because the output voltage is proportional to the input voltage only within a narrow voltage range or slice. The sliced output of the length-modulated pulses will consist of a series of relatively "clean" constant-amplitude length-modulated pulses suitable for immediate conversion to a-m pulses.

As in the case of a-m pulses, gating can be employed within the limits of pulse lengths used. A gate length as long as the longest pulse must be used; this would appear to favor slightly the use of a-m pulses where accurate gating of a size equal to the pulse length at all times is possible.

Frequency or Phase Modulation.—In this type of modulation one can think first of an ordinary f-m or p-m continuous wave as described in Secs 2·3 and 2·4. The pulses merely select short segments out of this r-f wave; they therefore bear defined frequency and/or phase changes determined by the original modulation. The process of reception consists of limiting the pulses, then passing them through a frequency-to-amplitude slope filter. From this point they are handled like a-m pulses. The pulse frequencies spread out over a band about equal in width to the reciprocal of the pulse length. Therefore the frequency deviation should be made large compared with this band of frequencies. In the true pulsed case, it is not really essential that the phase of the r-f signal which is being frequency modulated be accurately defined at the start of each pulse, since the frequency-to-amplitude converter is itself insensitive to phase. Unlike the case of f-m continuous waves, the starting phase of each pulse may be made random because of the dead time between pulses; no difficulties are caused thereby with f-m pulses, but phase-modulation schemes are, of course, upset. Likewise schemes can be considered in which the phase is modulated *without* changing the center frequency during each pulse. Such modulation is again made possible by the discontinuity between pulses; either frequency or phase can be arbitrarily set. For the detection of the phase modulation, a scheme similar to that discussed in Sec. 2·6 can be used. One may use a coherent local c-w source whose frequency is that of the pulses and whose phase is in quadrature with the pulse phase in the absence of a modulating signal, that is, carrier present only. As can be seen, variations in pulse phase caused by modulation, for small phase changes, will cause amplitude changes substantially proportional to these phase changes. These a-m pulses are then handled in the usual manner.

Modulation of PRF.—In this scheme the variable that is modulated is the PRF itself. The maximum range of variation is kept smaller than one octave to prevent harmonics of the lowest PRF from interfering with the highest frequency. As in the other sampling schemes the average

PRF must be about three times as high as the highest desired modulating frequency. Detection of the pulses is made in the usual way. The audio output is obtained by putting the video signals into a filter designed to pass only the audio frequencies. It should be remembered that since the incoming signal amplitude is constant, limiting and slicing can be employed; but because of the variable PRF, gating is impossible.

Other Schemes.—Other schemes of modulation are possible, and methods for their reception are obvious. Among these may be mentioned a double-pulse scheme in which the spacing between the two pulses is modulated. Clearly, this scheme is similar to pulse-length modulation. Again frequency or phase differences between the two pulses can be used if desired.

CHAPTER 3

THEORETICAL INTRODUCTION

3·1. The Mathematical Description of Noise.—It is well known that the output of a receiver when *no* signal is present is not always zero but fluctuates more or less irregularly around some average value. On an A-scope, for instance, these fluctuations produce the typical noise that often prevents weak signals from being detected. This noise has several origins, to be discussed in detail in the next chapters; the question that concerns us here is how to describe quantitatively the noise output of a receiver.

The answer is perhaps not obvious. Merely observing the output $y(t)$ of a receiver over a period of time (y may be a voltage, a current, or the deflection on an A-scope) does *not* make it possible to predict the output for any later time or to predict the output as a function of time for another receiver identical with the first. Then how can any theory at all be formulated? The answer is, of course, by using the notion of probability. As we shall see, certain probability distributions can be predicted and observed. The noise output of a receiver is a typical example of a *random* (or *stochastic*) *process*. The systematic study of such a process forms a recently developed part of the theory of probability.[1]

Let us assume that there are a great number of macroscopically identical receivers (called an "ensemble" of receivers) all turned on simultaneously. The noise outputs $y_1(t)$, $y_2(t)$, . . . , are then observed.

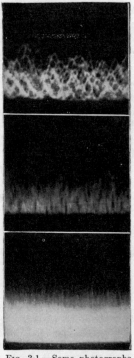

Fig. 3·1.—Some photographs of typical noise on an A-scope.

All these functions will be different. At a definite time t it can be observed for what fraction of the total number of cases y occurs in a

---

[1] Several aspects and applications of the general theory of random processes are reviewed and extensive references to the literature given by S. O. Rice, "Mathematical

given interval between y and $y + \Delta y$. This fraction will depend on y and t and will be proportional to Δy when Δy is small. It is written $W_1(y,t) \, dy$ and called the *first probability distribution*. Next can be considered all the pairs of values of y occurring at two given times t_1 and t_2. The fraction of the total number of pairs in which y occurs in the range $(y_1, \ y_1 + \Delta y_1)$ at t_1 and in the range $(y_2, \ y_2 + \Delta y_2)$ at t_2 is written $W_2(y_1, \ t_1; \ y_2, \ t_2) \, dy_1 \, dy_2$ and is called the *second probability distribution*. We can continue in this manner, determining all the triples of values of y at three given times to arrive at the third probability distribution, etc.

The objection immediately occurs that observations of the noise outputs on an ensemble of receivers can never be made. Such observations are not necessary, however, when the noise output is *stationary*. This means that the influence of the transients (because of the switching on of the receivers) has died down and that all tubes have warmed up properly with the result that the receiver is in a stationary state. If *one* observation is then made of the noise output $y(t)$ of the receiver for a very long time, all the information desired will be received. The record can be cut in pieces of length Θ (where Θ is long compared with all "periods" occurring in the process), and the different pieces can then be considered as the different records of an ensemble of observations from which the different probability distributions can be determined. Furthermore, these distributions now become somewhat simpler. The first one, for instance, will be independent of t; the second one will depend only on the time difference $t_2 - t_1$, etc.; hence the stationary noise output will be described by the series of functions:

$$W_1(y) \, dy = \text{probability of finding } y \text{ between } y \text{ and } y + dy;$$

$$W_2(y_1,y_2,t) \, dy_1 \, dy_2 = \text{joint probability of finding a pair of values of } y \text{ in the ranges } (y_1, \ y_1 + dy_1) \text{ and } (y_2, \ y_2 + dy_2), \text{ which are a time interval } t \text{ apart from each other;}$$

Analysis of Random Noise," *Bell System Techn. J.*, **23**, 282 (1944); **25**, 46 (1945); S. Chandrasekhar, "Stochastic Problems in Physics and Astronomy," *Rev. Mod. Phys.*, **15**, No. 1, 1 (1943); Ming Chen Wang and G. E. Uhlenbeck, "On the Theory of the Brownian Motion II," *Rev. Mod. Phys.*, **17**, 322 (1945). Discussion in this chapter will be restricted to the minimum requirements for the understanding of noise problems in radio receivers. It may be well to point out, however, that these problems form only a small part of the general theory of random processes. Other applications of the theory are made in many branches of physics (as, for instance, in the theory of Brownian motion and the theory of other fluctuation phenomena), in hydrodynamics (especially in the theory of turbulence), in the theory of the errors in gunnery and bombing, in economics (especially in the theory of time series), etc. Another application, the so-called "random walk" problem, will be treated in Chap. 6.

$W_3(y_1, y_2, y_3, t_1, t_2) \, dy_1 \, dy_2 \, dy_3 =$ joint probability of finding a triple of values of y in the ranges dy_1, dy_2, dy_3, where dy_1 and dy_2 are the time interval t_1 apart and dy_2 and dy_3 the time interval t_2 apart, etc.

It should be emphasized that these probability distributions represent everything that can be found out about the random process, and one may therefore say that the random process is *defined* by these distributions. Of course, the functions W_n are not arbitrary and unrelated to each other; they must fulfill the three obvious conditions:

$W_n \geqq 0$, because the W_n are probability densities,

$W_n(y_1, t_1; y_2, t_2 \ldots y_n, t_n)$ must be a symmetric function in the set of variables $y_1, t_1; y_2, t_2, \ldots, y_n, t_n$, since W_n is a *joint* probability, and

$W_k(y_1, t_1; \cdots, y_k, t_k)$

$$= \int \cdots \int dy_{k+1} \cdots dy_n \, W_n(y_1, t_1; \cdots y_n, t_n), \quad (1)$$

since each function W_n must imply all the previous W_k with $k < n$. The set of functions W_n form therefore a kind of hierarchy; they describe successively the random process in more and more detail. A *complete* theory of the random process should make it possible to derive the general distribution function W_n from an analysis of the origins of the random process. For the noise produced in or passing through *linear* networks this can actually be done (see Sec. 3·6). However, the investigations here will usually be restricted to the first two probability distributions.

3·2. Average Values.—From the *first* probability distribution $W_1(y,t)$ the average value of y can be found.

$$\bar{y} = \int dy \, y W_1(y,t). \quad (2)$$

Clearly, this average value will in general depend on the time t. It can be determined by averaging, at the time t, the noise outputs $y_1(t)$, $y_2(t)$, . . . of the ensemble of receivers mentioned in Sec. 3·1. It will be spoken of, therefore, as the *ensemble average* and indicated by a bar. It must be distinguished from the *time average*, defined and denoted by

$$\tilde{y} \equiv \lim_{\Theta \to \infty} \frac{1}{\Theta} \int_{-\frac{\Theta}{2}}^{+\frac{\Theta}{2}} dt \, y(t). \quad (3)$$

This will be independent of the time, of course, but will, in general, differ for the various functions $y_1(t)$, $y_2(t)$, . . . of the ensemble. We can still average over the ensemble; then the same result will be obtained as the time average of $\bar{y}$.   Or in a formula

$$\bar{\tilde{y}} = \tilde{\bar{y}}. \tag{4}$$

Only for a *stationary* process will the two ways of averaging give the same result, since then $\bar{y}$ will be independent of the time and $\tilde{y}$ will be the same for the different functions $y_i(t)$ of the ensemble.

The same distinction must, of course, be made for the average values of functions of y.   Usually it will be clear from the context which kind of averaging is meant.   Especially important are the different moments of the distribution W_1, defined by

$$m_n = \overline{y^n} = \int dy\, y^n W_1. \tag{5}$$

From the first and second moments there is derived the *fluctuation* or variance

$$\overline{(y - \bar{y})^2} = \overline{y^2} - (\bar{y})^2 = \int dy\, (y - \bar{y})^2 W_1, \tag{6}$$

which is a measure of the width of the distribution $W_1(y)$ about the average value $\bar{y}$.   From the third moment can be obtained an idea of the skewness of the probability distribution, more and more information about $W_1(y)$ being acquired as additional moments are known.   The problem whether or not the knowledge of *all* moments determines the probability distribution uniquely is a famous one, but it will not concern us.[1]   In certain instances this is actually the case, as, for example, when the m's fulfill the relations

$$\left. \begin{aligned} m_{2k+1} &= 0, \\ m_{2k} &= 1 \cdot 3 \cdot 5 \cdots (2k - 1)(m_2)^k. \end{aligned} \right\} \tag{7a}$$

The $W_1(y)$ is then the Gaussian distribution

$$W_1(y) = \frac{1}{\sqrt{2\pi m_2}} e^{-\frac{y^2}{2m_2}}. \tag{7b}$$

Of special importance is the combination of the moments embodied in the so-called *characteristic function*

$$\phi_1(s) = \overline{e^{isy}} = \sum_{n=0}^{\infty} \frac{(is)^n}{n!} m_n = \int dy\, e^{isy} W_1(y). \tag{8}$$

---

[1] *Cf.*, for instance, M. G. Kendall, *Advanced Theory of Statistics*, Vol. I, Griffin, London, 1943, Chap. 4.

The significance of the characteristic function lies especially in the following two theorems:

1. The characteristic function determines uniquely the probability distribution. In fact, from the Fourier integral theorem it follows[1] that

$$W_1(y) = \frac{1}{2\pi} \int_{-\infty}^{+\infty} ds \, e^{-isy} \phi_1(s). \tag{9}$$

2. If the characteristic functions of two *independent* random variables y and z are $\phi(s)$ and $\psi(s)$, then the characteristic function of the distribution of the sum $y + z$ is given by the product $\phi(s) \cdot \psi(s)$.[2]

Let us now turn to the *second* distribution function $W_2(y_1, t_1; y_2, t_2)$. The most important average value derived from it is

$$\overline{y_1 y_2} = \int \int dy_1 \, dy_2 \, y_1 y_2 W_2(y_1, t_1; y_2, t_2). \tag{10}$$

In general, this will be a function of t_1 and t_2. Letting $t_2 = t_1 + \tau$, we can perform an additional time average over t_1 and then obtain a function of τ

$$R(\tau) = \lim_{\theta \to \infty} \frac{1}{T} \int_{-\frac{\theta}{2}}^{+\frac{\theta}{2}} dt_1 \, \overline{y_1 y_2}(t_1, t_1 + \tau) = \overline{\overline{y_1 y_2}}. \tag{11}$$

The same function $R(\tau)$ is obtained, of course, by taking the ensemble average of

$$\overline{\overline{y(t_1)y(t_1 + \tau)}} = \lim_{\theta \to \infty} \frac{1}{T} \int_{-\frac{\theta}{2}}^{+\frac{\theta}{2}} dt_1 \, y(t_1)y(t_1 + \tau). \tag{12}$$

For a stationary process Eqs. (10) and (12) give the same result. The function $R(\tau)$ gives a measure for the correlation between successive values of y and is therefore called the correlation function. When $y(t_1)$ and $y(t_2)$ are independent of each other,

$$W_2(y_1, t_1; y_2, t_2) = W_1(y_1, t_1) \cdot W_1(y_2, t_2)$$

and

$$\overline{y_1 y_2} = \bar{y}_1 \cdot \bar{y}_2.$$

[1] One might think that Eqs. (8) and (9) answer the previously mentioned question of moments in the affirmative. In fact, it can be proved in this way that Eq. (7b) follows from Eq. (7a). The general mathematical problem, however, is to find the conditions that the m_n have to fulfill so that $\phi_1(s)$ exists and has a Fourier transform that is always positive.

[2] For a proof and also many examples and references, *cf.* Kendall, *loc. cit.* For the strict mathematical discussion of the notion of characteristic function, see H. Cramer, *Random Variables and Probability Distributions*, Cambridge, London, 1937.

For noise (without signal), this situation will occur when the time interval $t_2 - t_1 = \tau$ is sufficiently large. For $\tau = 0$, it is obvious that

$$\overline{y_1 y_2} \to \overline{y^2} = \int dy \, y^2 W_1(y_1, t_1).$$

It is sometimes convenient to work with the function[1]

$$\rho(\tau) = \frac{\overline{(y_1 - \bar{y})(y_2 - \bar{y})}}{\overline{(y - \bar{y})^2}}, \tag{13}$$

which will be called the normalized correlation function. We may note some properties of $\rho(\tau)$:

1. $\rho(0) = 1$.
2. $\rho(\tau) \leqq \rho(0)$.
3. For noise without signal $\rho(\tau) \to 0$ as $\tau \to \infty$.
4. If $\rho(\tau) = 0$ for $\tau \geqq \tau_0$, then[2]

$$\rho\left(\frac{\tau_0}{n}\right) \leqq \rho(0) \cos \frac{\pi}{n+1},$$

where n is an integer.

As already mentioned in Sec. 3·1, $W_2(y_1, t_1; y_2, t_2)$ gives *more* information about the random process than the first probability distribution $W_1(y,t)$. In fact, W_1 follows from W_2, since one has

$$W_1(y_1, t_1) = \int dy_2 \, W_2(y_1, t_1; y_2, t_2) \tag{14}$$

and

$$W_2(y_2, t_2) = \int dy_1 \, W_2(y_1, t_1; y_2, t_2),$$

which is a special case of the general Eq. (1). It is sometimes important to introduce instead of W_2 the *conditional probability distribution* $P_2(y_1, t_1 | y_2, t_2)$, which gives the probability of finding y between y_2 and $y_2 + dy_2$ at time t_2, *given* that $y = y_1$ at time t_1. Of course,

$$W_2(y_1, t_1; y_2, t_2) = W_1(y_1, t_1) P_2(y_1, t_1 | y_2, t_2), \tag{15}$$

and P_2 must fulfill the relations

$$\left. \begin{array}{l} \displaystyle\int dy_2 \, P_2(y_1, t_1 | y_2, t_2) = 1, \\[2mm] \displaystyle\int dy_1 \, W_1(y_1, t_1) P_2(y_1, t_1 | y_2, t_2) = W_1(y_2, t_2), \end{array} \right\} \tag{16}$$

---

[1] This function is written for a stationary process, with which we shall be concerned most often.

[2] For the proof, *cf.* R. P. Boas and M. Kac, "Inequalities for Fourier Transforms of Positive Functions," *Duke Math. J.*, **12**, 189 (1945).

which follow from Eq. (14). From P_2 may be obtained *conditional average values*, as, for instance,

$$\overline{y_2}^{y_1} = \int dy_2 \, y_2 P_2(y_1, t_1 | y_2, t_2),$$

which is the average value of y at t_2 when one *knows* that $y = y_1$ at time t_1. For a stationary process, P_2 and, therefore, $\overline{y_2}^{y_1}$ also will depend only on $t_2 - t_1 = \tau$.

The notion of the characteristic function for W_2 can also be generalized by forming

$$\phi_2(s_1, s_2) = \overline{e^{i(s_1 y_1 + s_2 y_2)}} = \int \int dy_1 \, dy_2 \, e^{i(s_1 y_1 + s_2 y_2)} W_2(y_1, y_2). \quad (17a)$$

We again have analogous theorems; in particular W_2 is found from ϕ_2 by

$$W_2(y_1, y_2) = \frac{1}{(2\pi)^2} \int \int ds_1 \, ds_2 \, e^{i(s_1 y_1 + s_2 y_2)} \phi_2(s_1, s_2). \quad (17b)$$

3·3. The Relation between the Correlation Function and the Spectrum.—Of special significance for the applications to signal detectability is the notion of the spectrum[1] of a random process. Let us suppose that a function $y(t)$ is observed for a long time Θ. Assuming that $y(t) = 0$ outside the time interval Θ, the resulting function can be developed in a Fourier integral,

$$y(t) = \int_{-\infty}^{+\infty} df \, A(f) e^{2\pi i f t}, \quad (18)$$

where if $A^*(f)$ denotes the complex conjugate, $A(f) = A^*(-f)$, since $y(t)$ is real. It is well known (Parseval theorem) that

$$\int_{-\infty}^{+\infty} y^2(t) \, dt = \int_{-\frac{\Theta}{2}}^{+\frac{\Theta}{2}} y^2(t) \, dt = \int_{-\infty}^{+\infty} df \, |A(f)|^2.$$

Using the fact that $|A(f)|^2$ is an even function of f and going to the limit $\Theta \to \infty$, this equation can be written as

$$\overline{y^2} = \lim_{\Theta \to \infty} \frac{1}{\Theta} \int_{-\frac{\Theta}{2}}^{+\frac{\Theta}{2}} y^2(t) \, dt = \int_0^{\infty} df \, G(f), \quad (19)$$

where

$$G(f) = \lim_{\Theta \to \infty} \frac{2}{\Theta} |A(f)|^2 \quad (20)$$

---

[1] *Cf.* Rice, *Bell System Tech. J.*, **23**, 310 (1944); Wang and Uhlenbeck, *Rev. Mod. Phys.*, **17**, 326 (1945); further references are given in these papers.

and will be called the *spectral density* or the *power spectrum* of the function $y(t)$.

Let us consider next the average value,

$$\overline{y(t)y(t + \tau)} = \lim_{\Theta \to \infty} \frac{1}{\Theta} \int_{-\frac{\Theta}{2}}^{+\frac{\Theta}{2}} y(t)y(t + \tau) \, d\tau.$$

By introducing the Fourier expansion [Eq. (18)] and using the Fourier integral theorem, it is easily shown that

$$\overline{y(t)y(t + \tau)} = \int_0^\infty df \, G(f) \cos 2\pi f\tau, \qquad (21a)$$

from which it follows by inversion that

$$G(f) = 4 \int_0^\infty d\tau \, \overline{y(t)y(t + \tau)} \cos 2\pi f\tau. \qquad (21b)$$

All this holds for any function $y(t)$. Let us assume, now, that we have a random process and that $y(t)$ is a member of the ensemble of functions $y_1(t)$, $y_2(t)$, . . . , mentioned in Sec. 3·1. Each of these functions can be developed in a Fourier integral, and the corresponding $G(f)$ can be averaged over the ensemble. The resulting $\overline{G(f)}$ will be called the spectral density or the power spectrum of the random process. From Eqs. (21a) and (21b) it follows that the correlation function $R(\tau)$ and this spectrum are each other's Fourier cosine transform, or

$$\left. \begin{array}{l} R(\tau) = \displaystyle\int_0^\infty df \, \overline{G(f)} \cos 2\pi f\tau, \\[2mm] \overline{G(f)} = 4 \displaystyle\int_0^\infty d\tau \, R(\tau) \cos 2\pi f\tau. \end{array} \right\} \qquad (22)$$

This is the relation referred to in the title of this section.

The following additional remarks may be helpful.

1. Equation (19) can also be averaged over the ensemble, which gives

$$\overline{\overline{y^2}} = \int_0^\infty df \, \overline{G(f)}. \qquad (23)$$

2. For a *stationary* process the averaging over the ensemble can be omitted, since each member $y_i(t)$ will lead to the same spectral density $G(f)$.

3. The spectral density $\overline{G(f)}$ may contain singular peaks of the well-known Dirac δ-function type. This certainly occurs, for instance,

when $\tilde{y}$ is *not* zero or, in electrical language, when there is a d-c term. Then

$$G(f) = 2(\tilde{y})^2\delta(f) + G_1(f), \tag{24}$$

where $\delta(f)$ is the Dirac δ-function.[1]

4. For pure noise the peak at $f = 0$, corresponding to the d-c term will usually be the only peak, so that $G_1(f)$ will be a regular function, representing the really continuous spectrum. From Eqs. (19) and (24) it is apparent that the area under this continuous spectrum is equal to the fluctuation or variance of $y(t)$. In this case it is sometimes convenient to introduce the *normalized power spectrum*

$$S(f) = \frac{G_1(f)}{\displaystyle\int_0^\infty df\, G_1(f)};$$

it becomes apparent that $S(f)$ and the normalized correlation function $\rho(\tau)$ of Sec. 3·2 are each other's Fourier cosine transform.

5. The relations [Eqs. (21a) and (21b)] are perfectly general. They hold, for example, when

$$y(t) = A + B \sin 2\pi(f_0 t + \alpha).$$

We then have

$$\widetilde{y^2} = A^2 + \tfrac{1}{2}B^2,$$
$$\widetilde{y(t)y(t + \tau)} = A^2 + \tfrac{1}{2}B^2 \cos 2\pi f_0\tau,$$

and from Eq. (21b) it follows that

$$G(f) = 2A^2\delta(f) + \tfrac{1}{2}B^2\delta(f - f_0),$$

where the following relations have been made use of:

$$\left.\begin{array}{l} 2\displaystyle\int_0^\infty d\tau \cos 2\pi f\tau = \delta(f); \\[2ex] 4\displaystyle\int_0^\infty d\tau \cos 2\pi f\tau \cos 2\pi f_0\tau = \delta(f - f_0). \end{array}\right\} \tag{25}$$

The spectrum therefore consists, as it should, of the two frequencies $f = 0$ and $f = f_0$, corresponding to the power in the d-c term A^2 and the power $\tfrac{1}{2}B^2$ in the a-c term.

6. When there are noise and a signal, the spectral density $G(f)$ will consist (in addition to the d-c term) of a continuous spectrum and a number of peaks at the discrete frequencies f_i of the signal. The

---

[1] This function has the following properties: $\delta(x) = 0$ for $x \neq 0$ and $\delta(x) = \infty$ for $x = 0$ in such a way that the integral, $\displaystyle\int_{-\infty}^{+\infty} \delta(x)\, dx = 1$; $\delta(x) = \delta(-x)$ so that $\displaystyle\int_0^\infty \delta(x)\, dx = \tfrac{1}{2}$.

magnitudes of the peaks—or better, the area under the peaks—correspond to the power spectrum of the signal.

7. When a stationary random process with spectral density $G_i(f)$ passes through a linear device that is described by an impedance function $Z(f)$, then the output will again be a stationary random process and the spectral density will be

$$G_o(f) = |Z(f)|^2 G_i(f). \tag{26}$$

3·4. Examples of Spectra.—The importance of the relation in Eqs. (21) or (22) between the correlation function and the spectrum lies in the fact that it is often easier to calculate the $R(\tau)$ or $\rho(\tau)$ by means of Eqs. (10) and (11) than to calculate the spectrum directly. To elucidate the relations in Eqs. (22), consider, for example, the case where[1]

$$\rho(\tau) = e^{-\beta\tau}.$$

Then

$$S(f) = \frac{4\beta}{\beta^2 + (2\pi f)^2}, \tag{27}$$

when

$$\rho(\tau) = e^{-\alpha^2\tau^2},$$
$$S(f) = \frac{2\sqrt{\pi}}{\alpha} e^{-\frac{\pi^2 f^2}{\alpha^2}}. \tag{28}$$

When $\rho(\tau)$ is a monotonically decreasing function of τ, $S(f)$ is also a monotonic decreasing function of f. The function $S(f)$ will become flatter and flatter as $\rho(\tau)$ becomes narrower. If $\rho(\tau)$ drops to zero in a very short time Δ, then $S(f)$ will be essentially constant up to a very high frequency of the order of magnitude $1/\Delta$. We call this a *white spectrum*. The limiting case—where $S(f)$ = constant for all f—would correspond to no correlation at all between successive values of y; hence for all t,

$$W_2(y_1, t_1; y_2, t_2) = W_1(y_1,t_1)W_1(y_2,t_2),$$

and we have what is called a *purely random process*. This is, of course, an idealization that in actual cases can only be approximated.

When $S(f)$ has a maximum at some high frequency f_0 and is symmetrical around the maximum, so that

$$S(f) = F(f - f_0),$$
$$F(x) = F(-x),$$

then

$$\rho(\tau) \approx \cos 2\pi f_0\tau \cdot \int_{-\infty}^{\infty} dx\, F(x) \cos 2\pi x\tau, \tag{29}$$

---

[1] In these examples the normalized correlation function $\rho(\tau)$ is used and the resulting spectrum is therefore also normalized; $\rho(0)$ is always unity, and consequently the total area of the spectrum is $\int_0^{\infty} S(f)\, df = 1$.

as long as the width of $S(f)$ is small compared with f_0. To illustrate, when $S(f)$ is constant over a band of frequencies of width B around f_0, then

$$\rho(\tau) \approx \cos 2\pi f_0\tau \, \frac{1}{\pi B\tau} \sin \pi B\tau, \tag{30}$$

as long as $B \ll f_0$. The correlation function will therefore be like a damped oscillation with frequency f_0. The smaller B is, the farther the correlation goes out in time. A limiting case is when $S(f) = \delta(f - f_0)$; then $\rho(\tau)$ is strictly given by $\cos 2\pi f_0\tau$.

It is not necessary, of course, to calculate the power spectrum by means of the correlation function. Sometimes it is just as easy to derive the spectrum directly. Let us consider, for example, the case where

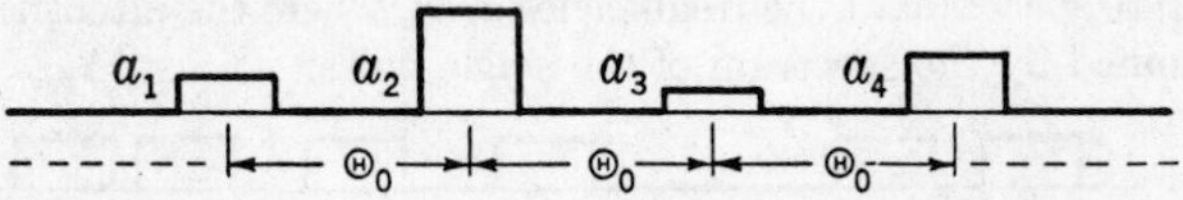

FIG. 3·2.—Series of pulses of random height but fixed repetition interval.

$y(t)$ consists of a series of pulses that have identical shape and a constant repetition frequency but whose heights vary according to some probability distribution (see Fig. 3·2, where the shape of the pulse is assumed to be rectangular).
Then

$$y(t) = \sum_k a_k F(t - k\Theta_0), \tag{31}$$

where Θ_0 is the repetition period and the a_k are the heights that are distributed according to a probability distribution, say $P(a)$. From Eq. (18) is obtained

$$A(f) = \int_{-\infty}^{+\infty} dt \, y(t)e^{-2\pi ift} = B(f) \sum_{k=-N}^{+N} a_k e^{-2\pi ikf\Theta_0}, \tag{32}$$

where

$$B(f) = \int_{-\infty}^{+\infty} dx \, F(x)e^{-2\pi ifx},$$

and where it has been assumed that there are approximately $(2N + 1)$ pulses between the times $-N\Theta_0$ to $+N\Theta_0$. From Eq. (32) it follows that the average power spectrum is given by

$$\overline{G(f)} = \lim_{N \to \infty} \frac{2}{2N\Theta_0} \overline{|A(f)|^2}$$

$$= \frac{2}{\Theta_0} |B(f)|^2 \left\{ [\overline{a^2} - (\bar{a})^2] + (\bar{a})^2 \lim_{N \to \infty} \frac{1}{2N + 1} \left| \sum_{-N}^{+N} e^{-2\pi if\Theta_0 k} \right|^2 \right\}. \tag{33}$$

The sum inside the braces will be $(2N + 1)$ for $f = n/\Theta_0$ when n is an integer; hence in the limit $\overline{G(f)}$ will be infinite. For other values of f the sum will be oscillatory, and for $N \to \infty$ the limiting value will be zero. Clearly, the limit has the character of a series of peaks, or δ-functions, at the frequencies n/Θ_0, and $\overline{G(f)}$ can be written

$$\overline{G(f)} = \frac{2}{\Theta_0} |B(f)|^2 \left\{ [\overline{a^2} - (\bar{a})^2] + \frac{(\bar{a})^2}{\Theta_0} \sum_{n=0}^{\infty} \delta\left(f - \frac{n}{\Theta_0}\right) \right\}.$$

Therefore, a continuous spectrum is obtained that has the same shape as the power spectrum of a single pulse. The total intensity is determined by the fluctuation $\overline{a^2} - (\bar{a})^2$ of the pulse heights. There is, in addition, a discrete spectrum at the frequencies n/Θ_0, where the intensities are also determined by the spectrum of the single pulse.

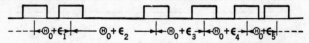

FIG. 3·3.—Series of pulses of fixed height but variable repetition interval.

Let us consider next a series of pulses that have identical shape and height but a repetition period varying around an average value according to some probability distribution (see Fig. 3·3, where the pulse shape is again taken to be rectangular). Now

$$y(t) = \sum_k F(t - k\Theta_0 - \epsilon_k), \tag{34}$$

where Θ_0 is the average repetition period and ϵ_k is the deviation of the kth spacing from Θ_0, so that $\bar{\epsilon} = 0$. Let $P(\epsilon)$ be the probability distribution for ϵ, and let

$$\phi(f) = \int_{-\infty}^{+\infty} d\epsilon \, e^{2\pi i f \cdot \epsilon} P(\epsilon).$$

Then the following expression for the power spectrum is obtained:

$$\overline{G(f)} = \frac{2}{\Theta_0} |B(f)|^2 \left\{ [1 - |\phi(f)|^2] + \frac{|\phi(f)|^2}{\Theta_0} \sum_{n=0}^{\infty} \delta\left(f - \frac{n}{\Theta_0}\right) \right\}. \tag{35}$$

Here, the shape of the continuous spectrum and the intensities of the discrete spectrum are no longer determined solely by the spectrum of the single pulse but depend also on the function $\phi(f)$.

Suppose that the function $y(t)$ consists of pieces of the function $e^{2\pi i f_0 t}$, the lengths l_i of these pieces being distributed according to the probability distribution $P(l)$ (see Fig. 3·4). Let us suppose further that at the end of each piece the phase changes and that these phase changes are governed by the probability distribution $Q(\alpha)$. The normalized power spectrum is given by[1]

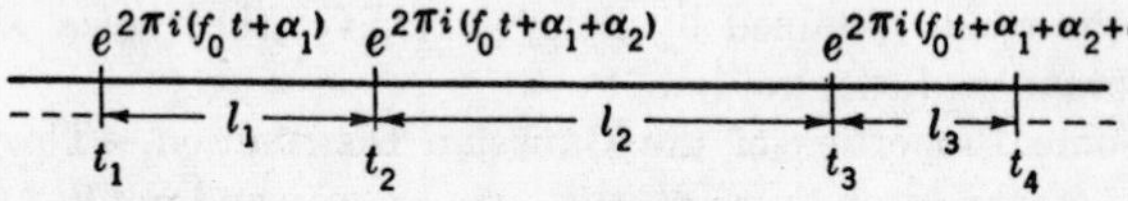

FIG. 3·4.—Series of pieces of the function $e^{2\pi i f_0 t}$ of random lengths and with random phase changes.

$$S(f) = \frac{1}{\pi^2 \bar{l}(f - f_0)^2}$$
$$\times \frac{1 - A + (A^2 + B^2 - 1)\phi(f) - (A^2 + B^2 - A)\,[\phi^2(f) + \psi^2(f)]}{[1 - A\phi(f) + B\psi(f)]^2 + [A\psi(f) + B\phi(f)]^2}, \quad (36a)$$

where

$$A + iB = \int_{-\pi}^{+\pi} d\alpha\, Q(\alpha) e^{2\pi i\alpha},$$

$$\phi(f) + i\psi(f) = \int_0^\infty dl\, P(l) e^{2\pi i l(f_0 - f)},$$

$$\bar{l} = \int_0^\infty dl\, lP(l).$$

Some special cases are of interest. that $A = -1$, $B = 0$; this leads to a step curve of height ± 1, in which the lengths of the steps are distributed according to the probability law $P(l)$. From Eq. (36a) is obtained

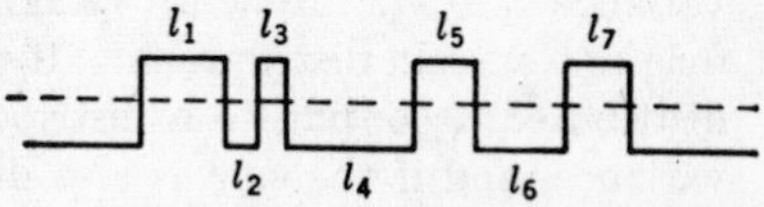

Let $f_0 = 0$ and $Q(\alpha) = \delta(\pi - \alpha)$, so

FIG. 3·5.—Step curve of height ± 1 with random lengths of steps.

$$S(f) = \frac{2}{\pi^2 \bar{l} f^2}\frac{1 - \phi^2 - \psi^2}{(1 + \phi)^2 + \psi^2}, \quad (36b)$$

where now, of course,

$$\phi(f) + i\psi(f) = \int_0^\infty dl\, P(l) e^{-2\pi i l f}.$$

For $P(l) = \beta e^{-\beta l}$ this becomes

$$S(f) = \frac{8\beta}{4\beta^2 + (2\pi f)^2},$$

which is analogous to Eq. (27). For $f_0 \neq 0$ and $P(l) = e^{-\beta l}$, Eq. (36a)

[1] This equation is a generalization of a result obtained by H. M. Foley, "An Investigation in the General Theory of Pressure Broadening and an Experimental Study of Pressure Effects in the 14μ Band of Hydrogen Cyanide," Ph.D. Thesis, U. of Mich., 1942.

reduces to

$$S(f) = \frac{4\beta(1 - A)}{\beta^2(1 - A)^2 + [2\pi(f - f_0)^2 + \beta B]^2},$$ (36c)

which is the result obtained by Foley. It gives the typical shape of a pressure-broadened spectral line.

3·5. Some Properties of the Gaussian Distribution.—The following are some of the properties of the one-, two-, and multidimensional Gaussian distribution that are of importance for future applications.

The One-dimensional Gaussian Distribution.—The *one-dimensional* Gaussian distribution

$$W(y) = \frac{1}{\sigma \sqrt{2\pi}} e^{-\frac{(y-a)^2}{2\sigma^2}}$$ (37a)

with the average value $\bar{y} = a$ and the variance $\overline{(y - \bar{y})^2} = \sigma^2$ has for its characteristic function

$$\psi(t) = \int_{-\infty}^{+\infty} dy \, e^{ity} W(y) = e^{ita - (\sigma^2 t^2/2)}.$$ (37b)

From the second theorem on characteristic functions mentioned in Sec 3·2 it follows that the sum of two independent random variables, each of which have a Gaussian distribution with means a_1, a_2 and variances σ_1^2, σ_2^2, will *also* have a Gaussian distribution with a mean $a_1 + a_2$ and a variance $\sigma_1^2 + \sigma_2^2$. Roughly speaking, this property is also characteristic for the Gaussian distribution. If two independent random variables are distributed according to a distribution function $W(y)$ that has a *finite* variance, and if the sum is also distributed according to the same law, then W must be the Gaussian distribution.[1]

The significance of the Gaussian distribution law lies especially in the so-called *central limit theorem* of the theory of probability. The following is a special case of this theorem: If $x_1, x_2, \ldots, x_n$ are n independent random variables, which are distributed according to the *same* probability distribution and which have a zero mean value and the finite variance σ, then the distribution of

$$y = \frac{x_1 + x_2 + \cdots + x_n}{\sqrt{n}}$$

will approach the Gaussian distribution for large n,

$$\frac{1}{\sigma \sqrt{2\pi}} e^{-\frac{y^2}{2\sigma^2}},$$

---

[1] For proofs and more precise formulation, see H. Cramer, *Random Variables and Probability Distributions*, Cambridge, London, 1936, Chap. VI, Theorems 17, 18, 19. That the variance be finite is an essential condition.

whatever the original distribution function[1] of the x_i. This independence of the original distribution function is the surprising feature of the theorem. Of course, how the Gaussian distribution law is approached will depend on further features of the distribution function of the x_i. It can be shown,[2] for instance, that asymptotically

$$W(y) \approx \frac{1}{\sigma \sqrt{2\pi}} \left(e^{-\frac{y^2}{2\sigma^2}} - \frac{\rho}{6\sqrt{n}} \frac{d^3}{dy^3} e^{-\frac{y^2}{2\sigma^2}} + \cdots \right), \qquad (38)$$

where $\rho = \overline{x_1^3}$ and where the further terms in the development contain higher powers of $n^{-\frac{1}{2}}$ and, also, the higher moments of the distribution function of the x_i. Usually the Gaussian distribution already becomes a very good approximation once n is greater than 10.

The n-dimensional Gaussian Distribution.—This can be written

$$W(y_1, y_2, \cdots, y_n) = \frac{1}{(2\pi)^{n/2}} \frac{1}{\sqrt{b}} e^{-\frac{1}{2b} \sum_{k,l=1}^{n} B_{kl} y_k y_l}, \qquad (39)$$

where we have already assumed, for simplicity, that the y_i's are measured from their mean value, so that $\overline{y_i} = 0$. The matrix **B** is a symmetric and positive definite matrix; the meaning of the elements B_{kl} and of the constant b is connected with the quadratic averages

$$b_{kl} = \overline{y_k y_l} = \int_{-\infty}^{+\infty} \cdots \int y_k y_l W(y_1 \cdots y_n) \, dy_1 \cdots dy_n. \qquad (40)$$

It can be shown that B_{kl} is the cofactor of the element b_{kl} in the matrix b whereas b is the determinant of the matrix b. To do this, let us first show that the characteristic function of the n-dimensional Gaussian distribution is given by

$$\psi(t_1 \cdots t_n) = e^{-\frac{1}{2} \sum_{k,l=1}^{n} b_{kl} t_k t_l} \qquad (41)$$

For this we must calculate the integral

$$\frac{1}{(2\pi)^n} \int_{-\infty}^{+\infty} \cdots \int dt_1 \cdots dt_n e^{i \sum_{1}^{n} y_k t_k} \psi(t_1 \cdots t_n).$$

---

[1] For a proof and more precise formulation, see *ibid.*, p. 52. The condition that $\overline{x_i} = 0$ is, of course, no restriction, since that x can always be measured from its mean value. For the connection with the random-walk problem, see Sec. 3·6.

[2] This is a special case of Theorem 25 in *ibid.*, p. 81. For a formal proof see Sec. 3·6.

Introduce instead of the t_k new variables u_k by means of

$$t_k = u_k - i \sum_{r=1}^{n} \frac{B_{kr}}{b} y_r.$$

By using the well-known theorem

$$\sum_{r=1}^{n} b_{ri} B_{rj} = \delta_{ij} b,$$

we find

$$i \sum_k t_k y_k - \frac{1}{2} \sum_{k,l} b_{kl} t_k t_l = -\frac{1}{2} \sum_{k,l} b_{kl} u_k u_l - \frac{1}{2} \sum_{k,l} \frac{B_{kl}}{b} y_k y_l.$$

Thus the integral becomes

$$\frac{1}{(2\pi)^n} e^{-\frac{1}{2b} \sum_{k,l} B_{kl} y_k y_l} \int_{-\infty}^{+\infty} \cdots \int du_1 \cdots du_n e^{-\frac{1}{2} \sum_{k,l} b_{kl} u_k u_l}.$$

By transforming the quadratic form $\Sigma\, b_{kl} u_k u_l$ to principal axes the last integral is shown to be $(2\pi)^{n/2} b^{-\frac{1}{2}}$, so that we really get the Gaussian distribution [Eq. (39)].

It remains to be shown that the b_{kl} are really the quadratic averages $\overline{y_k y_l}$. The simplest way is to use the characteristic function. In fact, if $F(y_1 \cdots y_n)$ is a polynomial in $y_1 \cdots y_n$, it follows from the Fourier integral theorem that

$$\overline{F(y_1 \cdots y_n)} = \int_{-\infty}^{+\infty} \cdots \int dy_1 \cdots dy_n F(y_1 \cdots y_n) W(y_1 \cdots y_n)$$

$$= \frac{1}{(2\pi)^n} \int_{-\infty}^{+\infty} \cdots \int dy_1 \cdots dy_n F(y_1 \cdots y_n) \int_{-\infty}^{+\infty} \cdots \int$$

$$dt_1 \cdots dt_n e^{i \sum_{1}^{n} y_k t_k} \psi(t_1 \cdots t_n) = \left[F\left(\frac{1}{i}\frac{\partial}{\partial t_1}, \frac{1}{i}\frac{\partial}{\partial t_2}, \cdots, \right. \right.$$

$$\left. \left. \frac{1}{i}\frac{\partial}{\partial t_n} \right) \psi(t_1 \cdots t_n) \right]_{t_1 = t_2 = \ldots = t_n = 0}. \quad (42)$$

Therefore,

$$\overline{y_k y_l} = \left(-\frac{\partial^2}{\partial t_k\, \partial t_l} e^{-\frac{1}{2} \sum_{kl} b_{kl} t_k t_l} \right)_{t_1 = \ldots = t_n = 0} = b_{kl}.$$

This result could also have been proved directly by calculating the integral in Eq. (40). Since the matrix b/b is the inverse of the matrix $\mathbf{B}$, it follows that b will also be a symmetric and positive definite matrix.

As a special case of Eq. (39), let us consider the *two-dimensional* Gaussian distribution. The matrix b is usually written

$$b = \left\{ \begin{matrix} \overline{y_1^2} & \overline{y_1 y_2} \\ \overline{y_1 y_2} & \overline{y_2^2} \end{matrix} \right\} = \left\{ \begin{matrix} \sigma^2 & \rho \sigma \tau \\ \rho \sigma \tau & \tau^2 \end{matrix} \right\},$$

calling $\overline{y_1^2} = \sigma^2$, $\overline{y_2^2} = \tau^2$, $\overline{y_1 y_2} = \rho \sigma \tau$; ρ is the correlation coefficient. This gives

$$B_{11} = \tau^2; \qquad B_{12} = -\rho \sigma \tau; \qquad B_{22} = \sigma^2; \qquad b = \sigma^2 \tau^2 (1 - \rho^2),$$

so that the distribution can be written

$$W(y_1, y_2) = \frac{1}{2\pi\sigma\tau \sqrt{1-\rho^2}} \exp\left[-\frac{1}{2(1-\rho^2)} \left(\frac{y_1^2}{\sigma^2} + \frac{y_2^2}{\tau^2} - \frac{2\rho y_1 y_2}{\sigma\tau} \right) \right]. \quad (43)$$

The general theorems mentioned in connection with the one-dimensional Gaussian distribution can also be generalized to the n-dimensional case. First of all one has again a central limit theorem. Interpreting $y_1 \ldots y_n$ as the n components of a vector $\mathbf{Y}$, and providing $\mathbf{Y}_1, \mathbf{Y}_2, \ldots, \mathbf{Y}_N$ are N independent random vectors, which are distributed according to the *same* probability distribution and which have a zero mean value and finite quadratic averages, then according to this theorem, the distribution of

$$\mathbf{Y} = \frac{\mathbf{Y}_1 + \mathbf{Y}_2 + \cdots + \mathbf{Y}_N}{\sqrt{N}}$$

will for large N approach the Gaussian distribution, regardless of the original distribution function[1] of the $\mathbf{Y}_i$. There is, furthermore, the theorem that when $\mathbf{Y}_1$ and $\mathbf{Y}_2$ are two independent random vectors, each of which has a Gaussian distribution, the sum $\mathbf{Y}_1 + \mathbf{Y}_2$ will also have a Gaussian distribution. This *stability property* is, with certain restrictions, again typical of the Gaussian distribution.

Another aspect of the stability of the Gaussian distribution is expressed by the following theorem (needed in Sec. 3·7). Suppose the variables $x_1, x_2, \ldots, x_n$ are distributed according to

$$W(x_1 \cdots x_n) = \frac{1}{(2\pi)^{n/2}} \frac{1}{\sigma_1 \sigma_2 \cdots \sigma_n} e^{-\frac{1}{2} \sum_1^n x_i^2 / \sigma_i^2}. \quad (44)$$

Let $y_1, y_2, \cdots, y_s$ $(s \leqq n)$ be s linear combinations of the x_i's,

[1] *Cf. ibid.*, Chap. 10, Theorem 20a.

$$y_k = \sum_{i=1}^{n} a_{ki} x_i, \qquad k = 1, 2, \cdots, s,$$

where the a_{ki}'s are constants. The y_k's will then be distributed according to an s-dimensional Gaussian distribution of the form in Eq. (39) (with n replaced by s) and with

$$b_{kl} = \overline{y_k y_l} = \sum_{i=1}^{n} a_{ki} a_{li} \sigma_i^2. \tag{45}$$

To prove this, there may be used the integral representation of the Dirac δ-function

$$\delta(x - x') = \frac{1}{2\pi} \int_{-\infty}^{+\infty} dt \, e^{it(x-x')}, \tag{46}$$

which allows one to write for the distribution function $P(y_1 \ldots y_s)$ of the y_i the expression

$$P(y_1 \cdots y_s) = \int_{-\infty}^{+\infty} \cdots \int dx_1 \cdots dx_n \, W(x_1 \cdots x_n)$$

$$\times \prod_{k=1}^{s} \delta\left(y_k - \sum_{i=1}^{n} a_{ki} x_i\right) = \frac{1}{(2n)^{n/2+s}} \frac{1}{\sigma_1 \cdots \sigma_n} \int_{-\infty}^{+\infty} \cdots \int$$

$$dx_1 \cdots dx_n \, e^{-\frac{1}{2}\sum_{1}^{n} x_i^2/\sigma_i^2} \int_{-\infty}^{+\infty} \cdots \int dt_1 \cdots dt_s \prod_{k=1}^{s} e^{it_k\left(y_k - \sum_{i=1}^{n} a_{ki} x_i\right)}$$

Interchanging the integrations over the x_i with those over the t_k, the integrations over the x_i can easily be carried out, obtaining

$$P(y_1 \cdots y_s) = \frac{1}{(2\pi)^s} \int_{-\infty}^{+\infty} \cdots \int dt_1 \cdots dt_s \, e^{i\sum_{1}^{s} y_k t_k - \frac{1}{2}\sum_{k,l} b_{kl} t_k t_l},$$

where the b_{kl}'s are given by Eq. (45). Or, in other words, the characteristic function of $P(y_1 \ldots y_s)$ is exp $(-\frac{1}{2} \Sigma b_{kl} t_k t_l)$, which is nothing but Eq. (41). Therefore P must be a Gaussian distribution of the form in Eq. (39).

3·6. The Random-walk Problem.—Consider a point that can move on a straight line with successive steps, either to the right or to the left. The steps will not be of equal size, but there is a basic probability $\phi(x) \, dx$ that the point will make a step of length between x and $x + dx$. What is the probability $\phi_n(z)\,dz$ that after n steps the displacement of the point lies between z and $z + dz$?

This is the famous random-walk problem formulated for the *one-dimensional* case. Clearly it is intimately connected with the central limit theorem of the probability theory, since $z = x_1 + x_2 + \cdots + x_n$, when the x_i's are the successive displacements of the point. But the problem occurs in many branches of physics; and especially for the *two-dimensional* case, the problem can be interpreted as the problem of the composition of n isoperiodic vibrations with given probability distribution for the amplitudes and for the phases.[1] The problem occurs in this form, for instance, when one investigates the return of a radar signal from a cloud. The different water drops produce scattered waves, each having different amplitude and phase. What we want to known is the probability for a certain amplitude and phase of the resultant of all these scattered waves. The problem is of fundamental importance and merits a brief solution here. For the detailed application to the problem of the radar return from a number of independent scatterers (clouds, "window," etc.), see Chap. 6.

Since the successive steps are independent of each other, $\phi_n(z)$ will fulfill the equation[2]

$$\phi_n(z) = \int_{-\infty}^{+\infty} \phi_{n-1}(z - x)\phi(x)\,dx, \tag{47}$$

with $\phi_1(x) \equiv \phi(x)$. The solution of this equation follows immediately from the convolution theorem of the Fourier transform. Let $\psi_n(u)$ be the Fourier transform of $\phi_n(x)$; then we obtain from Eq. (47),

$$\psi_n(u) = \psi_{n-1}(u)\psi(u),$$

with $\psi_1(u) \equiv \psi(u)$. Therefore $\psi_n(u) = [\psi(u)]^n$, and

$$\phi_n(x) = \frac{1}{2\pi} \int_{-\infty}^{+\infty} du\, e^{iux}[\psi(u)]^n, \tag{48a}$$

[1] This was the formulation of J. W. S. Rayleigh, *Scientific Papers*, Cambridge, London, 1899–1920, Vol. I, p. 491; Vol. IV, p. 370, who first gave a solution of the problem for large n. For a complete discussion of the problem and for further references, *cf.* S. Chandrasekhar, "Stochastic Problems in Physics and Astronomy," *Rev. Mod. Phys.*, **15**, No. 1, 1 (1943).

[2] The variables x and y can have all values between $-\infty$ and $+\infty$. Of course,

$$\int_{-\infty}^{+\infty} \phi_n(x)\,dx = 1,$$

since $\phi(x)$ is a probability density. From Eq. (47) it follows that

$$\int_{-\infty}^{+\infty} \phi_n(y)\,dy = \int_{-\infty}^{+\infty} \phi_{n-1}(z)\,dz,$$

so that the total probability remains 1, as it should.

with

$$\psi(u) = \int_{-\infty}^{+\infty} dx \, \phi(x) e^{-iux}. \tag{48b}$$

To discuss the behavior for large n and, especially, to see the connection with the central-limit theorem, let

$$y = \frac{z}{\sqrt{n}} = \frac{x_1 + x_2 \cdots + x_n}{\sqrt{n}}; \qquad u = \frac{v}{\sqrt{n}},$$

and assume that

$$\bar{x} = \int_{-\infty}^{+\infty} x\phi(x) \, dx = 0.$$

Developing Eq. (48b) in powers of v one obtains

$$\psi(v) = 1 - \frac{v^2}{2n} \overline{x^2} + \frac{iv^3}{6n^{3/2}} \overline{x^3} + O\left(\frac{1}{n^2}\right)$$

$$= e^{-\frac{v^2}{2n} \overline{x^2}} \left[1 + \frac{iv^3}{6n^{3/2}} \overline{x^3} + O\left(\frac{1}{n^2}\right) \right].$$

Therefore,

$$\Phi_n(y) = \sqrt{n} \, \phi_n(z) = \frac{1}{2\pi} \int_{-\infty}^{+\infty} dv \, e^{iyv - \frac{v^2}{2} \overline{x^2}} \left[1 + \frac{iv^3}{6\sqrt{n}} \overline{x^3} + O\left(\frac{1}{n}\right) \right]$$

$$= \frac{1}{2\pi} \left(1 - \frac{\rho}{6\sqrt{n}} \frac{d^3}{dy^3} + \cdots \right) \int_{-\infty}^{+\infty} dv \, e^{iyv - \frac{v^2\sigma^2}{2}}$$

$$= \frac{1}{\sigma\sqrt{2\pi}} \left(1 - \frac{\rho}{6\sqrt{n}} \frac{d^3}{dy^3} + \cdots \right) e^{-\frac{y^2}{2\sigma^2}},$$

calling $\overline{x^2} = \sigma^2$ and $\overline{x^3} = \rho$. This is Eq. (38); for large n, $\Phi(y)$ becomes therefore the Gaussian distribution and the error is of order $n^{-1/2}$ when the third moment[1] $\rho \neq 0$.

For the *two-dimensional* problem the treatment is similar. One obtains, for the probability that after n steps the point lies in the region $dx\,dy$, the general expression

$$W_N(x,y) = \frac{1}{(2\pi)^2} \int\!\!\int_{-\infty}^{+\infty} du \, dv \, e^{i(ux+vy)} [\psi(u,v)]^N,$$

where

$$\psi(u,v) = \int\!\!\int_{-\infty}^{+\infty} dx \, dy \, e^{-ij(ux+vy)} w(x,y), \tag{49}$$

---

[1] Note that the error is of order $1/n$ when $\phi(x)$ is an even function of x. It is also easy to carry the development one step further; the next term in the parentheses is

$$\frac{1}{24n} \left[(\overline{x^4} - 3\sigma^4) \frac{d^4}{dy^4} + 2\rho^2 \frac{d^6}{dy^6} \right].$$

and $w(x,y) \equiv W_1(x,y)$ is the probability density for one step. The most important case for the applications to be discussed in Chap. 6 is the one in which $w(x,y)$ is isotropic, so that one can write, introducing polar coordinates,

$$w(x,y) \, dx \, dy = \frac{1}{2\pi} f(r) \, dr \, d\phi.$$

By a calculation similar to that in the one-dimensional problem, it can be shown that for large N,

$$W_N(x,y) = \left\{ 1 + \frac{I_0^2}{64N} \left[\frac{\overline{r^4}}{(\overline{r^2})^2} - 1 \right] \left(\frac{\partial^2}{\partial x^2} + \frac{\partial^2}{\partial y^2} \right)^2 + \cdots \right\} \frac{1}{\pi I_0} e^{-\frac{x^2+y^2}{I_0}}, \tag{50}$$

where

$$\overline{r^2} = \int_0^\infty dr \, f(r) r^2 \qquad \overline{r^4} = \int_0^\infty dr \, f(r) r^4,$$

and $I_0 = N\overline{r^2}$. Except[1] for x, $y \gg I_0$ (where W_N is small anyway), W_N can be replaced by the isotropic two-dimensional Gaussian distribution

$$W(x,y) = \frac{1}{\pi I_0} e^{-\frac{x^2+y^2}{I_0}}, \tag{51}$$

with an error of the order $1/N$. For $I = x^2 + y^2$ this leads to the distribution

$$W(I) \, dI = \frac{dI}{I_0} e^{-\frac{I}{I_0}}, \tag{52a}$$

from which follows

$$\bar{I} = I_0, \qquad \overline{(I - I_0)^2} = I_0^2. \tag{52b}$$

This is sometimes called the *Rayleigh distribution*.

3·7. The Gaussian Random Process.—Noise problems in radio receivers, at least up to the detector stage where nonlinear elements begin to enter, involve a special type of random process (the Gaussian random process), for which a complete theory can be given. These processes are characterized by the fact that *all* the basic distribution functions W_n, mentioned in Sec. 3·1, are Gaussian distributions. This fact could be taken as the defining property of the process. But since, as we shall see, the spectrum essentially determines everything, it is, from the physical point of view, more natural to start with the Fourier development of the Gaussian random function $y(t)$.

Consider again, as in Sec. 3·3, the stationary random function $y(t)$ over a long time interval Θ. In contrast to what was done[2] in Sec. 3·3,

---

[1] This is of course a special case of the central limit theorem for two dimensions.

[2] Where $y(t)$ was taken zero outside the time interval Θ, and the resulting function

let us assume now that $y(t)$ is repeated periodically with the period Θ so that $y(t)$ can be developed in a Fourier *series*

$$y(t) = \sum_{k=1}^{\infty} (a_k \cos 2\pi f_k t + b_k \sin 2\pi f_k t), \qquad (53)$$

where $f_k = k/\Theta$. There is no constant term, since we shall assume that the average value of $y(t)$ is zero, an assumption that does not constitute a restriction, of course. The different members of the ensemble of functions $y_i(t)$ will have different Fourier coefficients a_k, b_k. These coefficients are therefore random variables, and we shall *assume* that they are all independent of each other and have Gaussian distribution with average values zero and with variances which may depend on the order k but which are the same for the a's and the b's. Or, in formula,

$$\left. \begin{array}{c} \overline{a_k} = \overline{b_k} = 0, \\ \overline{a_k a_l} = \overline{b_k b_l} = \sigma_k^2 \delta_{kl}; \qquad \overline{a_k b_l} = 0. \end{array} \right\} \qquad (54)$$

The probability that the a_k and b_l are in certain ranges da_k, db_l can be expressed as follows:

$$W(a_1, a_2, \cdots ; b_1, b_2, \cdots) = \prod_{k=1}^{\infty} \frac{1}{2\pi \sigma_k^2} e^{-\frac{a_k^2 + b_k^2}{2\sigma_k^2}}. \qquad (55)$$

The variances σ_k^2 are connected with the spectral density or power spectrum[1] $G(f)$; in fact,

$$\sigma_k^2 = \frac{1}{\Theta} G(f_k), \qquad (56)$$

since

$$\overline{y^2(t)} = \sum_k [\overline{a_k^2} \cos^2 2\pi f_k t + \overline{b_k^2} \sin^2 2\pi f_k t] = \sum_k \sigma_k^2$$

$$= \frac{1}{\Theta} \sum_k G(f_k) \approx \int_0^{\infty} G(f)\, df = \sigma^2, \qquad (57)$$

when $\Theta \to \infty$. This is identical with Eq. (12) or (23).

It follows from these assumptions that the basic distributions of Sec. 3·1 are all Gaussian. The method is best explained by considering a few examples.

---

was developed in a Fourier *integral*. Of course, both methods are artifices to obtain convergent expressions. Afterward one goes to the limit $\Theta \to \infty$; the two methods will then give the same results, and Θ will drop out of all the final formulas.

[1] The bar is omitted since $y(t)$ was assumed to be stationary.

The Distribution of y at Fixed t.—According to Eq. (53), y is, for a given t, a *linear* function of the basic random variables a_k, b_l. From the theorem proved in Sec. 3·5 (see page 49) we know that the probability distribution will be Gaussian with a variance given by Eq. (57) and a mean value zero. The time t has disappeared; this is as it should be, since $W_1(y)$ must be independent of t because the process is stationary.

The Joint Distribution of $y(t_1)$ and $y(t_2)$.—Since $y(t_1)$ and $y(t_2)$ are both linear functions of a_k, b_l, one will obtain, according to the theorem of Sec. 3·5, a two-dimensional Gaussian distribution; $\overline{y^2(t_1)}$ and $\overline{y^2(t_2)}$ are again given by Eq. (57), and

$$\overline{y(t_1)y(t_2)} = \sum_k \left(\overline{a_k^2} \cos 2\pi f_k t_1 \cos 2\pi f_k t_2 + \overline{b_k^2} \sin 2\pi f_k t_1 \sin 2\pi f_k t_2 \right)$$

$$= \sum_k \sigma_k^2 \cos 2\pi f_k(t_1 - t_2) \approx \int_0^\infty df\, G(f) \cos 2\pi f \tau = \rho(\tau)\sigma^2. \quad (58)$$

The correlation depends therefore only on $\tau = t_2 - t_1$, as it should, since the process is stationary. The distribution function [*cf.* Eq. (43)] is

$$W_2(y_1, y_2, \tau) = \frac{1}{2\pi\sigma^2 \sqrt{1 - \rho^2}} \exp\left[-\frac{1}{2\sigma^2(1 - \rho^2)}(y_1^2 + y_2^2 - 2\rho y_1 y_2) \right].$$

$$(59)$$

The quantity $\rho(\tau)$ is the normalized correlation function, and Eq. (58) expresses again the connection with the normalized spectrum,

$$S(f) = \frac{1}{\sigma^2} G(f) = \frac{G(f)}{\int_0^\infty df\, G(f)}.$$

The Joint Distribution of $y(t_1)$, $y(t_2)$, and $y(t_3)$.—We can go on in the manner just described. We can consider the third distribution function $W_3(y_1, t_1; y_2, t_2; y_3, t_3)$, which will be a three-dimensional Gaussian distribution depending only on $t_2 - t_1$ and $t_3 - t_2$. And from the theorem of Sec. 3·5 it follows clearly that *all* the distributions W_n will be Gaussian and will depend only on σ^2 and $\rho(\tau)$.

Distribution Functions of the Derivatives of y.—In the same way there can also be derived distribution functions in which the derivatives $y'(t)$, $y''(t)$, . . . appear. Since $y'(t)$, $y''(t)$, . . . are also linear functions of the random variables a_k, b_l, it is clear that their distribution functions will also be Gaussian, and we find, for instance, that

$$\left. \begin{aligned} \overline{y'(t)^2} &= \int_0^\infty (2\pi f)^2 G(f)\, df, \\ \overline{y''(t)^2} &= \int_0^\infty (2\pi f)^4 G(f)\, df, \end{aligned} \right\} \quad (60)$$

etc. We can also consider joint distributions of $y(t)$ and its derivatives, as, for example, the distribution of y and y' at a fixed t. This will be a two-dimensional Gaussian distribution, which is especially simple, however, since y and y' at a given t are *not* correlated. One gets, namely,

$$\overline{y(t)y'(t)} = \sum_k 2\pi f_k \sin 2\pi f_k t \cos 2\pi f_k t (-\overline{a_k^2} + \overline{b_k^2}) = 0.$$

It should still be pointed out that sometimes the distribution functions derived in this way will have no meaning, since some of the integrals over the spectrum are divergent. For instance, when $\rho(\tau) = e^{-\beta\tau}$ so that $G(f)\alpha 1/[\beta^2 + (2\pi f)^2]$ [see Eq. (27)], the distribution functions in which the velocity $y'(t)$ appears will have no meaning, since [see Eq. (60)] $\overline{y'^2}$ will not exist. In this case one may call the process *nondifferentiable*. The degree of differentiability will be characteristic for the process and will depend on the behavior of $G(f)$ for large f.

Finally, a few words should be said about the justification of the assumptions, embodied in Eq. (55), made in the beginning of this section. In the actual problems of the signal threshold in radio receivers the convenient fiction is always allowed that the signal, before it enters the receiver, is accompanied by a certain amount of noise. This will be called the *primary noise* and can be shown to be Gaussian, with a spectrum that is constant up to a very high frequency, so that for all practical purposes one can consider it a white spectrum (see Sec. 3·4). It can therefore be said that the *primary noise is a purely random, Gaussian process*. The proof of this statement must come from the analysis of the origins of the primary noise. In Chap. 4 this analysis will be given in detail for a few cases like thermal noise and shot noise. It is clear, however, that when this primary noise goes through a *linear* device (as, for instance, an i-f amplifier), which is characterized by an impedance function $Z(p)$, the output will again be Gaussian noise with a spectral density $D|Z(i\omega)|^2$, when D is the constant spectral density of the primary noise source. In the next section we shall see what happens when Gaussian noise passes through a *nonlinear* device.

3·8. Spectrum after a Nonlinear Device. *Method of North.*—Let us suppose we have an s-dimensional Gaussian process $y_1(t)$, $y_2(t)$, $\cdots$, $y_s(t)$, so that *all* the probability distributions are known, and let us suppose that

$$z = F(y_1, y_2, \cdots, y_s). \tag{61}$$

It is clear that in principle one can also find *all* the probability distributions for the random process $z(t)$. For instance, $W_1(z)\,dz$ would follow from $W_1(y_1 \ldots y_s)\,dy_1 \ldots dy_s$ by integrating over the y's with the condition that the function $F(y_1 \ldots y_s)$ must lie between z and $z + dz$.

It is also clear that *only* when the function F is *linear* will the resulting process $z(t)$ again be Gaussian. In all other cases one obtains a non-Gaussian process. The great difficulty then is in finding out what happens when such non-Gaussian noise passes through a linear network like, for instance, a filter. This is the reason why the main concentration has been on the calculation of the *spectral density*, since this will give at least some idea of the possible response of such a linear network. D. O. North[1] has pointed out that the spectral density can be calculated by first calculating the correlation function,

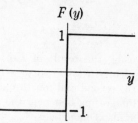

FIG. 3·6.—Characteristic for strong clipping.

$$\overline{z(t_1)z(t_2)} = \int \cdots \int dY_1 \, dY_2 \, F(Y_1)F(Y_2)W_2(Y_1, Y_2, t_2 - t_1), \quad (62)$$

where Y_1 is an abbreviation of $y_1(t_1)$, $y_2(t_1)$, . . . , $y_s(t_1)$. From the correlation function the spectrum can be obtained by means of the

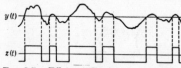

FIG. 3·7.—Effect of clipping on noise; large bandwidth.

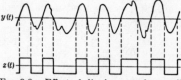

FIG. 3·8.—Effect of clipping on noise; small bandwidth.

general formula of Sec. 3·3. Most calculations of spectra have been made by this method, which we shall call the method of North. The following examples serve to illustrate the method.

Spectrum of Strongly Clipped Noise.[2]—Suppose that $y(t)$ is a one-dimensional Gaussian process and that $F(y) = 1$ for $y > 0$ and $= -1$ for $y < 0$ (see Fig. 3·6). The effect this has on the random function $y(t)$ is shown in Figs. 3·7 and 3·8; $z(t)$ will be a step curve between $+1$ and -1, which is more or less irregular depending on whether $y(t)$ is more or less sinusoidal. To find the spectrum of $z(t)$ we must calculate the correlation function [Eq. (62)]

---

[1] See for reference S. O. Rice, "Mathematical Analysis of Random Noise," *Bell System Techn. J.*, **25**, 45 (1945).

[2] The spectrum of strongly and partially clipped noise has been investigated in detail by J. H. van Vleck, "The Spectrum of Clipped Noise," RRL Report 51, July 21, 1943. One special case will be discussed here; some further results will be given in Sec. 12·5.

$$R(t) = \frac{1}{2\pi\sigma^2 \sqrt{1 - \rho^2}} \int\limits_{-\infty}^{+\infty} \int dy_1\, dy_2\, F(y_1)F(y_2) \cdot$$

$$\exp\left[-\frac{1}{2\sigma^2(1 - \rho^2)}\, (y_1^2 + y_2^2 - 2\rho y_1 y_2)\right],$$

using the result of Eq. (59) for the second probability distribution. Clearly, $F(y_1)F(y_2) = +1$ in the first and third quadrant and $= -1$ in the second and fourth quadrant. By introducing polar coordinates and integrating first over the radius vector, the integral can be easily evaluated. One gets

$$R(t) = \frac{2}{\pi} \sin^{-1} \rho(t). \tag{63}$$

To find the spectrum one must calculate the Fourier cosine transform of $R(t)$. The discussion is complicated and depends, of course, on what one assumes for $\rho(t)$. Most interesting is the case in which the spectrum $S(f)$ of $y(t)$ has a maximum at some high frequency f_0 and is symmetric around f_0 [cf. Sec. 3·4, Eq. (29)]. Then $\rho(t) = \cos 2\pi f_0 t \Phi(t)$, where $\Phi(t)$ is the Fourier transform of the spectrum of $y(t)$ with f_0 as origin; $\Phi(0) = 1$, since $S(f)$ is assumed normalized to unity. Developing the $\sin^{-1}$ in a power series

$$R(t) = \frac{2}{\pi}\left(\rho + \frac{1}{2}\frac{\rho^3}{3} + \frac{1\cdot3}{2\cdot4}\frac{\rho^5}{5} + \cdots\right) = \frac{2}{\pi}\sum_{p=0}^{\infty} a_p \rho^{2p+1},$$

and using

$$\cos^{2p+1}\alpha = \frac{1}{2^{2p}} \sum_{s=0}^{p} \binom{2p+1}{p-s} \cos(2s+1)\alpha,$$

we can write for the spectrum of $z(t)$

$$G(f) = \frac{4}{\pi}\sum_{s=0}^{\infty} \int_0^{\infty} d\tau \cos 2\pi\tau\,[f - (2s+1)f_0] \sum_{p=s}^{\infty} \frac{a_p}{2^{2p}}\binom{2p+1}{p-s}\Phi^{2p+1}(\tau), \quad (64)$$

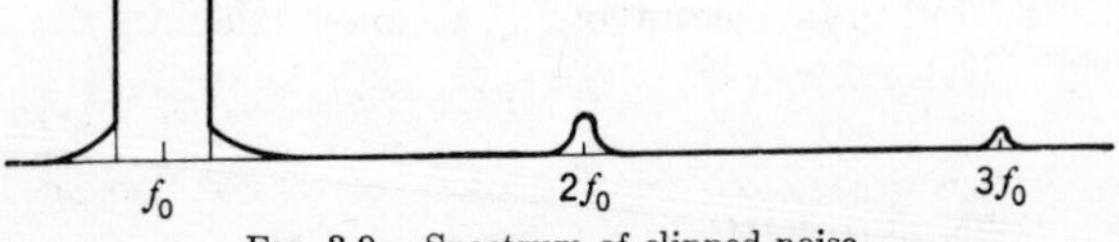

Fig. 3·9.—Spectrum of clipped noise.

where we have neglected terms with $\cos 2\pi\tau[f + (2s+1)f_0]$, which is consistent with the assumption that f_0 is large compared with the bandwidth of $S(f)$. The expression shows that there are overtones. The spectrum will consist of bands around f_0, $2f_0$, $3f_0$, . . . , each of approximately the same bandwidth as $S(f)$ (see Fig. 3·9). Of special interest is the deformation of the band around f_0 from the original form $S(f)$. Taking $s = 0$ in Eq. (64) and making special assumptions for $S(f)$, the calculation can be carried out; for $S(f)$, a square band, the result is shown in Fig. 3·10, which is taken from Van Vleck's report. The deformation is small.   There is, of course, less energy in the fundamental, since we have the higher harmonics also.   From Eq. (64) it can be proved that the area under the fundamental is reduced from 1 to $8/\pi^2$, so that a fraction $1 - 8/\pi^2$ of the total energy is converted into harmonics. This fraction and in fact the whole distribution of energy over the different harmonics are the same as for a square wave of frequency f_0. This conclusion is also plausible, since $y(t)$ will be very much like a sinusoidal curve, the bandwidth of $S(f)$ being supposed small compared with f_0.

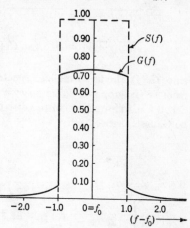

FIG. 3·10.—Spectrum of clipped noise; shape of the fundamental. The quantity $(f - f_0)$ is in units of the half bandwidth of the noise before clipping.

Spectrum of Gaussian Noise after a Linear or Square-law Detector.— Suppose that the spectrum of the original Gaussian random process $V(t)$ is again concentrated around the high carrier frequency f_0 and that it is again symmetric around f_0. It is often convenient to measure the frequency from f_0 and to write the Fourier development of $V(t)$ in the form

$$V(t) = x(t) \cos 2\pi f_0 t + y(t) \sin 2\pi f_0 t, \tag{65}$$

where

$$\left. \begin{aligned} x(t) &= \sum_{-\infty}^{+\infty} (a_k \cos 2\pi f_k t + b_k \sin 2\pi f_k t), \\ y(t) &= \sum_{-\infty}^{+\infty} (-a_k \sin 2\pi f_k t + b_k \cos 2\pi f_k t), \end{aligned} \right\} \tag{66}$$

and $f_k = k/\Theta$ is measured[1] from f_0.   From the basic properties [Eqs. (54)

[1] The lower limit in the sums should, of course, be $-k_0$, when $f_0 = k_0/\Theta$, but it may be replaced by $-\infty$.

and (56)] of the a_k, b_l it is easily proved that

$$\left. \begin{array}{c} \overline{x^2(t)} = \overline{y^2(t)} = \int_{-\infty}^{+\infty} df\, G_V(f) = \sigma^2, \\[2mm] \overline{x(t)x(t+\tau)} = \overline{y(t)y(t+\tau)} = \int_{-\infty}^{+\infty} df\, G_V(f)\cos 2\pi f\tau, \\[2mm] \overline{x(t)y(t+\tau)} = \int_{-\infty}^{+\infty} df\, G_V(f)\sin 2\pi f\tau = 0, \end{array} \right\} \qquad (67)$$

since $G_V(f)$, the unnormalized spectrum of $V(t)$—always with f measured from f_0—is supposed to be an *even* function of f. From the theorem of Sec. 3·5 it follows that all the distribution functions of the $x(t)$, $y(t)$ will be Gaussian, specifically,

$$W_1(x,y) = \frac{1}{2\pi\sigma^2} e^{-\frac{x^2+y^2}{2\sigma^2}}, \qquad (68a)$$

$$W_2(x_1, y_1; x_2 y_2; \tau) = \frac{1}{(2\pi\sigma^2)^2(1-\rho^2)} \exp$$

$$\left\{ -\frac{1}{2\sigma^2(1-\rho^2)} [x_1^2 + y_1^2 + x_2^2 + y_2^2 - 2\rho(x_1 x_2 + y_1 y_2)] \right\} \quad (68b)$$

with[1]

$$\sigma^2 = \int_{-\infty}^{+\infty} G_V(f)\, df; \qquad \sigma^2\rho(\tau) = \int_{-\infty}^{+\infty} df\, G_V(f)\cos 2\pi f\tau.$$

When noise of the general form [Eq. (65)] enters a *linear detector*, the output, as explained in Chap. 2, will be linearly proportional to the *envelope* of the r-f or carrier wave. That is, the output $L(t)$ is given by

$$L(t) = \sqrt{x^2(t) + y^2(t)}. \qquad (69)$$

Analogously, for a *square-law detector* the output $Q(t)$ is proportional to the square of the envelope, or

$$Q(t) = x^2(t) + y^2(t). \qquad (70)$$

It will be important in these two cases to know what the probability distributions and the spectra of the random functions $L(t)$ and $Q(t)$ are. The first two probability distributions follow, of course, from Eqs. (68a) and (68b) by introducing polar coordinates and integrating over the angles. One finds, for the first probability distributions,

---

[1] Note in the expression for $\rho(\tau)$ that the lower limit of the integral is $-\infty$ in contrast to Eq. (22) or (58); $\rho(\tau)$ is the same as the $\Phi(\tau)$ in our first example, since there the spectrum of $y(t)$ was assumed to be normalized.

$$W_1(L) = \frac{L}{\sigma^2} e^{-\frac{L^2}{2\sigma^2}},$$
$$\bar{L} = \sigma \sqrt{\frac{\pi}{2}},$$

$$(71a)$$

$$W_1(Q) = \frac{1}{2\sigma^2} e^{-\frac{Q}{2\sigma^2}},$$
$$Q = 2\sigma^2.$$

$$(71b)$$

(See Figs. 3·11 and 3·12; note that for the square-law detector the most probable value of Q is zero whereas in the linear case the most probable

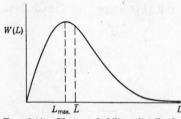

FIG. 3·11.—First probability distribution for the deflection; linear detector.   FIG. 3·12.—First probability distribution for the deflection; square-law detector.

value of L is σ.)   The second probability distributions are more complicated and less important.   Only the result for the linear case is given, namely,

$$W_2(L_1,L_2,\tau) = \frac{L_1 L_2}{\sigma^4(1-\rho^2)} e^{-\frac{L_1{}^2+L_2{}^2}{2\sigma^2(1-\rho^2)}} I_0\left[\frac{\rho L_1 L_2}{\sigma^2(1-\rho^2)}\right], \qquad (72)$$

where $I_0(x)$ is the Bessel function of order zero and imaginary argument.[1]

To find the spectra the correlation functions are computed.   This means, according to Eq. (62), that we have to calculate the integral (in the square-law case)

$$\overline{Q(t)Q(t+\tau)} = \int\int_{-\infty}^{+\infty}\int\int dx_1\, dy_1\, dx_2\, dy_2\, (x_1^2+y_1^2)(x_2^2+y_2^2)$$

$$W_2(x_1y_1; x_2y_2; \tau).$$

This can be done quite simply.[2]   We find

$$\overline{Q(t)Q(t+\tau)} = 4\sigma^4(1+\rho^2). \qquad (73)$$

[1] $I_0(x) = J_0(ix)$; one has made use in the derivation of Eq. (72) of the integral

$$I_0(x) = \frac{1}{2\pi}\int_0^{2\pi} d\theta\, e^{x\cos\theta}.$$

[2] Note that W_2 according to Eq. (68b) can be considered as the product of two independent two-dimensional Gaussian distributions in x_1, x_2 and y_1, y_2. Using, for instance, the general formula [Eq. (42)] for the calculations of average values, we easily obtain

$$\overline{x_1^2 x_2^2} = \overline{y_1^2 y_2^2} = \sigma^4(1+2\rho^2); \qquad \overline{x_1^2 y_2^2} = \overline{x_2^2 y_1^2} = \sigma^4,$$

from which Eq. (73) follows.

For the linear detector the calculation is more involved. Only the following result is given here:

$$\overline{L(t)L(t+\tau)} = \sigma^2[2E(\rho) - (1-\rho^2)K(\rho)]$$

$$= \frac{\pi}{2}\sigma^2\left(1 + \frac{\rho^2}{4} + \frac{\rho^4}{64} + \cdots\right), \tag{74}$$

where K and E are the complete elliptic integrals of the first and second kind.

Finally the Fourier transform of Eqs. (73) and (74) must be determined to obtain the spectra of $Q(t)$ and $L(t)$. Equations (73) and (74) contain a *constant* term equal to $(\bar{Q})^2$ and $(\bar{L})^2$, respectively, and these

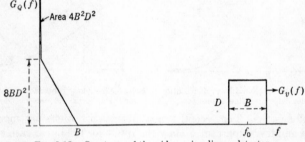

Fig. 3·13.—Spectrum of the video noise; linear detector.

terms, of course, will give the d-c terms [*cf.* Eq. (24)]. The terms with ρ^2, according to the convolution theorem of the Fourier transform, contribute to the spectrum

$$\int_{-\infty}^{+\infty} \sigma^4\rho^2(\tau)\cos 2\pi f\tau \, d\tau = \int_{-\infty}^{+\infty} df_1 \, G_V(f_1)G_V(f-f_1). \tag{75}$$

By applying the convolution theorem over and over again we can find the contribution of the higher powers of ρ in Eq. (74) and in this way express the spectrum of $Q(t)$ and $L(t)$ completely in terms of the original spectrum $G_V(f)$ of $V(t)$. Fortunately the convergence of the series [Eq. (74)] is so rapid that it is usually possible to stop with the term in ρ^2.

The precise shape of the spectra depends, of course, on the shape of $G_V(f)$. Figures 3·13 and 3·14 give the results when $G_V(f)$ is a square band of height D and width B. These results represent the equations

$$G_Q(f) = 8B^2D^2 \, \delta(f) + 8D^2(B-f),$$

$$G_L(f) = \pi BD \, \delta(f) + \frac{\pi D}{4B}(B-f) + \cdots.$$

Besides the d-c peak there is a triangular continuous spectrum. For the square-law case this is exact; note that the width is B and that the height at the origin is proportional to B; the area is

$$4B^2D^2 = 4\sigma^2 = \overline{Q^2} - (\overline{Q})^2,$$

as it should be. For the linear case, the triangle is only an approximation, though a very good one. The area of the triangle is

$$\left(\frac{\pi}{8}\right) BD = 0.39\sigma^2;$$

the true area is, of course,

$$\overline{L^2} - (\overline{L})^2 = \left[2 - \left(\frac{\pi}{2}\right) \right] \sigma^2 = 0.43\sigma^2.$$

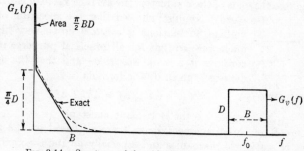

FIG. 3·14.—Spectrum of the video noise; square-law detector.

The height of the spectrum at the origin is $(\pi/4)D$ and therefore independent of the bandwidth[1] B; this remains true for the exact spectrum; the height, however, is not $(\pi/4)D$ but about 6 per cent greater. The width of the triangle is again B, whereas the true spectrum also contains higher frequencies than B, with, however, very small intensities.

[1] This was pointed out by J. R. Ragazzini, "The Effect of Fluctuation Voltage on the Linear Detector," *Proc. I.R.E.*, **30**, 277 (1942).

CHAPTER 4

BASIC ORIGINS OF INTERNAL NOISE[1]

THERMAL NOISE

4·1. Statistical Derivation of the Thermal Noise Spectrum.—Suppose one has a conductor of resistance R at temperature T. Because of the random motion of the electrons there will be small fluctuations of the voltage across the ends of the conductor; the average value of the fluctuations is, of course, zero. Nyquist[2] showed that the spectrum of these voltage fluctuations is *constant* up to very high fre-

FIG. 4·1.—Two resistors at the same temperature T.

quencies[3]—so that for all practical purposes one can consider it a *white spectrum*—and that the spectral density is given by the formula

$$G_V(f)\, \Delta f = 4RkT\, \Delta f, \qquad (1)$$

where k is the Boltzmann constant.

The proofs of this fundamental result are all based on the general principles of statistical mechanics and especially on the theorem of the equipartition of energy. The proof of Nyquist is outlined first.

Consider two conductors with resistances R_1 and R_2 at the same temperature T connected to each other (see Fig. 4·1). Suppose, furthermore, that the resistances are independent of frequency and that their self-capacitances and self-inductances are negligibly small for all frequencies that are of interest. Nyquist first observes that for *any* frequency range Δf the power transferred from R_1 to R_2 must be the same as the power transferred back from R_2 to R_1. This must be so because by interposing a suitable ideal filter that will pass only frequencies in the range Δf one can ensure that currents of these frequenices are the only ones that can exchange energy between the two resistors. And since they are at the same temperature, the second law of thermody-

[1] The authors will attempt no more than a summary of the main theoretical results and of some of the experiments. The literature on the subject is very large, and the authors feel that they may have overlooked some significant contribution. They regret especially that space does not permit a more detailed account of the many experimental investigations. For this and for the literature up to 1938, reference is made especially to E. B. Moullin, *Spontaneous Fluctuations of Voltage*, Oxford, New York, 1938.

[2] H. Nyquist, *Phys. Rev.*, **32**, 110 (1928).

[3] For the discussion of this upper limit, see Sec. 4·5.

namics (which is, of course, a consequence of statistical mechanics) requires that, on the average, no energy is transferred from the one resistor to the other. Now the spontaneous voltage fluctuations across each of the two resistors may be represented by the electromotive forces E_1 and E_2, whose average values are zero and whose spectral densities $G_{E_1}(f)$ and $G_{E_2}(f)$ are still unknown functions of f. It follows then from simple circuit theory that the average power transferred from R_1 to R_2 in the frequency range Δf is given by

$$G_{E_1}(f) \, \Delta f \, \frac{R_2}{(R_1 + R_2)^2}, \tag{2a}$$

and the average power transferred back from R_2 to R_1 is

$$G_{E_2}(f) \, \Delta f \, \frac{R_1}{(R_1 + R_2)^2}. \tag{2b}$$

Since these must be equal, one obtains

$$G_{E_1}(f)R_2 = G_{E_2}(f) \, R_1. \tag{3}$$

In particular, if $R_1 = R_2$, it is clear that the spectral density of the fluctuating voltage must be a universal function of the resistance, temperature, and frequency and that it must be independent of the nature of the two resistors and of the mechanism of the conduction of electricity through them.

To find the universal function, Nyquist imagines that the interchange of energy between the two conductors[1] takes place by means of a lossless transmission line of characteristic impedance R, so that both resistors are matched. There is then no reflection at either end of the line; all power emitted by one resistor is absorbed by the other, and vice versa. When equilibrium has been established there will be present in the line electromagnetic energy of an amount[2]

$$\frac{2L}{v} \, kT \, \Delta f$$

in the frequency range Δf. Here L is the length of the line and v the velocity of propagation of the waves. This expression follows from the fact that there are $(2L/v) \, \Delta f$ modes of vibration in the range Δf and that each mode, according to the equipartition law, has the energy kT (namely, $\frac{1}{2}kT$ electric and $\frac{1}{2}kT$ magnetic energy). The energy density in the range Δf is therefore $(2kT/v) \, \Delta f$; half of this is carried by waves going to the right, and the energy that flows into the resistor on the right per

---

[1] Now supposed to have the *same* resistance R.

[2] This is the one-dimensional form of the well-known Rayleigh-Jeans law of radiation theory.

second is therefore $v(kT/v) \, \Delta f = kT \, \Delta f$. This is the average power transferred from one resistor to the other, which, on the other hand, according to Eqs. (2) (with $R_1 = R_2$) is equal to $G_E(f) \, \Delta f/4R$. By equating these two expressions for the power transfer, one obtains Eq. (1).

4·2. The Gaussian Character of Thermal Noise.—One can also connect the resistance R, possessing the fluctuating electromotive force $E(t)$, to an inductance or capacitance or, in general, to an ideal network made up of inductances and capacitances. By applying the equipartition theorem to the electric or magnetic energy of the network one may obtain another proof of the fundamental formula [Eq. (1)]; this method can also be generalized so that one can prove in addition that $E(t)$ must be a Gaussian random process.[1]

Fig. 4·2.—Thermal noise source connected to a self-inductance.

The simplest method of procedure is to connect R to an inductance L (Fig. 4·2). The circuit equation[2] is then

$$L \frac{di}{dt} + Ri = E(t). \tag{4}$$

If for $t = 0$ the current is i_0, then

$$i(t) = i_0 e^{-\frac{R}{L}t} + \frac{1}{L} e^{-\frac{R}{L}t} \int_0^t d\xi \, E(\xi) e^{+\frac{R}{L}\xi}. \tag{5}$$

Since $\bar{E} = 0$ (the averaging is now over an *ensemble*),

$$\overline{i(t)} = i_0 e^{-\frac{R}{L}t}.$$

The average current goes down exponentially. Squaring Eq. (5) and taking the average gives

$$\overline{i^2(t)} = i_0^2 e^{-2\frac{R}{L}t} + \frac{1}{L^2} e^{-2\frac{R}{L}t} \int_0^t \int_0^t d\xi \, d\eta \, e^{+\frac{R}{L}(\xi+\eta)} \overline{E(\xi)E(\eta)}. \tag{6}$$

We shall now *assume* that

$$\overline{E(\xi)E(\eta)} = \sigma^2 \delta(\xi - \eta), \tag{7}$$

where σ^2 is an unknown constant. This assumption is, of course, equi-

---

[1] In this form the theory of thermal noise in linear networks becomes mathematically completely analogous to the theory of the Brownian motion of a system of coupled harmonic oscillators; *cf.* for instance, Ming Chen Wang and G. E. Uhlenbeck, "The Theory of the Brownian Motion, II" *Rev. Mod. Phys.*, **17**, 323 (1945).

[2] This is completely analogous to the equation of motion of a free particle in Brownian motion. *Cf.* especially G. E. Uhlenbeck and L. S. Ornstein, "The Theory of the Brownian Motion, I," *Phys. Rev.*, **36**, 823, Sec. 2 (1930).

valent to the assumption that the spectral density of $E(t)$ is constant; in fact, one can see that

$$G_E(f) = 4 \int_0^\infty d\tau \, \cos 2\pi f \tau \overline{E(t)E(t+\tau)} = 2\sigma^2. \qquad (8)$$

If, in Eq. (6), we let $\xi + \eta = v$, $\xi - \eta = w$, the double integral becomes

$$\frac{1}{2L^2} e^{-\frac{2R}{L}t} \int_0^{2t} dv \, e^{\frac{R}{L}v} \int_{-\infty}^{+\infty} dw \, \sigma^2 \delta(w) = \frac{\sigma^2}{2RL} \left(1 - e^{-\frac{2R}{L}t} \right),$$

so that

$$\overline{i^2(t)} = \frac{\sigma^2}{2RL} + \left(i_0^2 - \frac{\sigma^2}{2RL} \right) e^{-\frac{2R}{L}t}. \qquad (9)$$

This equation shows that $\overline{i^2}$ starts from a value i_0^2 and for $t \to \infty$ reaches the constant value $\sigma^2/2RL$. On the other hand it is known from the equipartition theorem that in the equilibrium state

$$\tfrac{1}{2}L\overline{i^2} = \tfrac{1}{2}kT.$$

Therefore σ^2 must be $2RkT$; or according to Eq. (8), $G_E(f) = 4RkT$. Equation (9) shows in detail, then, how the equipartition value is reached.

Of course, one could have reached the conclusion $\sigma^2 = 2RkT$ more directly by observing that as a consequence of Eq. (4) the spectral density of the current is

$$G_i(f) = \frac{G_E(f)}{|R + 2\pi i f L|^2}. \qquad (10a)$$

With Eq. (8), this yields

$$\overline{i^2} = \int_0^\infty df \, G_i(f) = 2\sigma^2 \int_0^\infty \frac{df}{R^2 + 4\pi^2 f^2 L^2} = \frac{\sigma^2}{2RL}, \qquad (10b)$$

and σ^2 is again determined by the equipartition theorem. It should be pointed out that in this derivation the constancy of the spectral density $G_E(f)$ is assumed, whereas in Nyquist's proof of Sec. 4·1 it is derived. With our method, however, we can now go a step further. In the equilibrium state we know not only that $L\overline{i^2} = kT$ but also that the first probability distribution $W(i)$ for the current must be the Maxwell-Boltzmann distribution

$$W(i) = \sqrt{\frac{L}{2\pi kT}} \, e^{-\frac{Li^2}{2kT}}. \qquad (11)$$

This is equivalent [see Eq. (3·7a)] to

$$\overline{i^{2k+1}} = 0,$$
$$\overline{i^{2k}} = 1 \cdot 3 \cdot 5 \cdots (2k-1) \, (\overline{i^2})^k.$$

The higher moments of $i(t)$ can be calculated from Eq. (5). If the foregoing requirements are to be fulfilled as $t \to \infty$, it is necessary and sufficient[1] that $E(t)$ fulfill, *besides* Eq. (7), the relations

$$\overline{E(t_1) E(t_2) \cdots E(t_{2k+1})} = 0; \tag{12a}$$

$$\overline{E(t_1) E(t_2) \cdots E(t_{2k})} = \sum_{\text{(all pairs)}} \overline{E(t_i) E(t_j)} \cdot \overline{E(t_k) E(t_l)} \cdots, \tag{12b}$$

where the sum has to be taken over all the different ways in which one can divide the $2k$ time points $t_1, t_2, \ldots, t_{2k}$, into k pairs.

It clearly follows from Eqs. (7) and (12) that $E(t)$ is a Gaussian random process with the constant spectral density $2\sigma^2$. First, from Eq. (12a) it follows that the average values of all the *odd* powers of the Fourier coefficients of $E(t)$ in the time interval Θ,

$$a_k = \frac{2}{\Theta} \int_0^\Theta dt \cos 2\pi f_k t E(t), \qquad b_l = \frac{2}{\Theta} \int_0^\Theta dt \sin 2\pi f_l t E(t),$$

are zero. Furthermore, from Eq. (12b)

$$\overline{a_k^{2n}} = \left(\frac{2}{\Theta}\right)^{2n} \int \cdots \int_0^\Theta dt_1 \cdots dt_{2n} \cos 2\pi f_k t_1 \cdots \cos 2\pi f_k t_{2n}$$
$$\overline{E(t_1) \cdots E(t_{2n})}$$

$$= 1 \cdot 3 \cdot 5 \cdots (2n-1) \left[\frac{4}{\Theta^2} \int\int_0^\Theta dt_1\, dt_2 \cos 2\pi f_k t_1 \cos 2\pi f_k t_2 \right.$$
$$\left. \overline{E(t_1) E(t_2)} \right]^n$$

$$= 1 \cdot 3 \cdot 5 \cdots (2n-1)(\overline{a_k^2})^n,$$

since there are $1 \cdot 3 \ldots (2n-1)$ ways in which one can divide the $2n$ time points $t_1 \cdots t_{2n}$ into n pairs. The distribution function for the a_k is therefore Gaussian, and analogously one can show that the b_l's have a Gaussian distribution and that the different a_k's and b_l's are independent of each other; hence the complete distribution function $W(a_1, a_2, \ldots; b_1, b_2, \ldots)$ is given by Eq. (3·55), with

$$\sigma_k^2 = \overline{a_k^2} = \overline{b_k^2} = \frac{2\sigma^2}{\Theta}.$$

This last fact follows from Eq. (7) and is equivalent to the statement that the spectral density is $2\sigma^2\, \Delta f$.

[1] See G. E. Uhlenbeck and L. S. Ornstein, *op. cit.*, Note 1, for details of the proof.

4·3. Kinetic Derivation of the Thermal Noise Spectrum.—Although the fundamental result [Eq. (1)] is independent of the mechanism of the conduction of electricity, it is of great interest to show how one can obtain Eq. (1) from a definite model for the electric conduction through a metal.[1]

Consider a piece of metal of length L and cross section Q. We shall assume the simplest possible picture of the electronic conduction through

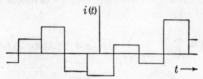

FIG. 4·3.—Current as a function of the time for one electron.

the metal, the so-called "Drude model." All the electrons are independent of each other, have the same speed v, and have the constant mean free path λ, so that there is also a constant time $\tau = \lambda/v$ between successive collisions. The velocity v is connected to the temperature T by the equipartition theorem,

$$\tfrac{1}{2}mv^2 = \tfrac{3}{2}kT. \tag{13}$$

If we follow one electron in the course of time, then it is clear[2] that the current produced will consist of blocks of height ev_x/L and of width τ, where v_x is the component of the velocity along the metal (see Fig. 4·3). The blocks will be assumed to be independent of each other, which means that the v_x before collision does not affect the probability of the v_x after collision. The average value of $i(t)$ is, of course, zero. Introducing again a long periodicity interval Θ (*cf.* Sec. 3·7), one can develop $i(t)$ in the Fourier series

$$i(t) = \sum_{k=0}^{\infty} (a_k \cos 2\pi f_k t + b_k \sin 2\pi f_k t).$$

[1] This was performed by J. Bernamont, *Ann. phys.*, **7**, 71 (1937). The authors follow essentially the simple proof given by D. A. Bell, *J.I.E.E.*, **82**, 522, (1938). *Cf.* also S. Goudsmit and P. Weiss, RL Report No. 43-20 (1943). More refined analyses have been attempted by C. J. Bakker and G. Heller, *Physica*, **6**, 262 (1939), and by E. Spenke, *Wiss. Veröffentl. Siemens-Werken*, **18**, 54 (1939). In the opinion of the authors, however, a completely satisfactory kinetic proof of Eq. (1), based on the modern theory of metals, is still lacking.

[2] Consider the metal to be in the shape of a ring. If the electron always had the velocity v_x, then the charge passing through any cross section per second would be e divided by the time L/v_x necessary to go around the conductor; the current would therefore be ev_x/L. After each time τ, however, this value changes, since v_x changes at each collision of the electron with an ion.

For all frequencies f_k that are small compared with $1/\tau$, we obtain for the Fourier coefficients

$$a_k = \frac{2}{\Theta} \int_0^\Theta dt\, i(t) \cos 2\pi f_k t = \frac{2\tau}{\Theta} \sum_{i=1}^n \frac{ev_{x_i}}{L} \cos 2\pi f_k t_i,$$

where the t_i's are $n = (\Theta/\tau)$ time points spaced τ apart from each other. We must now calculate the ensemble average of a_k^2 ($\bar{a}_k$ is, of course, zero, since $\bar{v}_{x_i} = 0$). We have

$$\overline{a_k^2} = \frac{4e^2\tau^2}{\Theta^2 L^2} \sum_i \sum_j \overline{v_{x_i} v_{x_j}} \cos 2\pi f_k t_i \cos 2\pi f_k t_j.$$

Because of independence assumption $\overline{v_{x_i} v_{x_j}} = \bar{v}_{x_i} \bar{v}_{x_j} = 0$ when $i \neq j$. On the other hand $\overline{v_{x_i}^2} = \frac{1}{3}v^2 = kT/m$ because of the isotropy of the metal and Eq. (13). We therefore obtain

$$\overline{a_k^2} = \frac{4e^2\tau^2 kT}{m\Theta^2 L^2} \sum_i \cos^2 2\pi f_k t_i.$$

The sum can again be replaced by an integral, and it then becomes apparent that the sum is equal to $\frac{1}{2}(\Theta/\tau)$. Calculating $\overline{b_k^2}$ and $\overline{a_k b_k}$ in the same way, we finally find

$$\overline{a_k^2} = \overline{b_k^2} = \frac{2e^2\tau kT}{m\Theta L^2}; \qquad \overline{a_k b_k} = 0.$$

This is also the mean-square value of the component of the current of frequency f_k, since

$$\overline{i_k^2} = \overline{a_k^2} \cos^2 2\pi f_k t + \overline{b_k^2} \sin^2 2\pi f_k t = \overline{a_k^2}.$$

Since in a frequency range Δf there are $\Theta\, \Delta f$ of such components and since there are, say, N electrons that are completely independent of each other, one obtains, for the spectral density of the total current,

$$G_i(f)\, \Delta f = N\overline{i_k^2}\Theta\, \Delta f = \frac{2e^2\tau kTN}{mL^2}\, \Delta f. \tag{14}$$

The value of the resistance for this model must now be calculated. If an electric field F is applied along the metal, it is clear that between two collisions each electron will gain $eF\tau/m$ in velocity. The average drift velocity will clearly be half of this, and the average current density is therefore

$$j = \frac{e^2 n\tau}{2m}\, F,$$

where n is the electron density. The electric conductivity σ is, therefore, $en\tau/2m$, and the resistance

$$R = \frac{L}{\sigma Q} = \frac{2mL}{e^2 n\tau Q} = \frac{2mL^2}{e^2 N\tau}. \tag{15}$$

Combining Eqs. (14) and (15) we find, for the spectral density of the voltage,

$$G_V(f) = R^2 G_i(f) = 4RkT,$$

which is the formula of Nyquist.

From the general statistical arguments of Secs. 4·1 and 4·2 it follows that the result should be independent of the many special assumptions we made. Some of these can be removed quite easily. For instance, the successive blocks do not have to be independent of each other; the whole series of blocks can always be divided into groups that *are* independent and each group replaced by the average value of the blocks in the group. It is more important and more difficult to take the velocity distribution of the electrons into account. These questions will not be gone into, since a quite satisfactory analysis has not yet been given. It should be pointed out, however, that the velocity distribution (or, better, the fluctuation of the total energy of the electrons) *must* be taken into account, since on the basis of the Drude model it is *not* possible to prove the Gaussian character of the thermal noise. For instance, to show that

$$\overline{a_k^4} = 3(\overline{a_k^2})^2,$$

which is necessary when the a_k's have a Gaussian distribution, it is necessary that

$$\overline{v_{x_i}^4} = 3(\overline{v_{x_i}^2})^2,$$

which is not the case when the averages are taken over the different directions of the constant speed v.

4·4. Generalizations. *Theorems of Nyquist and Williams.*—We have seen that the voltage fluctuations across a resistance R at temperature T can be accounted for by a fluctuating electromotive force $E(t)$ of average value zero and of constant spectral density $4RkT$. Of course, we could

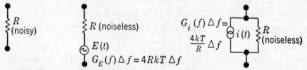

FIG. 4·4.—Equivalent representations of the noise in a resistor.

also have said that the voltage fluctuations are due to a fluctuating current source of average value zero and of constant spectral density $4kT/R$ (see Fig. 4·4 where the equivalent representations are presented).

In this section some generalizations of the theory given in Secs. 4·1 and 4·2 will be discussed. These generalizations are useful in practice and further strengthen the representations made above.

1. Let us suppose that the resistance R is connected to a resonant circuit (see Fig. 4·5). It will be shown that as a consequence of $G_E(f) = 4RkT$, both the average magnetic energy $\frac{1}{2}L\overline{i^2}$ and the average electric energy $\overline{Q^2}/2C$ are equal to $\frac{1}{2}kT$, where Q is the charge on the capacitor C. One finds [analogous to Eq. (10a)]

FIG. 4·5.—Thermal noise source connected to a series-resonant circuit.

$$\frac{1}{2} L\overline{i^2} = 2RLkT \int_0^\infty \frac{df}{R^2 + \left(\omega L - \dfrac{1}{\omega C}\right)^2},$$

$$\frac{1}{2} \frac{\overline{Q^2}}{C} = \frac{2RkT}{C} \int_0^\infty \frac{df}{\omega^2 \left[R^2 + \left(\omega L - \dfrac{1}{\omega C}\right)^2 \right]},$$

where $\omega = 2\pi f$. It is merely an exercise in integral calculus to show that the right-hand sides are *independent* of R and both equal to $\frac{1}{2}kT$.

2. One can generalize the above result to an arbitrary linear network of n meshes. This may be of interest, since the way in which the resistance dropped out of the expression for the total energy may seem rather accidental. If associated with each resistance is a noise emf, the circuit equations can be written[1]

$$\sum_{j=1}^n \left(L_{ij} \frac{d^2 y_j}{dt^2} + R_{ij} \frac{dy_j}{dt} + S_{ij} y_j \right) = \sum_{j=1}^n E_{ij}, \qquad i = 1,2,\cdots,n, \quad (16)$$

The term E_{ii} is the fluctuating emf in that part of the resistance of the ith mesh which is not in common with any other mesh. The term $E_{ij}(i \neq j)$ is the fluctuating emf in the resistance R_{ij}. If in R_{ij} the positive directions chosen for the currents are in the same direction, $E_{ij} = E_{ji}$; if they are opposite each other, then $E_{ij} = -E_{ji}$. The E_{ij} are again supposed to be Gaussian random processes with a constant spectrum. We assume especially [*cf.* Eq. (7)]

[1] For the precise definition of the matrix elements L_{ij}, R_{ij}, S_{ij}, see, for instance, E. A. Guillemin, *Communication Networks*, Vol. 1, Wiley, New York, 1931, Chap. 4. All these matrices are symmetrical. Note, however, that R_{ij} ($i \neq j$) does *not* need to be positive. It is negative, when, in the resistance common to the ith and jth meshes, the positive directions chosen for the currents are opposite each other. The y_j are the mesh charges.

$$\left.\begin{aligned}
\overline{E_{ij}(t)} &= 0, \\
\overline{E_{ij}(t_1)E_{ji}(t_2)} &= 2R_{ij}kT\delta(t_2 - t_1), \\
\overline{E_{ij}(t_1)E_{ij}(t_2)} &= 2|R_{ij}|kT\delta(t_2 - t_1), \\
\overline{E_{ij}(t_1)E_{kl}(t_2)} &= 0.
\end{aligned}\right\} \tag{17}$$

The electric energy and the magnetic energy are given, respectively, by the quadratic forms (the primes indicate differentiation with respect to the time)

$$U_{\text{elec}} = \tfrac{1}{2} \sum_{r,s} S_{rs} y_r y_s,$$

$$U_{\text{magn}} = \tfrac{1}{2} \sum_{r,s} L_{rs} y_r' y_s'.$$

To prove the equipartition theorem,[1] it must be shown

$$\overline{y_r \frac{\partial U_{\text{elec}}}{\partial y_r}} = \overline{y_r' \frac{\partial U_{\text{magn}}}{\partial y_r'}} = kT, \qquad r = 1, 2, \cdots, n. \tag{18}$$

To do this, one calculates from the circuit Eqs. (16) for each frequency f the stationary values of the mesh charges y_i and of the mesh currents y_i'. With Eq. (17), it is easily found, for instance, that

$$\overline{y_r \frac{\partial U_{\text{elec}}}{\partial y_r}} = \sum_s S_{rs}\overline{y_r y_s} = \frac{kT}{\pi} \int_{-\infty}^{+\infty} d\omega \, [\mathsf{S}\mathsf{Z}^{-1}(i\omega)\mathsf{R}\mathsf{Z}^{-1}(-i\omega)]_{rr}, \tag{19}$$

where $\mathsf{Z}(p)$ is the matrix,

$$\mathsf{Z}(p) = \mathsf{L}p^2 + \mathsf{R}p + \mathsf{S}, \tag{20}$$

and L, R, and S are the inductance, resistance, and elastance matrices.

To calculate the integral in Eq. (19), we observe that

$$\mathsf{Z}(i\omega) - \mathsf{Z}(-i\omega) = 2i\omega\mathsf{R},$$

which follows from Eq. (20). Substituting this value of R in Eq. (19), one obtains

$$\overline{y_r \frac{\partial U_{\text{elec}}}{\partial y_r}} = -\frac{kT}{\pi i} \int_{-\infty}^{+\infty} \frac{d\omega}{\omega} [\mathsf{S}\mathsf{Z}^{-1}(i\omega)]_{rr},$$

where the principal value of the integral has to be taken. Use is

[1] For this formulation of the equipartition theorem *cf.*, for example, R. Tolman, *The Principles of Statistical Mechanics*, Oxford, New York, 1938, Chap. 4, Sec. 35.

now made of the well-known fact that the determinant of $Z(i\omega)$ has no zeros in the lower half of the complex ω-plane.[1] The value of the integral, taken around the closed path shown in Fig. 4·6, is therefore zero. In the limit the integral along the large half circle goes to zero; therefore the integral along the real axis must be equal to minus the integral along the small half circle around the origin. This latter, in turn, is equal to πi times the residue of the integrand at $\omega = 0$. Since $Z^{-1}(0) = S^{-1}$, it is clear that this residue is unity, and therefore the value of $\overline{y_r(\partial U_{\text{elec}}/\partial y_r)}$ is merely kT.

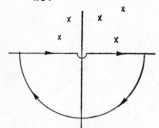

Fig. 4·6.—Integration path in the complex ω-plane; crosses are zeros of Det $[Z(i\omega)]$.

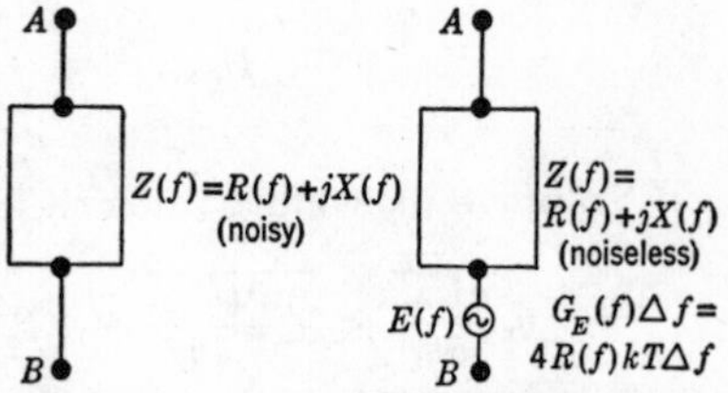

Fig. 4·7.—Equivalent representations of the noise in an arbitrary impedance.

3. *A Theorem of Nyquist.* Suppose one has an arbitrary two-pole linear passive network at temperature T; let the impedance between the poles be $Z = R + jX$, where R and X are now, in general, functions of the frequency f. Nyquist has shown that the spectral density of the voltage fluctuations across the impedance is given by

$$G_V(f) \, \Delta f = 4R(f)kT \, \Delta f. \tag{21}$$

This is clearly a generalization of Eq. (1). It can also be said that one must associate with the impedance Z a fluctuating emf $E(t)$ with average value zero and the spectral density given by Eq. (21). Note that the spectrum of $E(t)$ is no longer constant, so that successive instantaneous values of $E(t)$ will now be correlated.

The proof Nyquist gave for Eq. (21) is a generalization of the considerations presented in Sec. 4·1. Suppose one connects the impedance Z to a pure resistance R_1, which is also at the temperature T and with which is associated the fluctuating emf $E_1(t)$. By equating the average power transferred from Z to R_1 in the frequency range Δf to the average power transferred back from R_1 to Z, one finds, in exactly the same way as Eq. (3) was derived in Sec. 4·1,

$$G_E(f)R_1 = G_{E_1}(f)R(f). \tag{22}$$

[1] This is an expression of the fact that we are dealing with a passive network.

Since it is known that $G_{E_i}(f) = 4R_1kT$, one immediately obtains Eq. (21).

4. *A Theorem of Williams.* It must, of course, be possible to derive Eq. (21) by associating with each of the constant resistances a fluctuating emf having the constant spectrum of Eq. (1) [just as in the general circuit equations (16)], and then calculating the combined effect of all these fluctuating emf's on the voltage across the two poles of the network. This proof was given by Williams.[1] It is of special value, because one can also predict what will happen when the different resistances are *no longer at the same temperature.*

In this more general case it seems quite plausible still to associate with each constant resistance R_i a fluctuating emf $E_i(t)$ of average value zero and of spectral density $4R_ikT_i$, where T_i is the temperature of the resistance. In essence, this was first proposed by Ornstein[2] in his studies of how cooling the resistance influences the sensitivity of galvanometers. The first complete experimental confirmation of this assumption[3] was first given by F. C. Williams, however.

Let $Z_i(f)$ be the transfer impedance between the resistance R_i (temperature T_i) and the two poles A and B of the network. This means that a sinusoidal emf E of frequency f in series with R_i will produce a current E/Z_i in a link short-circuiting A and B. Williams shows that the spectral density of the voltage fluctuations across AB is given by

$$G_V(f) \, \Delta f = 4|Z|^2 k \, \Delta f \sum_i \frac{R_i T_i}{|Z_i|^2} \tag{23a}$$

and that the real part of the impedance Z is given by

$$R(f) = |Z|^2 \sum_i \frac{R_i}{|Z_i|^2}. \tag{23b}$$

Clearly, when all the temperatures T_i are the same, then Eq. (23a) reduces to Nyquist's result [Eq. (21)].

Finally it should be pointed out that in this way one can also see that although the spectrum of the voltage across AB is *no longer* constant, the voltage [or the emf $E(t)$ in Fig. 4·7] is still a Gaussian random process. The reason for this is that the different fluctuating emf's $E_i(t)$ in the

[1] F. C. Williams, *J.I.E.E.*, **81**, 751 (1937).

[2] L. S. Ornstein, *Z. Physik*, **41**, 848 (1927); L. S. Ornstein, H. C. Burger, J. Taylor, and W. Clarkson, *Proc. Roy. Soc.*, **115**, 391 (1927).

[3] One must call it an assumption, because *no* general statistical proof for this extension of the original picture can be given. However, the kinetic proof makes the assumption very plausible.

resistances R_i are Gaussian processes, which are independent of each other, and that the connection between the voltage across AB and the $E_i(t)$ is linear.

4·5. Experimental Confirmations. *The Upper Limit of the Thermal Noise Spectrum.*—Many experimental investigations have confirmed the

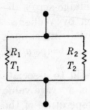

basic Nyquist formula [Eq. (1)]. Besides the original measurements of Johnson,[1] and those of Moullin and Ellis,[2] the careful work of Wilbur[3] should be mentioned. The voltage fluctuations across wire-wound resistors up to about 2 megohms were amplified and compared with the fluctuations due to pure "shot" noise, which are known to obey precisely the theoretical formula (see Sec. 4·6). In this way Wilbur could verify rather precisely the linear dependence of $G_V(f)$ on R and T (from liquid-air temperature to about

FIG. 4·8.—Two resistors at different temperatures.

380°K), and his measurements can almost be considered as a precision measurement of the Boltzmann constant k.

It has also been shown[4] that in metal resistors the voltage fluctuations are independent of whether a current is flowing through the resistance or not. This *cannot* be predicted on the basis of the general statistical theory of Secs. 4·1 and 4·2, since, with a current, the metallic electrons are, of course, no longer in a state of equilibrium. On the basis of the kinetic theory of Sec. 4·3 the independence of voltage fluctuations and current flow becomes plausible, since the drift velocity of the electrons in consequence of the outside constant emf is very small compared with the thermal velocities of the electrons. In nonmetallic conductors, however, the fluctuations usually increase when a current is passing through, producing the so-called "current noise" (see Sec. 4·11).

The most detailed verification of Eqs. (21) and (23a) has been made by Williams.[5] In one series of experiments the voltage fluctuations across two parallel resistances R_1 and R_2 at temperatures T_1 and T_2 were measured. Equation (23a) gives, for this case,

$$G_V(f) = 4 \frac{R_1^2 R_2^2}{(R_1 + R_2)^2} k \left(\frac{T_1}{R_1} + \frac{T_2}{R_2} \right)$$
$$= 4 R_1 k T_1 \left(\frac{R_2}{R_1 + R_2} \right)^2 \left(1 + \frac{T_2}{T_1} \cdot \frac{R_1}{R_2} \right).$$

[1] J. B. Johnson, *Phys. Rev.*, **32**, 97 (1928).

[2] E. B. Moullin and H. D. M. Ellis, *J.I.E.E.*, **74**, 331 (1934).

[3] D. A. Wilbur, "Thermal Agitation of Electricity in Conductors," Dissertation, U. of Mich., 1932.

[4] *Cf.* E. B. Moullin, *Spontaneous Fluctuations of Voltage*, Oxford, New York, 1938, Chap. 1.

[5] F. C. Williams, *J.I.E.E.*, **81**, 751 (1937).

The temperature T_2 was varied from 20° to 470°C, while R_1 remained at room temperature. The linear dependence of $G_V(f)$ on T_2/T_1 and the absolute value of $G_V(f)$ were well established.

In a second series a capacitance and an inductance were introduced in the two branches (see Fig. 4·9). In this case Eq. (23a) becomes

$$G_V(f) = 4|Z|^2 k \left[\frac{R_1 T_1}{R_1^2 + \omega^2 L^2} + \frac{R_2 T_2}{R_2^2 + (1/\omega C)^2} \right].$$

Again the temperature T_2 could be varied and the measurements could be made at three different frequencies f. The results again confirmed the theory.

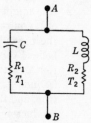

Finally, R_1, R_2, and L were kept at room temperature, and the voltage fluctuations across AB were measured as a function of the temperature of the condenser. The value of $G_V(f)$ did *not* change, confirming the picture that the fluctuating emf's must be associated *only with the resistances.*

This section is concluded with a discussion of the *upper limit of the thermal noise spectrum.* It is clear that the Nyquist formula must break down at some high frequency f_0 and that $G_V(f)$ must then go to zero. Otherwise (in the argument of Sec. 4·1) the total power transferred from one resistance to the other would be infinite.

FIG. 4·9.—Two impedances at different temperatures.

Various statements have been made in the literature about the value of f_0; they lead to several questions and difficulties, to be discussed briefly.

1. Nyquist pointed out that in his derivation (see Sec. 4·1) for very high frequencies one should replace the equipartition value kT for the energy of each of the modes of the transmission line by the Planck formula

$$\frac{hf}{e^{hf/kT} - 1}.$$

This would lead to

$$G_V(f) \, \Delta f = 4R \frac{hf}{e^{hf/kT} - 1} \, \Delta f. \tag{24}$$

The spectrum would, therefore, vanish at a frequency of the order of

$$f_0 \approx \frac{kT}{h} = 2 \cdot 1 \times 10^{10} T \quad \text{cps}, \tag{25}$$

and the total voltage fluctuation across the resistance R would be

$$\overline{V^2} = \int_0^\infty df \, G_V(f) = \frac{2\pi^2 R k^2 T^2}{3h}.$$

On the other hand, from the kinetic proof given in Sec. 4·3, the noise spectrum must be expected to drop to zero at a frequency of the order of

$$f_0 \approx \frac{1}{\tau} = \frac{v}{\lambda} \approx 10^{13} \text{ to } 10^{14} \qquad \text{cps}, \qquad (26)$$

and this has been corroborated by Bakker and Heller.[1] Both limits [Eqs. (25) and (26)] are, of course, much too high to be of any practical significance. However, the question still remains: Which is the correct limit? The essential difference between Eqs. (25) and (26) is that Eq. (25) is universal whereas Eq. (26) would, in principle, give different limits for different metals.

2. One might think that the transmission line (or waveguide) proof of Nyquist shows that the limit must be universal, since otherwise there would be a conflict with thermodynamics. The authors believe this is *not* so. Essential in Nyquist's proof is the assumption that the conductors have a *constant* resistance, independent of frequency. At high frequencies this will certainly no longer be true, and the dependence on frequency will be different for different conductors. The proof of Sec. 4·1 breaks down at very high frequencies because the conductors will no longer match the line, so that reflections will have to be taken into account.

3. The general argument of Nyquist leading to Eq. (21) makes it very plausible that one always will find

$$G_V(f) = 4R(f)kT. \qquad (27)$$

It seems, however, that the function $R(f)$ will usually not be determined by the nature of the resistor [a supposition that would lead to the limit expressed by Eq. (26)] but by the *shape* of the resistor, since this will determine its self-capacitance and self-inductance. Only when these are completely negligible will the limit given by Eq. (26) begin to play a rôle.

4. It is clear that at these high frequencies it is no longer permissible to consider only networks with lumped constants. The general statistical theory should be generalized, using the Maxwell equations, to an arbitrary system of bodies in equilibrium with the radiation field. Such an investigation would clarify the precise meaning of Eq. (27) and would then presumably also determine the function $R(f)$. It would also be of interest to see if a more general kinetic investigation would justify Eq. (27).

5. A difficulty of Eq. (27) is that with a frequency-dependent resistance, the proofs of the equipartition theorem given in Secs. 4·2 and

[1] *Physica*, **6**, 262 (1939).

4·4 break down. This difficulty is, however, only apparent, since the impedance of the conductor must now necessarily also have a complex part. Thus in the simple case of Sec. 4·2 (Fig. 4·2) the magnetic energy of the circuit will not be $\frac{1}{2}L\overline{i^2}$, for the resistance R also will carry some magnetic and electric energy. That we shall again arrive at the equipartition law can be shown only by the more general statistical investigation mentioned above.

NOISE DUE TO DISCRETENESS OF THE ELECTRONIC CHARGE

4·6. Derivation of the Schottky Formula.—Let us consider a temperature-limited diode connected to a resistance R.
Because of discreteness of the electronic charge, the number of electrons emitted in equal time intervals will fluctuate around an average value. As a result of this fluctuating current the voltage across the resistance will fluctuate too, and these fluctuations can be amplified and measured. This is the well known *shot effect*, first predicted and treated theoretically by Schottky. He showed that the spectral density of the current is *constant* up to frequencies of the order of the

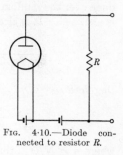

Fig. 4·10.—Diode connected to resistor R.

reciprocal of the transit time and that the spectral density (for the *temperature-limited case*) is given by the formula

$$G_I(f) \, \Delta f = 2eI \, \Delta f, \tag{28}$$

where e is the electronic charge and I is the average current.

Since the electrons may be taken as independent in the temperature-limited case, it is clear that the current through the resistance will consist of a series of short pulses, each pulse corresponding to the passage of an electron from cathode to anode. The current will therefore have the form

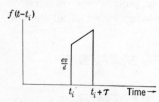

Fig. 4·11.—Current pulse corresponding to the passage of one electron.

$$I(t) = \sum_i f(t - t_i), \tag{29}$$

where the t_i's are the random and independent emission times of the successive electrons, and where $f(t)$ is almost like a Dirac δ-function (since the transit time τ is very short) with area equal to the electronic charge e (see Fig. 4·11).[1] Introducing a long periodicity interval Θ, $I(t) - \overline{I}$ can be developed in the Fourier series

---

[1] The statistical properties of sums of the type in Eq. (29) have often been investi-

$$I(t) - \bar{I} = \sum_{k=0}^{\infty} (a_k \cos 2\pi f_k t + b_k \sin 2\pi f_k t).$$

For frequencies f_k large compared with $1/\tau$, we obtain

$$a_k = \frac{2}{\Theta} \int_0^\Theta dt \, [I(t) - \bar{I}] \cos 2\pi f_k t = \frac{2e}{\Theta} \sum_{i=1}^{N} \cos 2\pi f_k t_i, \qquad (30)$$

where N is the total number of electrons passing from cathode to anode in the time Θ; N may be considered constant. The averaging has to be done over the random time points t_i, for which a uniform distribution law is assumed. It is clear that

$$\overline{\cos 2\pi f_k t_i} = \overline{\sin 2\pi f_k t_i} = 0,$$
$$\overline{\cos 2\pi f_k t_i \cos 2\pi f_k t_j} = \overline{\sin 2\pi f_k t_i \sin 2\pi f_k t_j} = \tfrac{1}{2}\delta_{ij},$$
$$\overline{\cos 2\pi f_k t_i \sin 2\pi f_k t_j} = 0;$$

therefore

$$\bar{a}_k = \bar{b}_k = 0,$$
$$\overline{a_k^2} = \overline{b_k^2} = \frac{4e^2}{\Theta^2} \cdot \frac{1}{2} N = \frac{2e^2 n}{\Theta}; \qquad \overline{a_k b_k} = 0,$$

where $n = N/\Theta$ is the average number of electrons passing per second. The average current $\bar{I}$ is therefore en, and we can write, for the mean square value of the component of the current of frequency f_k,

$$\overline{i_\kappa^2} = \overline{a_k^2} \cos^2 2\pi f_k t + \overline{b_k^2} \sin^2 2\pi f_k t = \frac{2e\bar{I}}{\Theta}.$$

Since in the frequency range Δf there are $\Theta \, \Delta f$ of such components, multiplication by this number yields the results given in Eq. (28).

To prove that $I(t)$ is a Gaussian random process requires a rather detailed investigation. It is clear that the mean values of all the odd powers of a_k and b_l vanish. Furthermore,

$$\overline{a_k^4} = \left(\frac{2e}{\Theta}\right)^4 \sum_{ijlm} \overline{\cos 2\pi f_k t_i \cos 2\pi f_k t_j \cos 2\pi f_k t_l \cos 2\pi f_k t_m}$$

$$= \left(\frac{2e}{\Theta}\right)^4 \left[3 \left(\sum_{\text{all } i} \overline{\cos^2 2\pi f_k t_i} \right)^2 - 3 \sum_{\text{all } i} \overline{(\cos^2 2\pi f_k t_i)^2} \right.$$

$$\left. + \sum_{\text{all } i} \overline{\cos^4 2\pi f_k t_i} \right] = \left(\frac{2e}{\Theta}\right)^4 \left(\frac{3}{4} N^2 - \frac{3}{4} N + \frac{3}{8} N \right).$$

gated. *Cf.* S. O. Rice, "Mathematical Analysis of Random Noise," *Bell System Techn. J.*, **23**, 282 (1944), Part I; see also for further references. For the most complete and exact treatment see H. Hurwitz and M. Kac, "Statistical Analysis of Certain Types of Random Functions," *Ann. Math. Statist.*, **15**, 173 (1944).

Since N can be chosen arbitrarily large, one might be inclined to conclude that the terms linear in N can be neglected; this would lead to

$$\overline{a_k^4} = 3 \left(\frac{2e^2N}{\Theta^2} \right)^2 = 3(\overline{a_k^2})^2.$$

In the same way the mean values of all the even powers of a_k could be calculated; and keeping only the highest power of N, we should get

$$\overline{a_k^{2m}} = 1 \cdot 3 \cdot 5 \cdots (2m - 1) \, (\overline{a_k^2})^m,$$

which is characteristic for the Gaussian distribution. The next question is whether or not the different Fourier coefficients are independent of each other. Here one gets into trouble. It can be shown that the coefficients $a_1, a_2, \ldots, a_s$ can be considered as independent (in the limit $N \rightarrow \infty$) if, and only if, s/N approaches zero as N approaches infinity. If we let only Θ approach infinity (keeping $n = N/\Theta$ fixed), we shall have independence only providing s is small compared with Θ. Thus independence of coefficients is obtained solely over narrow portions of the frequency range. To get a Gaussian process, where *all* the Fourier coefficients are independent, not only must N approach infinity (which can always be achieved by taking Θ large enough) but so must n *also*. The *essential* condition for the Gaussian nature of the shot noise is that the average number of electrons passing per second be very large. This conclusion is confirmed by an analysis of the distribution of $I(t)$ itself. Assuming, as before, that the time points t_i are distributed uniformly over the time interval Θ, we obtain

$$\bar{I} = \int_0^\Theta \frac{dt_1}{\Theta} \int_0^\Theta \frac{dt_2}{\Theta} \cdots \int_0^\Theta \frac{dt_N}{\Theta} \sum_{i=1}^N f(t - t_i)$$

$$= \frac{N}{\Theta} \int_{-\infty}^{+\infty} d\xi \, f(\xi).$$

Strictly speaking, we should still average over all possible values of N according to the Poisson distribution[1]

$$W(N) = \frac{(\bar{N})^N e^{-\bar{N}}}{N!},$$

with $\bar{N} = n\Theta$, where n is the average number of electrons passing per second. We then get

$$\bar{I} = n \int_{-\infty}^{+\infty} d\xi \, f(\xi). \tag{31}$$

[1] When $\bar{N}$ is large, $W(N)$ can be approximated by a Gaussian distribution around $\bar{N}$ and with a variance equal to $\bar{N}$; hence for large $\bar{N}$ the variation of N may be neglected. The formulas become simpler, however, by taking the variation of N into account.

In the same way we get

$$\bar{I}^2 = \frac{\bar{N}}{\Theta} \int_{-\infty}^{+\infty} d\xi\, f^2(\xi) + \frac{\overline{N(N-1)}}{\Theta^2} \left[\int_{-\infty}^{+\infty} d\xi\, f(\xi) \right]^2$$
$$= n \int_{-\infty}^{+\infty} d\xi\, f^2(\xi) + n^2 \left[\int_{-\infty}^{+\infty} d\xi\, f(\xi) \right]^2,$$

and it follows that

$$\overline{(I - \bar{I})^2} = n \int_{-\infty}^{+\infty} d\xi\, f^2(\xi). \tag{32}$$

To find the distribution of $I - \bar{I}$ it is best to calculate the characteristic function

$$\psi(u) = \overline{\exp\left[iu(I - \bar{I})\right]},$$

for which we obtain

$$\psi(u) = \exp\left[-iun \int_{-\infty}^{+\infty} f(\xi)\, d\xi + n \int_{-\infty}^{+\infty} d\xi\, (e^{iuf(\xi)} - 1) \right]. \tag{33a}$$

This is still exact. For large n we may develop the exponent in powers of u, leading to

$$\psi(u) \approx \exp\left[-nu^2 \int_{-\infty}^{+\infty} d\xi\, f^2(\xi) \right]; \tag{33b}$$

consequently (for large n) the distribution of $I - \bar{I}$ will be Gaussian with the variance given by Eq. (32). By a calculation similar to that given in Sec. 3·6, it can be shown that the error will be of the order of magnitude of $1/n^{1/2}$.

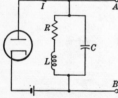

FIG. 4·12.—Diode connected to resonant circuit.

Experimentally, the Schottky formula [Eq. (28)] has been verified many times. In the original experiments of Hull and Williams[1] the current of a temperature-limited diode was passed through a lightly damped resonant circuit, and the fluctuation of the voltage between the poles A and B was measured (see Fig. 4·12).

To calculate this fluctuation from Eq. (28), the diode must be considered as a *fluctuating current source*. The spectral density of the voltage is therefore, in general,

$$G_V(f) = |Z(j\omega)|^2 G_I(f) = 2eI|Z(j\omega)|^2, \tag{34}$$

when Z is the impedance between the poles A and B. We therefore get

$$G_V(f) = \frac{2eI}{C^2\omega^2} \frac{R^2 + L^2\omega^2}{R^2 + \left(L\omega - \dfrac{1}{C\omega}\right)^2},$$

[1] A. W. Hull and N. H. Williams, "Determination of Elementary Charge E from Measurements of Shot-effect," *Phys. Rev.*, **25**, 147 (1925).

which gives for the fluctuation of the voltage

$$\overline{(V - \bar{V})^2} = \int_0^\infty df\, G_V(f) = \frac{eLI}{2RC^2}\left(1 + \frac{R^2C}{L}\right).$$

In subsequent experiments by Williams and collaborators the current of the diode was passed through a resistance R (see Fig. 4·10), and the voltage fluctuations, whose spectral density for this case is simply $2eIR^2$, were measured by a highly selective amplifier. The best results are probably those obtained by Williams and Huxford.[1] They can be considered as almost precision measurements of the electronic charge e.

4·7. Space Charge Depression of the Shot Noise.
—When the current through the diode is not temperature limited, the electrons cease to be independent, and the Schottky formula [Eq. (28)] breaks down. Many experimental and theoretical investigations[2] have

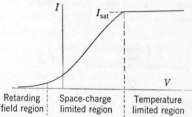

FIG. 4·13.—Current-voltage relation for a diode.

been devoted to the question of how the Schottky formula should be modified. One can say that this problem has now, except for the h-f region (see Sec. 4·8), been solved. The theory is complicated, however; only a short account of the main results will be attempted here.

It is necessary to recall, first, the well-known theory for the current-voltage characteristic of a diode.[3] For a given temperature of the cathode and for a given geometry, the characteristic has three distinct regions (see Fig. 4·13). When the voltage of the anode is sufficiently negative, the potential distribution between cathode and anode will be a monotonic decreasing function; the electrons will therefore always be in a retarding field. The current is extremely small and is produced only by those electrons which are emitted with such high velocities that they can overcome the retarding field and reach the anode. All other electrons will return to the cathode. As a result of the Maxwell distribution in

[1] N. H. Williams and W. S. Huxford, "Determination of the Charge of Positive Thermions from Measurements of Shot Effect," *Phys. Rev.*, **33**, 773 (1929).

[2] *Cf.* E. B. Moullin, *Spontaneous Fluctuations of Voltage*, Chaps. 3 and 4, Oxford, New York, 1938. The theory was developed independently by D. O. North, "Fluctuations in Space-charge-limited Currents at Moderately High Frequencies, Part II, Diodes and Negative-grid Triodes," *RCA Rev.*, **4**, 441 (1940); W. Schottky and E. Spenke, *Wiss. Veröffentl. Siemens-Werken*, **16** (No. 2), 1, 19 (1937); A. J. Rack, "Effect of Space Charge and Transit Time on the Shot Noise in Diodes," *Bell System Techn. J.*, **17**, 592 (1938).

[3] *Cf.*, for example, I. Langmuir, *Phys. Rev.*, **21**, 419 (1923).

velocity, the relation between the current and voltage in the retarded-field region is given by

$$I = I_{\text{sat}} e^{eV/kT}. \tag{35}$$

When the voltage of the anode increases the space-charge-limited region is reached; here there is a *minimum* in the potential distribution between cathode and anode. Therefore part of the field is retarding and part accelerating. The relation between I and V is in this case complicated and cannot be presented in a closed form. Increasing the anode voltage shifts the minimum toward the cathode. For high enough voltage the minimum will finally disappear, leaving only an accelerating field; one is then in the temperature-limited region. In this case the current is constant and equal to the saturation current I_{sat}.

The Schottky formula [Eq. (28)] is valid *only* in the temperature-limited region; then the density of the voltage fluctuations across an external resistance R (see Fig. 4·10) is consequently given by

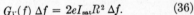

$$G_V(f)\,\Delta f = 2eI_{\text{sat}} R^2\,\Delta f. \tag{36}$$

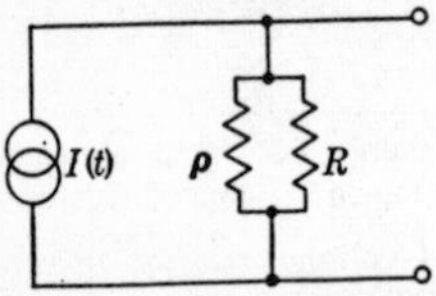

Fig. 4·14.—Equivalent circuit for a diode connected to a noiseless resistor R.

For the other regions of the characteristic, the first question that has to be considered is the part played by the differential resistance $\rho = dV/dI$ of the diode. It seems plausible and can also be strictly justified that the diode must always be considered as a fluctuating current source impressed on the resistances ρ and R in parallel (see Fig. 4·14). Equation (36) is therefore generalized as follows:

$$G_V(f)\,\Delta f = 2eI\Gamma^2\left(\frac{R\rho}{R+\rho}\right)^2\,\Delta f, \tag{37}$$

where Γ is a dimensionless quantity, which may still depend on the current I. For dimensional reasons, Γ must have the form

$$\Gamma = F\left(\frac{e\rho I}{kT_c}\right), \tag{38}$$

where T_c is the cathode temperature. The resistance ρ is, of course, also a function of I, which can be determined from the characteristic. In the temperature-limited region $\rho = \infty$, $\Gamma = 1$, and $I = I_{\text{sat}}$ so that Eq. (37) goes over into Eq. (36). Moullin[1] has shown experimentally that Eq. (37) gives the correct dependence on the resistance R. The point of view that the diode may always be considered as a fluctuating current source

[1] E. B. Moullin, "Measurement of Shot Voltage Used to Deduce the Magnitude of Secondary Thermionic Emission," *Proc. Roy. Soc.*, **147**, 109 (1934).

has also been confirmed by a series of interesting experiments by Williams.[1] Williams took into account the thermal noise of the resistance R, which he represented by a fluctuating emf $E(t)$ in series with the resistance R. For the voltage fluctuations across AB (see Fig. 4·15), we find

$$G_V(f) = \left(\frac{R\rho}{R + \rho}\right)^2 G_I(f) + \frac{\rho^2}{(R + \rho)^2} G_E(f)$$

$$= \left(\frac{R\rho}{R + \rho}\right)^2 \left(2eI\Gamma^2 + \frac{4kT}{R}\right), \tag{39}$$

using Eq. (37) and the Nyquist formula; T is the temperature of the resistance R. The dependence on R and on T was checked in detail.

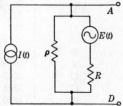

FIG. 4·15.—Equivalent circuit for a diode connected to a noisy resistor R.

There remains the problem of calculating the function Γ. The procedure may be roughly explained as follows: Just as in the temperature-limited case, it can be assumed here that the electrons emitted by the cathode emerge independent of each other and completely random in time. The average number ν emitted per second determines I_{sat}. Let us suppose that in a time Δt, which is short compared with the period $1/f$, *more* electrons than the average number $\nu \Delta t$ are emitted by the cathode, and let the excess be Δn. *Because of the existence of a potential minimum,* the number of electrons delivered at the anode in a time of the order of the transit time τ (which is also supposed to be small compared with $1/f$) will *not* exceed the average number by the same amount Δn. The excess will be *less,* because the Δn electrons will have somewhat lowered the potential minimum and will have thus prevented other electrons from reaching the anode. In the same way when *fewer* electrons than the average number $\nu \Delta t$ are emitted by the cathode, the raising of the potential minimum will diminish this defect at the anode. The fluctuations will consequently be cut down, and one must therefore expect Γ to be less than unity.

For the precise calculation the velocity distribution of the emitted electrons should of course be taken into account, since the effect on the potential minimum will depend strongly on the velocity of the group of electrons under consideration. Furthermore, one must distinguish between the *reflected electrons* (or electrons of Class α), which have insufficient energy to cross the potential minimum, and the *transmitted electrons* (or electrons of Class β), which are the only ones contributing to the

[1] F. C. Williams, "Fluctuation Voltage in Diodes and in Multi-electrode Valves," *J.I.E.E.*, **79**, 349 (1936). *Cf.* also Moullin, *op. cit.*, p. 74.

plate current. One finds that

$$\Gamma^2 = \Gamma_\alpha{}^2 + \Gamma_\beta{}^2. \tag{40}$$

For the usual operating conditions, $\Gamma_\alpha{}^2 \ll \Gamma_\beta{}^2$; hence the effect of the reflected electrons can often be neglected (*cf.* Table 4·1). The calcula-

TABLE 4·1.—VALUES OF THE REDUCTION FACTOR Γ

$\eta_2 = \dfrac{e(V - V_{\min})}{kT_c}$	$\chi = \dfrac{eI\rho}{kT_c}$	$\Gamma_\alpha{}^2$	$\Gamma_\beta{}^2$	$\Gamma^2 = \Gamma_\alpha{}^2 + \Gamma_\beta{}^2$	Γ	$\theta = \dfrac{T_{\text{eff}}}{T_c}$
0	1	0	1	1	1	0.500
5	6.76	0.0282	0.1663	0.1945	0.441	0.66
10	10.96	0.0167	0.1043	0.1210	0.348	0.66
15	14.9	0.0115	0.0775	0.0890	0.298	0.66
20	18.7	0.0086	0.0621	0.0707	0.266	0.66
25	22.5	0.0068	0.0519	0.0587	0.242	0.66
30	26.3	0.0056	0.0448	0.0504	0.224	0.66
35	29.9	0.0047	0.0394	0.0441	0.210	0.66
40	33.7	0.0040	0.0352	0.0392	0.198	0.66
45	37.3	0.0035	0.0319	0.0354	0.188	0.66
50	40.9	0.0031	0.0291	0.0322	0.179	0.655
60	48.0	0.0025	0.0248	0.0273	0.165	0.655
70	55.3	0.0020	0.0217	0.0237	0.154	0.65
80	62.2	0.0017	0.0192	0.0209	0.145	0.65
90	69.6	0.0015	0.0173	0.0188	0.137	0.65
100	76.4	0.0013	0.0157	0.0170	0.130	0.65

tions are complicated and involve a great deal of numerical computation.[1] The most complete calculations are those carried out by E. Spenke. Some of his results are shown in Fig. 4·16. Only *plane* diodes were considered; the geometry and operating conditions are characterized by the dimensionless quantity

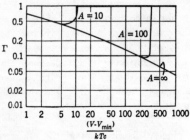

FIG. 4·16.—Reduction factor Γ as a function of the potential difference between the plate and the potential minimum:
$$A = 4\left(\frac{\pi}{2kT_c}\right)^{3/4} m^{1/4}(eI_{\text{sat}})^{1/2}d.$$

$$A = 4\left(\frac{\pi}{2kT_c}\right)^{3/4} m^{1/4}(eI_{\text{sat}})^{1/2}d$$
$$= 0.505 \times 10^4 \left(\frac{1000}{T_c}\right)^{3/4} I_{\text{sat}}{}^{1/2}d, \tag{41}$$

where I_{sat} is in amperes per square centimeter and the cathode-anode distance d is in centimeters. Usually A will be a large number. One

[1] In the theory the effect of the excess or defect in the number of emitted electrons on the position and magnitude of the potential minimum is calculated on the basis of

sees from Fig. 4·16 that for different values of A, Γ as a function of the plate voltage follows the curve for $A = \infty$ and then rapidly rises to the value unity when the temperature-limited region is reached.   For most purposes A can be taken infinite.   For this case the values of Γ are tabulated in Table 4·1 and shown in Fig. 4·17, both taken from North's

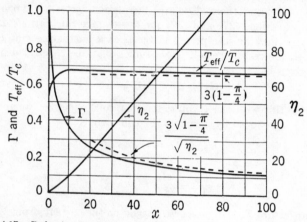

Fig. 4·17.—Reduction factor Γ, $\eta_2 = e(V - V_{min})/kT_c$, and T_{eff}/T_c as a function o $\chi = eI\rho/kT_c$. Dotted lines show the asymptotic behavior. The quantity A (see Fig. 4·16) is taken infinite.

paper.   In addition to Γ and Γ^2 one finds in this table $\Gamma_\alpha{}^2$ and $\Gamma_\beta{}^2$ as a function of the potential difference between the plate and the potential minimum and as a function of the perhaps more significant quantity

$$\chi = \frac{e\rho I}{kT_c} = 11.6 \frac{1000}{T_c} \rho I, \tag{42}$$

where T_c is in degrees Kelvin, ρ in ohms, and I in amperes.   Strictly speaking the results of the table can be used *only* when the current is *small* compared with the saturation current, although from Fig. 4·16 it can be seen that the results remain valid practically up to the saturation point.   It can further be shown that for large values of $\eta_2{}^2$

the continuum theory of the space-charge cloud.   This is really what makes the calculations possible at all, since the equations of the Epstein-Langmuir theory can then be used.   The method is justified because the fluctuations in emission are small and because the interaction of an electron with its immediate neighbors is always small compared with its interaction with the more distant electrons, which may be described by a continuous charge-density function.

[2] A simplified proof for this asymptotic behavior of Γ, based on the assumption that for large η_2 only the transmitted electrons need be considered, is attempted by C. J. Bakker, *Physica*, 8, 23 (1941).

$$\left.\begin{array}{l} \Gamma \approx \dfrac{3\sqrt{1 - \dfrac{\pi}{4}}}{\sqrt{\overline{\eta_2}}}, \\[4mm] \chi \approx \tfrac{2}{3}\eta_2. \end{array}\right\} \tag{43}$$

These asymptotic formulas can be given an interesting interpretation in terms of a pseudothermal voltage fluctuation across the diode resistance ρ. Equations (37) and (39) for the voltage fluctuations across a resistance R may be interpreted in terms of a fluctuating emf $E_1(t)$ in series with the resistance ρ if one assumes that the spectral density of $E_1(t)$ is given by

$$G_{E_1}(f)\,\Delta f = 2eI\Gamma^2\rho^2\,\Delta f. \tag{44a}$$

Comparing this with the Nyquist formula, an "effective" temperature T_{eff} can be introduced by means of the equation,

$$G_{E_1}(f)\,\Delta f = 4kT_{\text{eff}}\rho\,\Delta f, \tag{44b}$$

and

$$\theta = \frac{T_{\text{eff}}}{T_c} = \frac{eI\rho}{2kT_c}\Gamma^2 = \frac{1}{2}\chi\Gamma^2. \tag{45}$$

The temperature T_{eff} will of course depend on the current; from Eq. (43) it follows that, for large χ, $\Gamma^2 = 6\left(1 - \dfrac{\pi}{4}\right)\Big/\chi$; hence

$$\theta = \frac{T_{\text{eff}}}{T_c} = 3\left(1 - \frac{\pi}{4}\right) = 0.644. \tag{46}$$

It is surprising that for smaller currents θ remains near this value (see Table 4·1); hence *for all practical purposes one can consider the diode in the space-charge region as a resistance ρ at a temperature that is about two-thirds of the cathode temperature.*

This result breaks down, of course, in the temperature-limited region, where one has the normal shot effect. It also breaks down in the retarded-field region. In this region there is no potential minimum; hence it must be expected that $\Gamma^2 = 1$. On the other hand from the current-voltage relation, [Eq. (35)] it follows that

$$\rho = \frac{dV}{dI} = \frac{kT_c}{eI};$$

hence $\chi = e\rho I/kT_c = 1$. From Eq. (45) it follows therefore that in the retarded-field region

$$T_{\text{eff}} = \tfrac{1}{2}T_c. \tag{47}$$

This simple result, which has been checked experimentally by Pearson and by Williams,[1] can also be understood by the following simple argument of Schottky.[2] Suppose one has two identical diodes, of which the anodes are made of a poorly emitting substance but the cathodes are strong electron emitters. Let the diodes be arranged in parallel, and let the whole system be at the *same* temperature T_c. There will then be a potential difference between the cathodes and anodes, but the total current will be zero. In each diode the current from cathode to anode, which is in the retarded-field region, is balanced by the small but temperature-limited current from anode to cathode. According to the Nyquist formula, the voltage fluctuations across each diode must be $4kT_c\rho$. These fluctuations are produced by the normal shot-effect fluctuations of the cathode-anode and the anode-cathode currents. Therefore each of these currents must contribute *half* of the total fluctuation. Since the differential resistance ρ is due only to the cathode-anode current, the anode-cathode current being temperature-limited, it is clear that in the retarded-field region the normal shot-effect fluctuations must be equivalent to thermal fluctuations at a temperature that is *half* of the cathode temperature.

4·8. Experimental Confirmations; the Upper Limit of the Shot-noise Spectrum.—North and Jacoby and Kirchgeszner[3] have compared the theoretical results presented in Sec. 4·7 with experiment. For diodes,[4] qualitative agreement has been found with regard to the dependence of Γ on $\eta_2 = e(V - V_{\min})/kT_c$. The measured values of Γ are, however, always higher than the theoretical values. North has made it plausible that this discrepancy is due to the effect of electrons that are reflected elastically by the anode. Such electrons can return to the region of minimum potential and thus influence drastically the passage of other electrons.

Much better results are obtained for *negative-grid triodes*. The basic formula [Eq. (37)] must first be adapted to this case.[5] This can be done by introducing the familiar concept of the equivalent diode. The anode potential of the diode must be interpreted as the "effective" potential E_a of the grid plane, that is, that potential which, when applied to a solid sheet in the grid plane, would draw the same current. The voltage E_a is related to the actual grid and plate potentials E_g and E_p by

[1] G. L. Pearson, *Physics*, **6**, 6 (1935); F. C. Williams, *J.I.E.E.*, **79**, 349 (1936).

[2] W. Schottky, *Z. f. Physik.*, **104**, 248 (1937).

[3] D. O. North, "Fluctuations in Space-charge-limited Currents at Moderately High Frequencies, Part II, Diodes and Negative-grid Triodes," *RCA Rev.*, **4**, 441 (1940); H. Jacoby and L. Kirchgeszenr, *Wiss. Veröffentl. Siemens-Werken*, **16**, No. 2, 42 (1937).

[4] Or for triodes when operated as a diode, that is, when grid and anode are connected.

[5] *Cf.* North, *op. cit.*, p. 468.

$$E_a = \sigma \left(E_g + \frac{1}{\mu} E_p \right), \tag{48}$$

where σ and μ (the amplification factor) can, in principle, be calculated from the geometry of the tube. The factor σ lies between 0.5 and 1 and usually is nearly 1. The plate current is a function of E_a, and hence the conductance of the equivalent diode is given by

$$\frac{1}{\rho} = g = \frac{dI_p}{dE_a} = \frac{1}{\sigma} \left(\frac{\partial I_p}{\partial E_g} \right)_{E_p} = \frac{g_m}{\sigma}, \tag{49}$$

when g_m is the mutual conductance of the triode. Using Eqs. (44a), (45), and (49), one obtains for the voltage fluctuations across a resistance R in the plate circuit the formula

$$G_V(f) \, \Delta f = \frac{4\theta}{\sigma} kT_c g_m \left(\frac{r_p R}{r_p + R} \right)^2 \Delta f, \tag{50}$$

which replaces Eq. (37); r_p is the plate resistance, which is related to g_m and μ by the well-known relation

$$r_p = \frac{\mu}{g_m}. \tag{51}$$

Equation (50), with $\theta = 0.66$, has been thoroughly confirmed.[1]

In all results obtained so far the frequency f is supposed to be small compared with the reciprocal of the transit time τ of the electrons. All the spectral densities are then independent of the frequency. It is clear that this will cease to be valid when the frequency becomes comparable with $1/\tau$. In the *temperature-limited case* it is easy to see what will happen. In the Fourier analyses of the series of random current pulses (see Fig. 4·11) the *shape* of the pulses must now be taken into account. Taking the shape, for the sake of simplicity, as a rectangular block of height ev/d and width $\tau = d/v$, one gets, instead of Eq. (30),

$$a_k = \frac{2e}{\Theta} \frac{\sin \pi f_k \tau}{\pi f_k \tau} \sum_i \cos 2\pi f_k \left(t_i + \frac{\tau}{2} \right).$$

As a result, the spectral density of the current fluctuations becomes

$$G_I(f) \, \Delta f = 2eI \left(\frac{\sin \pi f \tau}{\pi f \tau} \right)^2 \Delta f, \tag{52}$$

which, of course, goes over into the Schottky formula [Eq. (28)] when

---

[1] *Cf. ibid.* Since the effect of the electrons in the grid-plate space on the space-charge reduction factor Γ^2 (or on the effective temperature θT_c of the cathode-grid region), has been neglected, Eq. (50) can be expected to hold only for *high-μ* tubes.

$f \ll 1/\tau$. For higher frequencies $G_I(f)$ is always less than the Schottky value; and for $f \gg 1/\tau$, $G_I(f)$ goes to zero. Spenke[1] has refined this rough calculation by taking into account the velocity distribution of the emitted electrons and the acceleration of the electrons between cathode and anode. Instead of Eq. (52), one then gets a completely monotonic decreasing function of f.

In the *space-charge-limited* region the problem is much more difficult. Rack[2] has given an analysis in which *only* the effect of the transmitted electrons was taken into account. He obtained for the spectral density the expression

$$G_E(f) \, \Delta f = 12 \left(1 - \frac{\pi}{4} \right) k T_c \rho S(\theta) \, \Delta f, \tag{53a}$$

where

$$S(\theta) = \frac{4}{\theta^4} (2 + \theta^2 - 2 \cos \theta - 2\theta \sin \theta) \tag{53b}$$

and $\theta = 2\pi f \tau$ is the transit angle. Equation (53a) is supposed to be a refinement of Eq. (44a) with the value given in Eq. (46) for the effective temperature of the cathode.[3] The function $S(\theta)$ is a monotonic decreasing function of θ, starting from unity for small θ and going to zero for large θ. The space-charge reduction of the fluctuations would therefore persist at high frequencies. It is doubtful, however, if this result is correct. Spenke[4] has shown that in the retarded-field region, values for Γ^2 can be obtained which are much larger than unity when the frequency is of the order of magnitude of $2/\tau$. The reason for this increase is that the *reflected* electrons then begin to contribute strongly to the fluctuations. It seems probable therefore that at high frequencies the effect of the reflected electrons cannot be neglected, and it may be that Γ^2 *rises* with increasing frequency and goes through a maximum before going to zero for very high values of f. Further theoretical investigations and experimental information, which we do not now have, are required with regard to this question.

4·9. Partition Noise.—In tubes that have more than one collecting electrode (tetrodes or pentodes) the random nature of the partition of the total current over the different electrodes provides an additional cause of fluctuations in current. The *mean* currents to the anode and to the screen grid are determined essentially by the ratio of the free area of

[1] E. Spenke, *Wiss. Veröffentl. Siemens-Werken,* **16**, No. 3, 127 (1937).

[2] A. J. Rack, "Effect of Space Charge and Transit Time on the Shot Noise in Diodes," *Bell System Techn. J.,* **17**, 592 (1938).

[3] The ρ in Eq. (53) is the diode resistance at *low* frequency and is therefore independent of f.

[4] *Op. cit.,* **17**, No. 3, 85 (1938).

the grid to its total area; the discrete nature of the electronic charge will give rise to fluctuations around these mean values.

Let us consider first the temperature-limited case. Since the electrons are completely independent of each other, and since the capture of an electron by the grid is a matter of pure chance, the times of arrival of the electrons at the anode will still be entirely random, just as for the diode in the temperature-limited case. The sole effect of the screen grid will be to diminish the average anode current. The density of the anode-current fluctuations will therefore be given by the Schottky formula

$$G_{I_a}(f) \, \Delta f = 2eI_a \, \Delta f, \qquad (54)$$

where I_a is the average anode current.

Let us imagine, on the other hand, the case where the electrons would be emitted by the cathode with absolute regularity in time, the time intervals between successive electrons being constant as a result. In a diode there would then be no current fluctuations at all; in other words, the shot fluctuations would have been completely suppressed. For a multicollector tube, however, the random nature of the capture of electrons by the grid would produce random gaps in the regular series of current pulses arriving at the anode; hence, there would again be some fluctuations in the current. What the spectrum will be is easily seen. Developing the anode current in a Fourier series in the usual fashion,

$$I_a = \sum_k (a_k \cos 2\pi f_k t + b_k \sin 2\pi f_k t),$$

we obtain

$$a_k = \frac{2}{\Theta} \int_0^\Theta dt \, I_a(t) = \frac{2}{\Theta} \sum_i e_i \cos 2\pi f_k t_i.$$

The time points t_i are now supposed to be spaced regularly with the constant interval Δ. The random variables are the charges e_i, which can have only two values, namely, e and zero with the probabilities p and $1 - p$. Therefore,

$$\overline{e_i} = pe \qquad \overline{e_i e_j} = \overline{e_i} \, \overline{e_j} = p^2 e^2,$$
$$\overline{e_i^2} = pe^2,$$

and we get

$$a_k^2 = \frac{4}{\Theta^2} \sum_i \sum_j \overline{e_i e_j} \cos 2\pi f_k t_i \cos 2\pi f_k t_j$$
$$= \frac{4}{\Theta^2} \left[p^2 e^2 \left(\sum_i \cos 2\pi f_k t_i \right)^2 + p(1 - p)e^2 \sum_i \cos^2 2k f_k t \right].$$

Or, again replacing the sums by integrals,

$$\overline{a_k^2} = \frac{2}{\Theta\Delta}\, p(1 - p)e^2.$$

Since Δ represents the spacing between successive electrons, it is clear that e/Δ is the sum of the average anode and grid current and that

$$\frac{pe}{\Delta} = I_a \qquad \frac{(1 - p)e}{\Delta} = I_{gr}.$$

We can therefore write

$$\overline{a_k^2} = \frac{2e}{\Theta} \frac{I_a I_{gr}}{I_a + I_{gr}}.$$

The same result is found for $\overline{b_k^2}$; and since $1/\Theta = \Delta f$, we get for the spectral density of the anode current

$$G_{I_a}(f)\,\Delta f = 2e \frac{I_a I_{gr}}{I_a + I_{gr}}\,\Delta f. \tag{55}$$

Comparing Eqs. (54) and (55), it can be seen that the complete suppression of the shot-effect fluctuation before the partition of the current reduces the fluctuations in the anode current by the factor $I_{gr}/(I_a + I_{gr})$. In the actual case when the initial current is space-charge limited, the shot-effect fluctuations are only partially suppressed; hence the fluctuations in the anode current must be expected to lie between the values given by Eqs. (54) and (55). A more precise analysis[1] shows that in the general case

$$G_{I_a}(f)\,\Delta f = 2eI_a \frac{I_{gr} + \Gamma^2 I_a}{I_a + I_{gr}}\,\Delta f, \tag{56}$$

where Γ^2 is the space-charge reduction factor that was discussed in Sec. 4·7. For $\Gamma^2 = 1$ (no space-charge suppression, temperature-limited case) Eq. (56) becomes Eq. (54), whereas for $\Gamma^2 = 0$ (complete space-charge suppression) Eq. (56) becomes Eq. (55).

In exactly the same way, we find, for the spectral density of the *screen-grid current*,

$$G_{I_{gr}}(f)\,\Delta f = 2eI_{gr} \frac{I_a + \Gamma^2 I_{gr}}{I_a + I_{gr}}\,\Delta f. \tag{57}$$

North[2] tested Eqs. (56) and (57) and found excellent agreement with experiment.

4·10. Transit-time Effects in Triodes and Multicollector Tubes; Induced Grid Noise.—Equations (56) and (57) of Sec. 4·9, for the spectral

---

[1] *Cf.* D. O. North, "Fluctuations in Space-charge-limited Currents at Moderately High Frequencies," *RCA Rev.*, **5**, 244 (1940).

[2] *Loc. cit.*

densities of the plate and screen-grid current, hold only for frequencies that are small compared with the reciprocal of the transit time. Because of our lack of knowledge about the frequency dependence of the space-charge reduction factor Γ (*cf.* Sec. 4·8), nothing can be said at present about the h-f end of the spectra $G_{I_a}(f)$ and $G_{I_g}(f)$.

There is one effect, however, for which an approximate theoretical treatment can be devised. It is clear that every time an electron passes through a grid, a current pulse will be induced (see Fig. 4·18). The

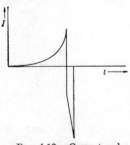

current will rise rapidly from zero to a maximum value during the period in which the electron approaches the grid. When the electron goes through the grid the current drops to a negative value; finally, while the electron recedes from the grid, the current passes through a minimum and subsequently goes back to zero. The *total* current is, of course, zero, since the electron is not captured. The duration of the pulse is of the order of the transit time. It is clear that these current pulses will contribute to the h-f part of the noise spectrum. For the case of the nega-

FIG. 4·18.—Current pulse in a grid when one electron passes through.

tive-grid triode this effect has been investigated, both experimentally and theoretically, by North and Ferris[1] and by Bakker.[2] In this case we speak of *induced grid noise*. Since the grid does not capture any electrons, the spectral density of the grid current will have no l-f components arising from the partition of the current, and for low frequencies it can be expected that

$$G_{I_g}(f) \approx f^2 G_{I_a}(f),$$

since each induced current pulse in the grid is like the derivative of the current pulse arriving at the anode. A more detailed analysis shows that

$$G_{I_g}(f) = \frac{1}{g}(\omega\tau_g)^2 G_{I_a}(f), \tag{58}$$

where $\omega = 2\pi f$ is the angular frequency and τ_g is the transit time between cathode and grid.

Equation (58) can be further transformed by introducing the concept of the *electronic load conductance* of the grid circuit. It is clear that the induced grid currents will give rise to an addition to the input conductance of the tube, and it can be easily seen[3] that this addition, called the

[1] D. O. North and W. R. Ferris, *Proc. I.R.E.*, **29**, 49 (1941).

[2] C. J. Bakker, *Physica*, **8**, 23 (1941).

[3] For a simple qualitative theoretical consideration (proposed by B. J. Thomson), see W. R. Ferris, *Proc. I.R.E.*, **24**, 82 (1936).

"electronic load conductance,"[1] is proportional to the square of the frequency and to the grid-plate transconductance g_m of the triode. More detailed calculations of g_g have been made by Bakker and deVries[2] and by North.[3] From these calculations it follows that, for high $-\mu$ tubes, operating under such conditions that the grid-plate transit time is negligible compared with the cathode-grid transit time,

$$g_g = \tfrac{1}{20} g_m (\omega \tau_g)^2. \tag{59}$$

For the spectral density of the anode current we can use the results derived in Sec. 4·8 [see Eq. (50)]. Taking $\sigma = 1$, we have

$$G_{I_a}(f) = 12 \left(1 - \frac{\pi}{4} \right) kT_c g_m. \tag{60}$$

Introducing this expression in Eq. (58) and by means of Eq. (59) expressing $\omega \tau_g$ in terms of g_g and g_m, we obtain

$$G_{I_g}(f) = \frac{20}{3} \left(1 - \frac{\pi}{4} \right) 4kT_c g_g. \tag{61}$$

The limitations of this formula should be kept in mind. Besides high-μ and negligible grid-plate transit time, the main assumption is that the transit angle $\omega\tau_g$ is so small that the space-charge reduction factor Γ can still be considered to be independent of the frequency.

It should be further emphasized that the fluctuation in the grid current is *coherent* with the fluctuation in the plate current. In general, therefore, these fluctuations *cannot* be compounded in the usual fashion by adding the mean square values. Since for small transit angles the phase angle is obviously nearly 90°, the addition of the mean square values is correct if the input impedance is a pure resistance. It is incorrect if the input impedance has an inductive part. By making use of this fact we can *cancel* part of the induced grid noise (see Sec. 5·5).

ADDITIONAL SOURCES OF NOISE

4·11. Current Noise; Flicker Effect; Positive Ion Fluctuations.— Thermal noise and shot noise are the two sources of noise that have been rather well investigated, both experimentally and theoretically. Usually they are also the most important sources of noise that occur in practice and that have to be considered in the construction of tubes and in the design of amplifiers and detectors. This does not imply that thermal noise and shot noise are the *only* sources of noise. There are other

---

[1] D. O. North, *Proc. I.R.E.*, **24**, 108 (1936).

[2] C. J. Bakker and G. de Vries, *Physica*, **2**, 683 (1935).

[3] *Loc. cit.*

sources, not so well investigated and understood, that may involve other fluctuation "mechanisms." Here only some of these additional sources of noise will be mentioned; more detailed discussion can be found in the literature.

In semiconductors, in thin metallic films,[1] and in resistance elements of the granular type (e.g., carbon microphone, commercial grid leaks)[2] the voltage fluctuations depend strongly on the current passing through the element.[3] Of course, when there is *no* current flowing, the spectrum of the voltage fluctuations $G_r(f)$ is given by the Nyquist formula. If a d-c current is passing through the resistance, the voltage fluctuations across the resistance increase by an amount that for small currents is approximately proportional to I^2 and for higher currents becomes proportional to I. Because of the dependence on I the additional noise is sometimes called *current noise*. The proportionality to I^2 suggests that the origin lies in a fluctuation of the resistance, either because the number of conduction electrons varies or because of random changes in the contact areas between the different granules that make up the resistance.

The frequency dependence of the current noise has also been investigated. In the a-f range it is found that $G_v(f)$ is inversely proportional to f; and above 10 kc/sec, $G_v(f)$ usually becomes small. A proposed explanation is that the cause of the fluctuations is connected with the presence of ions, which would affect the number of conduction electrons or the contact resistances. If we assume further that these ions have a certain lifetime, it may be expected that the current will consist of a random series of bursts of the form $e^{-\alpha t}$, where α is the reciprocal of the lifetime of the ion. This assumption leads to a spectrum of the form

$$G_v(f) \approx \frac{\alpha}{\alpha^2 + (2\pi f)^2} \tag{62}$$

For large f, $G_v(f)$ will be $\approx f^{-2}$, whereas for small f, $G_v(f)$ will be constant. One might think, therefore, that the experimental data may be represented by Eq. (62). For the current noise, nevertheless, this possibility seems unlikely.[4]

Additional sources of noise have also been found in electron tubes. In the a-f range the current fluctuations are much larger than would be expected from the shot-effect fluctuations. This increase is called the "flicker effect"; it has been investigated experimentally by Johnson,[5]

---

[1] *Cf.* J. Bernamont, *Ann. Phys.*, **7**, 71 (1937); *Proc. Phys. Soc.*, **49**, 138 (1937).

[2] E. Meyer and H. Thiede, *E.N.T.*, **12**, 237 (1935); C. J. Christensen and G. L. Pearson, *Bell System Techn. J.*, **15**, 197 (1936).

[3] This is in contrast to the thermal voltage fluctuations across a metallic resistance, which are independent of the current (see Sec. 4·5).

[4] For a discussion of the crystal noise, which belongs in this category, see Sec. 5·3.

[5] J. B. Johnson, *Phys. Rev.*, **26**, 71 (1925).

who found that the increase is proportional to the square of the average current and that it is strongly frequency-dependent. For frequencies above 5 kc/sec, the flicker effect disappears. A theory proposed by Schottky[1] attributes the flicker effect to random changes in the emissivity of the cathode produced by the presence of foreign atoms on the surface. Let us suppose that one foreign atom causes an additional current cI, where I is the average current and c a constant; let the average number of foreign atoms per square centimeter of the surface be N and the lifetime of a foreign atom be $1/\alpha$. Then the spectrum of the current fluctuations is given by the formula

$$G_I(f)\,\Delta f = 2eI\,\Delta f + 4Nc^2I^2\,\frac{\alpha}{\alpha^2 + (2\pi f)^2}\,\Delta f \qquad (63)$$

The second term represents the flicker effect and is in qualitative agreement with the observations of Johnson. The order of magnitude of the flicker effect is usually expressed in terms of an apparent electronic charge. For low frequencies apparent charges of the order $100e$ are common. For oxide-coated filaments the flicker effect is much more pronounced than for pure tungsten filaments, again in accord with the ideas of Schottky.

At higher frequencies (100 to 1000 kc/sec) increases of the current fluctuations have been observed when the tube is operated in the space-charge-limited region.[2] These increases (the apparent electronic charge can be of the order $10e$) are caused by the presence of positive ions trapped in the potential minimum. The slow motion of these ions releases random bursts of electrons. The positive ions are produced by evaporation from the cathode or by collision ionization of the residual gas atoms in the tube. This positive-ion effect disappears if the plate voltage is raised, and the current becomes temperature limited. The frequency dependence of the effect has not been investigated.

[1] W. Schottky, *Phys. Rev.*, **28**, 74 (1926).

[2] H. N. Kozanowski and N. H. Williams, *Phys. Rev.*, **36**, 1314 (1930). For a theoretical development and more recent experiments, see B. J. Thompson and D. O. North, *RCA Rev.*, **5**, 371 (1941).

CHAPTER 5

RECEIVER NOISE

5·1. Introduction. *Separation of Noise Contributions.*—The noise voltage appearing at the output terminals of a receiver actually arises from many sources. Some noise is generated by the antenna itself, which, as we shall see in Sec. 5·2, is due to incoming electromagnetic disturbances. In addition to this antenna noise there are several sources of noise within the receiver; chief among these noise contributions are the (crystal) converter noise, the local-oscillator noise, and the noise generated within the i-f amplifier. Here it need be noted only that these noise contributions are essentially independent. This fact assures that in a linear system the total noise *power* is the sum of the powers of the individual noise contributions. Furthermore this independence makes it possible to break the receiver into hypothetical pieces in each of which the detailed behaviors of signal and noise are studied, with a view toward ultimately synthesizing the over-all signal and noise contributions. Friis[1] has presented a method by which this analysis can be effected. The following analysis utilizes extensively the methods of Friis, with modifications devised by Roberts.[2]

The superheterodyne converter is essentially linear (see Sec. 2·2), and the i-f amplifier stages (at least at low level) are linear; let us thus assume that the over-all superheterodyne receiver consists of a series of linear networks; each of these networks is characterized by an input and output impedance and a gain that will shortly be defined. These three parameters are generally complex and depend upon frequency. It is not essential that the input and output signal frequencies be identical; it is necessary only that the network be linear, i.e., that the output signal voltage be linearly related to the input signal voltage.

Each of these linear networks serves to amplify (or to attenuate) the signal as well as any noise produced either in the device generating the signal or in preceding networks. In addition to this, the network in general adds some extra noise; this extra noise is the only quantity that prevents the network (or over-all receiver) from being "theoretically ideal." The attempt will be made therefore to specify the characteristics

---

[1] H. T. Friis, "Noise Figures of Radio Receivers," *Proc. I.R.E.*, **33**, 458 (1945).

[2] S. Roberts, "Some Considerations Governing Noise Measurements on Crystal Mixers," *Proc. I.R.E.*, **35**, 257 (1947).

of the over-all receiver in terms of this ideal receiver; this specification, to be definite, must assume certain properties of the input-signal generating device. [Since the properties of the antenna depend upon external radiation, which may be quite different under different conditions (see Sec. 5·2), it is customary to measure the properties of a receiver by means of a signal generator connected to its input terminals.] This signal generator is any device which can be represented, according to Thévenin's theorem, as a constant voltage source e_g in series with an impedance $R_g + jX_g$.

Available Power.—The available power from the signal generator or a linear network is simply the *maximum* power that can be taken from the network by a suitably adjusted load. In the case of the signal generator mentioned previously the available signal power S_g is

$$S_g = \frac{e_g^2}{4R_g}. \tag{1}$$

In addition to the available signal power from the generator, there is a noise fluctuation voltage due to R_g. The open-circuit mean-square noise voltage from the generator within a narrow frequency interval df (see Sec. 3·1) is

$$G_V(f)\,df = 4kTR_g\,df, \tag{2}$$

where k is Boltzmann's constant and T is the temperature of R_g. The quantity G_V is the power spectrum expressed in mean-square volts per unit frequency interval. Therefore, the available noise power dN_g from the signal generator is

$$dN_g = \frac{G_V(f)\,df}{4R_g} = kT\,df, \tag{3}$$

which does not depend upon the generator impedance but does depend upon the temperature of the generator resistance and the bandwidth df. To standardize the performance of the generator it is necessary to choose some standard temperature T_0; it is customary to choose T_0 as 292°K, since this is a reasonable approximation to the ambient temperature at which measurements are made, and since for this value of temperature there is obtained the simple relation

$$\frac{kT_0}{e} = \frac{1}{40} \quad \text{volt,} \tag{4}$$

where e represents the electronic charge.

The Gain of a Network.—The power gain G of a network will be defined here as the ratio of *available* output signal power to the *available* input signal power delivered either by the signal generator or by a preceding network. On the basis of this definition the gain is seen to depend upon the impedance of the generator but not upon the impedance of the load. It does not represent the actual power gain unless suitable matching loss-less networks are inserted between the generator and load. The over-all gain of a series of cascaded networks is the product of the gain factors of the individual networks.

The actual *measured* output power of the network is not necessarily the available output power. The quantity with which we are ultimately concerned, however, is the ratio of signal to noise power, i.e., the ratio of gain to noise power. The ratio of measured output power to available output power when the network is connected to a mismatched load will be identical for both signal and noise; hence only available gain need be dealt with in the analysis that follows.

Noise Figure.—As the noise and signal proceed from the signal generator through the various networks, the ratio of noise power to signal power increases. The reason for this increase is the extra noise contributions from the networks themselves. Let us consider the ratio of output noise to signal power (available) dN_o/S_o, where the output noise power dN_o is measured in a frequency band df centered at the signal frequency. This quantity is larger than the corresponding quantity at the signal generator by a factor F, which is called the noise figure of the network.

$$\frac{dN_o}{S_o} = F \frac{dN_g}{S_g}. \tag{5}$$

In this definition of noise figure the two signal frequencies can be different, but the noise at each point must be measured in a narrow band of given width df centered at the signal frequency. Furthermore, it is assumed that there is a one-to-one correspondence between input and output frequencies. This last assumption is not generally fulfilled in a super-heterodyne converter; but if the image response is suppressed by pre-selection or by other means (see Sec. 2·2), Eq. (5) is valid. If the image response is not suppressed, extra noise will be found in the output of the network. Therefore, presupposing good converter design, it will be assumed (in those cases where it matters) that the image response is properly suppressed.

The expression for the noise figure F may be written in a slightly different way. The increase of F over unity is explained by extra output noise dM_o generated within the network.

$$\frac{dN_o}{S_o} = \frac{GkT_0\,df}{GS_g} + \frac{dM_o}{GS_g} = F \frac{kT_0\,df}{S_g}, \tag{6}$$

or

$$F - 1 = \frac{dM_o}{GkT_0\,df}. \tag{7}$$

Integrated Noise Figure.—The noise figure is in general, as just defined, a function of frequency. It is useful, however, to speak of the *integrated* noise figure F_i of a network which represents the increase of the ratio of *total* noise to signal power by the network.

From Eq. (5) we may write

$$dN_o = FG \, dN_g = FGkT_0 \, df \qquad (8)$$

and

$$N_o = \int_0^\infty FGkT_0 \, df. \qquad (9)$$

The noise that would have appeared at the output from an ideal network is $\int_0^\infty GkT_0 \, df$; hence we may write

$$F_i = \frac{\int_0^\infty FGkT_0 \, df}{\int_0^\infty GkT_0 \, df}. \qquad (10)$$

If the bandwidth of the network Δf is defined as

$$\Delta f = \frac{1}{G_{\max}} \int_0^\infty G \, df, \qquad (11)$$

where $G_{\max}$ is the maximum of the gain vs. frequency characteristic, we may write

$$F_i = \frac{N_o}{G_{\max} k T_0 \, \Delta f}. \qquad (12)$$

Cascaded Networks.—When two networks in series follow the signal generator, an expression for the over-all noise figure of the combination may be derived in terms of the noise figures of each section.

The over-all output noise power $dN_{o_{12}}$ within a narrow band df centered at the signal frequency is made up of two parts. The first part is the output noise from the first section dN_o amplified by the second network according to its gain G_2, and the second part is the extra noise contributed by the second section. This second contribution can be derived from Eq. (7). We may write

$$dN_{o_{12}} = dN_{o_1} G_2 + (F_2 - 1)G_2 k T_0 \, df \qquad (13)$$

or

$$F_{12} G_1 G_2 k T_0 \, df = F_1 G_1 G_2 k T_0 \, df + (F_2 - 1)G_2 k T_0 \, df, \qquad (14)$$

where F_{12} is the over-all noise figure. From Eq. (14),

$$F_{12} = F_1 + \frac{F_2 - 1}{G_1}. \qquad (15)$$

Thus the over-all noise figure can be expressed in terms of the noise figures of the individual networks. This expression is especially useful in deriving the noise figure of the first network by measuring F_2, F_{12}, and G_1; this procedure is currently used in connection with crystal converters (see Sec. 5·3).

One can proceed from two to three networks by considering the first two networks as a single network and then applying Eq. (15).

$$F_{123} = F_{12} + \frac{F_3 - 1}{G_1 G_2} = F_1 + \frac{F_2 - 1}{G_1} + \frac{F_3 - 1}{G_1 G_2}. \tag{16}$$

If one proceeds in this way the over-all noise figure of n sections will be

$$F_{1\ldots n} = F_1 + \frac{F_2 - 1}{G_1} + \frac{F_3 - 1}{G_1 G_2} + \cdots + \frac{F_n - 1}{G_1 G_2 \cdots G_{n-1}}. \tag{17}$$

It can be seen (and a little reflection makes it obvious) that after any *high-gain* network the over-all noise figure is not markedly influenced by additional networks even though their individual noise figures are relatively high. Thus in the superheterodyne receiver one need be concerned only with the r-f amplifier, the converter—which in the microwave field generally has a gain less than unity—and with the first stage or two of the i-f amplifier.

An expression analogous to Eq. (17) can be derived for the over-all integrated noise figure of cascaded networks, but only if the bandwidth of the final network is narrow compared with the bandwidth of any preceding section.

By analogy with Eq. (10) the following equation may be written:

$$F_{i_1\ldots n} = \frac{\int_0^\infty F_{1\ldots n} G_1 G_2 \cdots G_n k T_0 \, df}{\int_0^\infty G_1 G_2 \cdots G_n k T_0 \, df}. \tag{18}$$

Since the bandwidth of the nth section is assumed narrow compared with that of any preceding network, the only quantities in Eq. (18) that depend upon the frequency are F_n and G_n. From Eqs. (10), (11), (17), and (18), we may write

$$F_{i_1\ldots n} = F_1 + \frac{F_2 - 1}{G_1} + \frac{F_3 - 1}{G_1 G_2} + \cdots + \frac{F_{n-1} - 1}{G_1 G_2 \cdots G_{n-2}} + \frac{F_{i_n} - 1}{G_1 G_2 \cdots G_{n-1}} \tag{19}$$

The form of this equation is similar to that of Eq. (17); it should be noted, however, that for the intermediate networks the noise figures themselves are used instead of the corresponding integrated noise figures.

5·2. Antenna Noise. *Introduction.*—The noise appearing at the output of a receiver has its origin partly in the receiver and partly outside the receiver. This external noise is picked up by the antenna and is generally referred to as "antenna noise." For receivers operating in the broadcast band this type of noise is largely either man-made or atmospheric in origin. For receivers operating in the short-wave bands these two effects are still important but an additional, new type of noise appears. This new random fluctuation, called cosmic noise, has its origin, as its name suggests, outside the solar system, in the direction of the center of the galactic system.[1] Because of the relative impenetrability of the ionosphere, cosmic noise is not of importance at broadcast frequencies.

Antenna noise at microwave frequencies is largely thermal in origin. It has been found experimentally that with few exceptions (e.g., radiation from fluorescent lights) antenna noise at microwave frequencies could be traced to thermal radiation emitted by surrounding objects. The antenna noise at microwave frequencies is, as will be shown later, nearly always small compared with the other sources of fluctuation in present-day microwave receivers. Any discussion of ultimate performance must be based, however, upon a knowledge of the antenna noise. Since the thermal radiation intercepted by an antenna depends upon the object at which the antenna is pointed, it is clear that there is no "best" performance for a receiver. The limiting sensitivity of a receiver will depend upon the nature of the objects at which the antenna is pointed.

Connection between Black-body Radiation and Electrical Noise.—Let us consider the hypothetical system shown in Fig. 5·1. An antenna is connected to a resistor by a transmission line. Both the antenna and resistor are assumed to be matched to the transmission line. The antenna is completely surrounded by the enclosure S, whose inside walls are assumed to be "black" at radio frequencies. The temperature of this black-body and of the resistor are assumed to be equal to T on the Kelvin scale. It is clear that the system is in thermal equilibrium and that the black-body radiation intercepted by the antenna must balance that lost by the resistor as a result of noise fluctuations in the resistor. It has been shown (Sec. 4·1) that, because of thermal fluctuations, the power P_1 that can be abstracted from the resistor by the matched antenna is simply kT per unit frequency interval. Therefore, in thermal equilibrium, the power P_2 absorbed by the antenna and delivered to the resistor is also equal to kT per unit frequency interval. We may calculate P_2 specifically in terms of the electrical properties of the antenna. The black-body radiation intensity per unit frequency interval and unit

---

[1] K. G. Jansky, *Proc. I.R.E.*, **25**, 1517 (1937); G. Reber, *ibid.*, **30**, 367 (1942).

solid angle is, according to the Rayleigh-Jeans law,

$$I = \frac{2}{c^2} f^2 kT. \tag{20}$$

The antenna is usually capable of absorbing only one of two orthogonal polarizations. Therefore,

$$P_2 = \int_\Omega \sigma \frac{I}{2} d\Omega, \tag{21}$$

where σ is the effective receiving area of the antenna. Since I is independent of the angle Ω,

$$P_2 = \frac{I}{2} \int_\Omega \sigma \, d\Omega = \frac{I}{2} 4\pi\sigma_{\text{avg}}, \tag{22}$$

where σ_{avg} is the average receiving area of the antenna for all directions. Since P_2 is also equal to kT per unit frequency interval,

$$kT = 4\pi\sigma_{\text{avg}} \frac{f^2}{c^2} kT, \tag{23}$$

$$\sigma_{\text{avg}} = \frac{\lambda^2}{4\pi}. \tag{24}$$

This is the well-known expression for the effective receiving area for any antenna (see Vol. 12 of the Radiation Laboratory Series).

The antenna, in so far as the generation of noise power is concerned, may therefore be viewed as a resistor whose value is the radiation resistance of the antenna at a temperature equal to the temperature of the

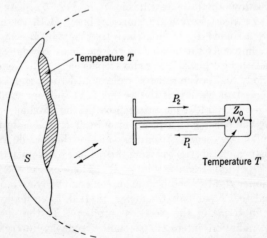

Fig. 5·1.—Thermal equilibrium between a resistor and a black-body.

antenna's surroundings. If the surroundings of the antenna are not all at the same temperature, an average temperature may be defined. This average temperature will be called the antenna temperature and may be defined as the temperature which a black-body (see Fig. 5·1) must have in order to duplicate the antenna noise.

Antenna Temperature of Sky.—Since the antenna temperature of a highly directive microwave antenna depends upon the direction in which the antenna is pointed, the antenna temperature must be investigated under a variety of conditions. First let us consider the temperature of

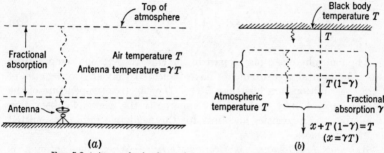

FIG. 5·2.—Atmospheric absorption as a source of thermal radiation.

a highly directive antenna pointed at the zenith. An experimental investigation has shown that with the exception of the sun and moon, radiation from astronomical bodies is negligibly small at wavelengths of the order of 1 cm. In particular, stellar radiation has been found experimentally to contribute less than 20°C to the antenna temperature for wavelengths of approximately 1 cm, and it can be easily calculated to contribute less than 10^{-8}°C. Thus it seems plausible that thermal radiation external to the solar system is completely negligible as a cause of antenna noise at microwave frequencies; hence it is necessary to examine the earth's atmosphere for sources of thermal radiation.

The atmosphere cannot radiate unless it absorbs at microwave frequencies. Figure 5·2a and b illustrates how the antenna temperature can be calculated in the case of a partially absorbing atmosphere. In Fig. 5·2b the earth's atmosphere is surrounded by an imaginary black-body at the same temperature as the atmosphere. The radiation x arising in the atmosphere must just compensate for the partial absorption of the black-body radiation in the atmosphere. This fact leads to the result

$$x = \gamma T \qquad\qquad (25)$$

for the antenna temperature, where γ is the fractional absorption of the atmosphere. Because of absorption in water vapor, the antenna tem-

perature can, in the 1-cm region, become as great as 70°K. At wavelengths of 2 to 10 cm the atmospheric absorption is so small that the
antenna temperature of an antenna directed at the zenith ought to be
extremely small.

When the antenna is directed at an angle θ from the zenith, the
increased path length through the atmosphere produces a greater amount
of absorption and hence a higher antenna temperature than for the
antenna pointed at the zenith. If T_θ is the antenna temperature at an
angle θ from the zenith and T is the atmospheric temperature, then

$$\frac{T_\theta}{T} = 1 - \left(1 - \frac{T_0}{T}\right)^{\sec \theta}. \tag{26}$$

The ionosphere can play a part in the effective antenna temperature,
but experimental measurements have indicated that at wavelengths of
1 cm contributions are less than 5°C. The effective temperature of the
ionosphere itself may be high, but apparently the negligible absorption
at microwave frequencies accounts for the negligible radiation emitted
by the ionosphere.

Antenna Temperature of Ground Objects.—When the antenna is
pointed at surrounding ground objects, the antenna temperature can vary
widely, depending upon the nature of the object. The amount of thermal
radiation from a body depends upon the degree of blackness of the body.
If the object at which the antenna is directed is not a black-body, it
reflects partially, and the total radiation from the object depends not
only on the temperature of the object but also on the temperatures of
reflected objects. For example, a metal does not emit at microwave
frequencies but merely acts as a mirror to reflect the radiation from other
objects or from the sky. A metallic object may appear very cold if it is
oriented in such a way as to reflect the radiation from the sky to the
antenna.

Figure 5·3 shows the antenna temperatures at a wavelength of 1 cm
resulting from pointing an antenna at ground objects. The curves are
measured antenna temperatures as a function of azimuth angle for various
declination angles. Several features merit special mention. (1) As the
declination angle was increased, the average antenna temperature
increased until at an angle of 91° the average antenna temperature
was approximately equal to the air temperature. (2) The presence
of the chimney A is indicated by its thermal radiation. The electro-
static-generator housing F is a metallic structure capped by a hemispher-
ical dome. It should also be noted that, at a declination angle of 91°,
the antenna temperature falls very low when the antenna is pointed at

the dome.   This fact indicates that the sky is reflected by the dome to the antenna.

Role of Antenna Noise in Receiver Performance.—If T, the temperature of the antenna, differs from T_0, the effective receiver noise figure must be

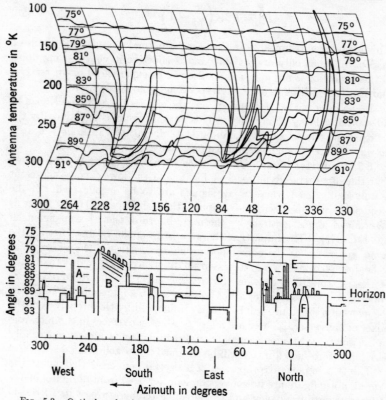

FIG. 5·3.—Optical and microwave radiometer panorama of the Cambridge, Mass., skyline from a point on Building 20, MIT.   The labels on the curves of the upper diagram are the antenna angles measured from the vertical.   Similarly, the angles indicated on the left side of the lower figure are measured from the vertical.

(A) Chimney of MIT powerhouse
(B) Radiation Laboratory, Building 24
(C) and (D) Sheds on Building 20
(E) Lever Brothers Company chimney
(F) Electrostatic accelerator, MIT

modified.   Let us denote the modified noise figure by F^*.   Analogously to Eq. (6),

$$\frac{dN_o}{S_o} = \frac{GkT\,df}{GS_a} + \frac{dM_o}{GS_a} = F^*\frac{kT_o\,df}{S_a}, \qquad (27)$$

where S_a refers to the signal power available from the antenna.   But from Eq. (7),

$$F - 1 = \frac{dM_o}{GkT_0\,df} = F^* - \frac{T}{T_0}.$$ (28)

Therefore,

$$F^* = F + \left(\frac{T}{T_0} - 1\right).$$ (29)

This expression assumes, as in the case for normal noise figures discussed in Sec. 5·1, that only one r-f sideband is effective in contributing noise. If this condition is not met, more noise will be experienced in the receiver and Eq. (29) will have to be correspondingly modified.

It can be seen that if T is very low, the effective noise figure F^* can be substantially lower than unity. This curious result is explained by the arbitrary way in which the "standard" temperature T_0 was chosen; it in no way violates fundamental noise principles.

5·3. Converter Noise. *Introduction.*—It is now generally recognized that the superheterodyne receiver has one of the lowest noise figures; it is universally used where weak signals are to be encountered. If the receiver is equipped with r-f amplification, the over-all noise figure is determined almost entirely by the noise figure of the r-f amplifier itself [see Eq. (17)]. The important characteristics of the r-f amplifier are the same, generally, as the corresponding characteristics of the i-f amplifier to be discussed in Sec. 5·5; the essential difference is the higher frequency of the r-f amplifier, causing transit-time effects to be relatively more important. If the receiver is not equipped with a high-gain r-f amplifier, the over-all noise figure will be greatly influenced by the properties of the mixer or converter. There are many types of converters in common use. In the microwave region a small crystal rectifier is now almost universally used; therefore such a mixer will be assumed in the following discussion.[1]

The two important properties of a crystal converter that affect the over-all noise figure are its conversion gain (or loss) from radio frequency to intermediate frequency and the effective temperature of its i-f resistance viewed at the i-f terminals of the mixer. The importance of these two quantities is shown by Eq. (15), which can be rewritten in a form containing the effective i-f temperature and the conversion gain. The noise figure of the converter F_1 is, specifically, the ratio of its noise output to that of an "ideal" converter, i.e., one that has an available noise output equal to $G_1 kT_0\,df$. If we write the effective i-f temperature of the converter as t, i.e., the ratio of actual available i-f noise power to the available noise power from an equivalent pure resistor, we may relate

---

[1] For vacuum-tube mixers, the reader is referred to W. A. Harris, "Fluctuations in Vacuum Tube Amplifiers and Input Systems," *RCA Rev.*, **5**, April 1941.

F_1, G_1, and t in the following way:

$$F_1 = \frac{t}{G_1};\tag{30}$$

and so, from Eq. (15),

$$F_{12} = \frac{t + F_2 - 1}{G_1}.\tag{31}$$

This equation shows how the crystal i-f temperature and gain influence the over-all receiver noise figure. In most cases G_1 is actually less than unity; i.e., the conversion gain is really a loss. Since G_1 is a factor that influences F_{12} in inverse fashion, it has been customary to express Eq. (31) logarithmically:

$$10 \log_{10} F_{12} = 10 \log_{10} (t + F_2 - 1) - 10 \log_{10} G_1,\tag{32}$$

where $(-10 \log_{10} G_1)$ is the conversion *loss* of the crystal expressed in decibels and $(10 \log_{10} F_{12})$ is the over-all noise figure also expressed in decibels. Thus an over-all noise figure of 3.01 db really means an over-all noise figure F_{12} of 2; likewise a conversion loss of 6.02 db really means a value for G_1 of $\frac{1}{4}$. The advantage of this loose way of expressing conversion loss and noise figures is that a change in loss of n db results in a change in over-all noise figure of just n db.

Crystal mixers in common use show an effective i-f temperature t ranging between 1.0 and very large numbers; the conversion loss is usually between 5 and 10 db. Since the i-f noise figure F_2 can usually be made less than 2 (see Sec. 5·5), the crystal characteristics play an extremely important part in the over-all noise figure. In the following discussion there will be given the important experimental observations, together with a brief explanation of current theories of crystal performance. For a complete treatment of this field the reader is referred to Vol. 15 of the Radiation Laboratory Series.

Experimental Observations.—A crystal rectifier consists of a small semiconducting block, such as germanium or silicon, embedded in a suitable case. On one exposed surface of the semiconductor a contact is made with a fine, pointed, metallic wire. The whole assembly is a two-terminal device, which acts much like a diode rectifier.

1. When crystal rectifiers are unexcited by direct or alternating current, the noise power available from them is just that given by the Nyquist formula, i.e., $kT\ df$. This is an experimental result and is in accord with the requirements of thermodynamics.

2. A crystal excited by either direct or alternating current puts out more noise in general than an equivalent resistor. This does not violate the laws of thermodynamics, since the system is not in

thermodynamic equilibrium. In a superheterodyne mixer or converter the quantity of interest is the effective i-f noise temperature t when the crystal is excited by local-oscillator power of the order of 1 mw. The corresponding rectified current ranges from 0.5 to 1.5 ma. It is found experimentally that t has values in the range from 1.0 to 3.0. In no authentic cases have values less than 1.0 been measured, although such values cannot be excluded on the basis of current theories. Values of $t < 1.0$ have been obtained with d-c excitation, however. For burned-out crystals t may become very large (10 to 20).

3. Miller *et al.*[1] have measured the noise temperature of crystals (excited either by d-c or microwave currents) for frequencies between 30 cps and 1 Mc/sec. They find that at low frequencies the noise temperature is inversely proportional to the frequency; this phenomenon appears to be independent of the means of excitation. The fact that this law holds down to a frequency of 30 cps indicates that the mechanism responsible has a very long time constant. In many ways this effect is like the "flicker" effect in thermionic tubes (see Sec. 4·11).

At the moderately high frequencies especially useful in i-f amplifiers, the noise temperature is essentially independent of frequency. It has been found, however, that there is a close correlation between audio noise temperatures and 30 Mc/sec noise temperatures; this suggests that the same mechanism may be responsible in both frequency regions.

4. The noise temperature (-1) is approximately proportional to rectified current up to 2 or 3 ma. At higher currents the curve departs from linearity, in the direction of smaller t.

5. The noise temperature and conversion loss of a crystal rectifier is a function of the termination of the two noise sidebands generated by the crystal. These sidebands, for an intermediate frequency f and local oscillator frequency f_0, occur at $f_0 + f$. R. Beringer[2] has shown that the conversion loss and noise temperature t go in opposite directions with image sideband tuning. However, the changes in loss are much greater than those of t; hence for minimum noise figure the sideband should be tuned for minimum loss.

6. With local-oscillator excitation the noise temperature is influenced by d-c bias; it changes very little for bias in the forward direction but may increase by a considerable amount for even a small back

[1] P. H. Miller, M. N. Lewis, L. I. Schiff, and D. E. Stephens, "Noise Spectrum of Silicon Rectifiers," NDRC 14-256, U. of Pa., Mar. 20, 1944; P. H. Miller and M. H. Greenblat, "Crystal Audio Noise," NDRC 14-387, U. of Pa., Jan. 5, 1945.

[2] Private communication.

bias (self-bias).   For example, a back bias of 0.1 volt may cause t
to increase by more than unity.   This effect is especially marked in
those crystals which are already somewhat noisy at zero bias.

7. A. Lawson et al.[1] have measured t as a function of the temperature
   of the rectifier.   Changes in t were observed, but they were as
   likely to have one sign as the other.

8. In addition to the influence of termination impedances at signal
   frequency and image frequency, it has been observed that termination impedances at harmonics of these frequencies contribute
   materially to noise temperature and conversion loss.   Since these
   termination impedances depend critically upon the particular
   circuit in which the crystal rectifier is placed, it follows that the
   two properties of the crystal rectifier with which we are concerned
   will also depend on the particular mixer circuit.

Theoretical Ideas.—Weisskopf[2] has examined the problem of crystal
noise and has suggested three sources of noise: (1) thermal noise of the
spreading (semiconductor) resistance, (2) shot noise caused by electrons
flying over the barrier, and (3) "fluctuation" noise caused by motion of
charges on the contact surface.   The effective noise temperature can be
easily calculated if "fluctuation" noise is assumed negligible; the result is

$$t = \frac{\dfrac{e}{2kT_0} IR^2 + \dfrac{T}{T_0} r}{R + r}. \tag{33}$$

where r is the spreading resistance, R is the dynamic resistance of the
barrier, T is the physical temperature of the semiconductor, and I is the
sum (arithmetic) of the electron currents from metal to semiconductor
and from semiconductor to metal, since both of these currents are equally
effective in producing shot noise.   For a voltage V such that $|V| > kT/e$,
I can be taken to be the actual direct current through the rectifier;
however, for $V = 0$ and $T = T_0$, I becomes equal to $e/2kT_0R$.

R. N. Smith[3] has measured the noise temperature with d-c excitation
as a function of voltage and, comparing his result with Eq. (33), has
found that the measured temperature generally exceeds the predicted
temperature, although in a few instances the observed noise was less
than predicted.   In at least three instances observed noise temperatures

[1] A. W. Lawson, P. H. Miller, and D. E. Stephens, "Noise in Silicon Rectifiers at
Low Temperatures," NDRC 14-189, U. of Pa., Oct. 1, 1943.

[2] V. F. Weisskopf, "On the Theory of Noise in Conductors, Semiconductors and
Crystal Rectifiers," NDRC 14-133, May 12, 1943.

[3] "Crystal Noise as a Function of D-c Bias," NDRC 14-167, Purdue U., June 25,
1943.

were less than unity at a forward bias of 0.1 volt. In each of these instances Eq. (33) correctly predicted the observed value.

It should be emphasized that Eq. (33) is valid only for d-c excitation; no useful formula for crystal noise with a-c excitation has yet been derived.

Observed noise in excess of the thermal and shot noises just mentioned has never been satisfactorily explained. Most of the mechanisms that have been suggested have not led to useful expressions, nor have they properly predicted the frequency dependence of audio noise. It is likely that most of this excess noise is caused by surface contamination of the contact; if this is true, it is not difficult to see why a quantitative formula is not yet available.

5·4. Local-oscillator Noise. *Introduction.*—In the preceding section the conversion gain and temperature of a crystal mixer was seen to depend upon many factors. Nevertheless one important source of noise appearing in the mixer was not mentioned for the reason that this noise has its origin not in the mixer but in the local oscillator. Furthermore, it is possible, by methods to be described, virtually to eliminate this local-oscillator noise. Even so, it is still important to understand the origin of local-oscillator noise.

The mixer has been considered as a (nonlinear) network upon which is impressed the r-f signal and the local-oscillator voltage and from which the i-f signal is taken. The local-oscillator voltage is generally assumed to be a pure sinusoid; but as we shall see, this assumption may not be valid. In fact the r-f terminals of the mixer may contain, besides the signal and local-oscillator sinusoid, r-f noise voltages generated within the local oscillator itself. These noise voltages, to be sure, are very small compared with the c-w local-oscillator voltage, but they may easily exceed a small signal voltage. It is clear that the only local-oscillator noise with which we shall be concerned is the noise appearing at the signal frequency and at the image frequency; these two noise sidebands, separated from the local-oscillator frequency f_0 by approximately the intermediate frequency f, are the only noise frequencies that will contribute to the mixer i-f noise temperature.

In conventional oscillators, noise is generated in the r-f resonant circuit principally because of shot and partition noise in the anode circuit; the spectral density in the resonant element simply follows the resonant response curve. In more complicated oscillators, such as the reflex variety, however, the spectral density is not so simple. Since this type of oscillator is of great importance in the microwave field, a brief account of its noise characteristics will be given.[1]

---

[1] For a complete discussion, see Vol. 7 of the Radiation Laboratory Series.

Experiments on Noise from Reflex Oscillators.—Kuper and Waltz[1] have investigated the noise output of reflex oscillators operating at wavelengths of approximately 3 and 1 cm. Their method was essentially a determination of the increase in i-f temperature of a crystal mixer resulting from the local oscillator noise. This increase in temperature Δt is simply

$$\Delta t = \frac{GP}{k T_0 \, \Delta f},\qquad(34)$$

where G is the crystal gain, Δf is the bandwidth of noise measured, and P is the noise power from the local oscillator appearing within the frequency interval Δf. In their experiments Kuper and Waltz used a bandwidth of 2.5 Mc/sec located either 30, 60, or 90 Mc/sec away from the local-oscillator frequency. Their results show many interesting features.

1. The total noise power in the 30-Mc/sec sidebands within a 2.5-Mc/sec bandwidth interval for the 3-cm oscillator varied between 10^{-12} and 10^{-11} watt. This is easily enough power to increase the effective crystal temperature by several units.

2. The noise power fell off rapidly with increasing intermediate frequency (larger sideband spacing). At an intermediate frequency of 90 Mc/sec the effective crystal temperatures were not seriously affected by local-oscillator noise.

3. The variation of total noise power with electrical tuning (reflector-voltage variation) was asymmetrical. This phenomenon was definitely established even though the r-f circuits were insensitive to frequency, i.e., the sidebands as well as the local-oscillator frequency were matched. Tuning to a higher frequency increased Δt.

4. The individual contributions of both sidebands were measured by means of r-f filters tuned to the appropriate frequencies; these contributions were, in general, unequal and influenced differently by the reflector-voltage electrical tuning. In particular, there appeared to be a crossover point, lying on the h-f side of the center of the tuning range, at which these two contributions were equal. Below this crossover point the h-f sideband contributed more noise, whereas above it the l-f sideband contributed more. Extreme values of the noise from the l-f sideband differed by as much as a factor of 10; extreme values from the h-f sideband differed by a factor of about 2.

5. The variation of total noise power with the impedance presented to the oscillator is different from the corresponding variation of

[1] J. B. H. Kuper and M. C. Waltz, "Measurements on Noise from Reflex Oscillators," RL Report No. 872, Dec. 21, 1945.

c-w power. In general, the ratio of noise to c-w power increases
with admittance; hence for a given c-w power the noise can be
minimized by presenting a low admittance to the oscillator.

Theoretical Ideas.—Pierce[1] has presented a theory of reflex-oscillator
noise that includes the effects from (1) shot and partition noise in the
electron beam coupled out through the cavity, (2) amplitude modulation
of the oscillator by i-f noise components in the beam, and (3) frequency
modulation of the oscillator at i-f rates caused by fluctuations in the phase
of returning electrons. Kuper and Waltz[2] have found experimentally
that with adequate bypassing of the oscillator leads the last two mechanisms are relatively unimportant. Knipp[3] has extended Pierce's calculations in two important directions: (1) He considers the noise produced
by the mixing of various electron-beam noise components with harmonics
of the oscillator current; (2) he takes into account the coherence, i.e.,
phase relationship, of the returning current with the incident current.
This coherence causes a marked difference in individual sideband contribution and also an asymmetry in noise output as a function of electrical
tuning.

In its final form Knipp's theory appears to account correctly for all
the important experimental facts discovered by Kuper and Waltz, not
only as to functional form but also as to magnitude.

Suppression of Local-oscillator Noise.—Although the local oscillator
has for a long time been known to be an important source of receiver
noise, it has also been recognized that this noise can be relatively easily
removed or suppressed. The most straightforward way of accomplishing
its elimination is by means of a tuned r-f filter inserted between the mixer
and local oscillator. If this filter is tuned to the local-oscillator frequency
and has a bandwidth small compared with the intermediate frequency
itself, the noise sidebands with which we are concerned will not be
transmitted through the filter to the mixer. For some oscillators we may
consider the resonant property of the oscillator cavity itself to constitute
such a filter; this is the usual reason why oscillator noise is relatively
unimportant for very high intermediate frequencies. In any case,
however, it is always possible to add a new filter in the local-oscillator
coupling that is sufficiently narrow (high-Q) to suppress local-oscillator
noise. The only flaw in this procedure is the necessity for continually
tuning the filter to the oscillator frequency; this disadvantage can be

---

[1] J. A. Pierce, "Noise Calculations for Reflex Oscillators," BTL Report MM-44-
140-4, Jan. 29, 1944.

[2] Kuper and Waltz, *loc. cit.*

[3] J. K. Knipp, "Theory of Noise from the Reflex Oscillator," RL Report 873,
Jan. 10, 1946.

overcome if a so-called "magic T" mixer is used, described in detail in Vol. 16 of the Radiation Laboratory Series. This form of mixer constitutes a sort of r-f bridge circuit in which the local-oscillator and signal voltages are applied to two crystal rectifiers. The connection is so made, however, that the r-f signal voltages applied to each of two crystals are in phase, the local-oscillator voltage being out-of-phase; therefore the cross products of the two voltage pairs (i.e., the i-f signals) are out of phase with respect to each other. The i-f connection is made in such a way that in-phase i-f contributions from the two crystals are canceled, and therefore only out-of-phase contributions (namely, i-f signals) are amplified. The principal local-oscillator contribution to the i-f noise comes from beats between the local-oscillator carrier and those components of its noise which are separated from it by the intermediate frequency. Since the intermediate frequency is small compared with the carrier frequency, the phase relationship between a noise component and the local-oscillator carrier at one crystal is virtually the same as that at the other crystal, even though the carrier itself is π radians out of phase. Therefore the i-f noise outputs from the local oscillator are in phase with respect to each other and cancel, whereas, as stated, the signal outputs add.

It is clear that there are other equally satisfactory ways of arranging the bridge so that LO noise is canceled and signal components properly handled. The fundamental reason why it is possible to suppress local-oscillator noise without at the same time suppressing desired signals is that the *sources* are different; this fact makes it possible to build circuits that discriminate in favor of the desired signals (see also Sec. 5·6).

5·5. Intermediate-frequency Noise. *Introduction.*—In a superheterodyne receiver the output voltage from the mixer is connected to the input terminals of an i-f amplifier. We have seen from Eq. (17) that if the gain of the first i-f stage is large, the over-all i-f noise figure depends only on the first stage itself; furthermore we have seen from Eq. (31) that if we use a crystal converter whose temperature is low ($t \approx 1$), the over-all receiver noise figure is approximately proportional to the noise figure of the i-f amplifier. Therefore the i-f amplifier noise is a very important matter. A great deal of effort has been expended in designing amplifiers with low noise figures.

Tubes used in i-f amplifiers have generally been of two kinds, pentodes and triodes. A pentode would appear to be more satisfactory since the plate-to-grid feedback (Miller effect) is so low; triodes, however, if properly used lead to lower noise figures because of the absence of partition noise. Circuits that have been found useful for triodes are of two kinds.

1. The *grounded-grid* triode, which does not need to be neutralized (out-of-phase feedback introduced that nullifies the output-to-input capacitance) but it can be used only where the relatively high input conductance can be tolerated. This input conductance is, in fact, simply the mutual conductance g_m of the triode.

2. The *grounded-cathode* triode (the conventional arrangement) would be very desirable because of its high input resistance; unfortunately, however, if the voltage gain of the tube is high, the necessary neutralization is extremely critical. For this reason this type of triode connection has been virtually abandoned.

Nevertheless a very ingenious circuit arrangement has been suggested that completely eliminates this difficulty. In this new circuit a grounded-cathode triode is immediately followed by a grounded-grid triode. If the triodes are alike, the voltage gain of the first triode is unity (its load conductance is essentially g_m); and since its current flows directly to the anode of the second triode (none is captured by the grid of the second triode), the over-all mutual conductance of the two tubes is just g_m. Wallman has shown that the noise contribution of the second triode is negligible; hence the over-all noise figure is essentially that of the grounded-cathode triode. Neutralization of the first triode is extremely easy, however, since its voltage gain is only unity; failure to neutralize at all results in no instability and in only a slight increase in noise figure.

Representation of Noise Generators.—It has been shown in Chap. 4 that the fundamental sources of i-f noise contributing to anode noise in a triode are (1) thermal noise in the signal generator, (2) thermal noise in circuit elements (such as transformer losses, tube glass losses, etc.), (3) shot noise in the anode, and (4) induced grid noise. For a pentode a fifth source of noise was mentioned, namely, partition noise caused by random current collection by the screen grid. In determining the noise figure of the i-f stage in terms of these noise contributions it is most convenient to introduce a hypothetical circuit whose over-all gain and noise output is in every way just the same as that of the actual i-f circuit. Such an equivalent circuit is shown in Fig. 5·4, in which it is assumed that a completely noiseless tube of the same mutual conductance as that of the actual tube is preceded by particular resistor elements. These resistor elements are so chosen that their noise contributions correspond to the various noise contributions in the actual tube. The noise in the grid circuit will be properly represented by the three load conductances g, g_l, g_o shown in Fig. 5·4; these symbols represent the conductances of the signal generator (applied directly to the grid), the conductance caused by grid-circuit losses, and the effective grid conductance caused by grid transit-time electronic loading.[1] The conductances g and g_l can usually be taken to be at standard room temperature T_0, but it has been shown [cf. Eq. (4.61)] that the effective temperature of g_g is several times T_0. The quantity g_g will be considered noiseless, but let us associate with it the proper (noise) current generator i_g as shown in Fig. 5·4.

The three conductances g, g_l, and g_g, together with the current generator i_g, can therefore represent the noise contributions in the *grid* circuit; there remains only the question of the contributions by shot and partition noise appearing in the anode circuit. It is convenient to introduce a *fictitious* resistor R_{eq} in series with the grid of the noiseless tube shown in Fig. 5·4; the thermal noise voltage of R_{eq} at temperature T_0

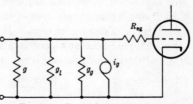

FIG. 5·4.—Equivalent input circuit.

produces noise currents in the tube just equal to the combined shot and partition noise in the actual tube. With this equivalent representation of actual tube noise we are in a position to calculate the noise figure and to examine the way in which the noise figure depends upon the various circuit parameters.

Calculation of Noise Figure.—The noise figure of the circuit shown in Fig. 5·4 can be easily calculated if one remembers that the noise figure is the ratio of the actual noise power output to that noise power coming from the signal generator resistance at a temperature T_0 (see Sec. 5·1). The total mean-square noise voltage at the grid terminal is clearly

$$G_V(f) \, \Delta f = \left[\frac{4kT_0(g + g_l) + 4kT_0 mg_g}{(g + g_l + g_g)^2} + 4kT_0 R_{eq} \right] \Delta f, \qquad (35)$$

where m is the ratio of the effective temperature of g_g (because of induced grid noise) to T_0 [see Eq. (4.59)]. The noise that would appear at the grid in an "ideal" condition, i.e., if the effective temperature of g_l and g_g and R_{eq} were zero, is

$$G_V(f) \, \Delta f = \frac{4kT_0 g \, \Delta f}{(g + g_l + g_g)^2}; \qquad (36)$$

hence the noise figure F is given by

$$F = 1 + \frac{g_l}{g} + \frac{mg_g}{g} + \frac{R_{eq}}{g}(g + g_l + g_g)^2. \qquad (37)$$

[1] These quantities are, in general, complex; however, for the sake of simplicity, they will be assumed to be pure conductances. Residual susceptances can always be tuned out with lumped reactive elements.

The first constant (unity) comes from the thermal noise in the signal generator itself; the remaining three terms, representing "excess" noise, come from circuit losses (usually small), induced grid noise, and shot (and partition) noise, respectively. Equation (37) can be written in a slightly different way:

$$F - 1 = [g_l + mg_g + R_{eq}(g_l + g_g)^2] \frac{1}{g} + 2R_{eq}(g_l + g_g) + R_{eq}g. \quad (38)$$

This expression shows that as a function of signal-generator conductance g, the noise figure (minus unity) has one independent term, one hyperbolic term, and one linear term. It is clear that (for small F) there is an *optimum* signal-generator conductance; for this value of conductance the first and third contributions are equal.

$$g_{opt} = \frac{[g_l + mg_g + R_{eq}(g_l + g_g)^2]^{1/2}}{R_{eq}^{1/2}}, \quad (39)$$

and

$$F_{opt} - 1 = 2[g_l + mg_g + R_{eq}(g_l + g_g)^2]^{1/2}R_{eq}^{1/2} + 2R_{eq}(g_l + g_g). \quad (40)$$

It is clear from Eq. (38) that a measurement of F as a function of g permits evaluation of all the quantities involved, namely, R_{eq}, g_l, g_g, and m. J. L. Lawson and R. R. Nelson[1] have used this method with partial success. The quantity R_{eq} can be obtained with good accuracy, but the other quantities cannot usually be determined with adequate precision. If circuit losses are small, g_l can be neglected; this fact helps somewhat in the determination of m and g_g. It is usually more satisfactory, however, to determine g_g by direct measurement.

In practice, g_l can usually be neglected. Furthermore, the contribution from the constant term in Eq. (38) is ordinarily negligible. Under these conditions the optimum noise figure (-1) depends linearly on the square root of the grid electronic loading conductance g_g [see Eq. (40)]. We saw in Sec. 4·10, however, that the electronic loading conductance is (for small transit angles) directly proportional to the square of the frequency; therefore it would be expected that

$$F_{opt} = 1 + kf, \quad (41)$$

where k is a function characteristic of the particular i-f tube. This relationship has been roughly verified by J. L. Lawson and R. R. Nelson, using a triode-connected 6AK5. They measured the noise figures at 6, 30, and 60 Mc/sec and found values of 1.06, 1.3, and 1.7, respectively, for F_{opt}.

Role of I-f Input Coupling Transformer.—It seldom happens that a signal generator (or the i-f terminals of a converter) has the optimum

[1] Unpublished.

conductance given by Eq. (39); a transformer is generally used, therefore, to change the effective generator impedance to the most suitable value. If the transforming network is lossless, we may simply view g as the transformed generator impedance. Losses in the transformer must be lumped with g_l; if this is done, the preceding development is valid and noise figures are easily calculated. It is obvious that the optimum (for optimum noise figure) transformed generator impedance is not generally equal to its load; i.e., impedance matching is not generally desirable.

In spite of the fact that the input coupling transformer is used for proper impedance transfer, it sometimes happens that, because of the input shunt capacitance of the tube, the circuit bandwidth is insufficient for the intended use. In this case a compromise between bandwidth and noise figure must be made; this compromise, however, is not usually serious. For instance, in the example just mentioned, i.e., triode-connected 6AK5, the optimum noise figure occurs when the circuit bandwidth is approximately 0.25 the center (intermediate) frequency. A larger bandwidth would hardly be useful in view of the difficult problem of adequately separating i-f and video voltage at the second detector.

Experimental Measurement of Noise Figures.—The noise figure of a receiver can be measured in many ways; however, the straightforward methods involving a direct comparison of the total equivalent noise power with a minute c-w signal power involve the difficult task of knowing accurately the power of the extremely minute signal. This task becomes especially difficult at high frequencies, where good attenuators are difficult to construct. There is a method of measuring noise figures which does not involve c-w signals and attenuators; it consists essentially of a comparison of "normal" noise (generator at temperature T_0) with the noise occurring when the generator is artificially changed to a new temperature. This change in temperature is most easily effected by impressing diode shot noise (temperature-limited) on the generator resistance.[1] Let us consider the case where a measurement is made of the d-c diode current I that just *doubles* the original receiver noise.

The original receiver (available) noise power is simply F (the noise figure) times the noise contribution arising in the generator resistance itself [see Eq. (5)], which is now to be set equal to the contribution of noise from the test diode operating into the generator resistance R_g. The available shot noise power W_s (per unit frequency interval) will be given by the Schottky formula [Eq. (4·28)], together with the generator resistance R_g:

$$W_s = \frac{eIR_g}{2} \Delta f, \qquad (42)$$

[1] E. J. Schremp showed (in December 1942) the validity of measuring noise figures by means of diodes.

which must be set equal to the original receiver noise power, i.e., $FkT_0\Delta f$. Therefore,

$$F = \frac{eIR_g}{2kT_0},\tag{43}$$

which, if T_0 is set equal to the "standard" figure of $292°$K, reduces to the simple expression

$$F = 20IR_g,\tag{44}$$

where I is that d-c diode current in amperes which just doubles the output noise and R_g is the generator resistance in ohms. In this fashion the noise figure is easily and accurately measured without recourse to long-range attenuators and complicated methods of accurate power measurements. The only precaution that must be taken is to ensure that the only source of noise from the diode is the one given by the Schottky formula; this appears to be the case when a temperature-limited tungsten or thoriated-tungsten cathode is used in a diode of good geometry. Diodes having oxide cathodes have proved to be somewhat unreliable, for what precise reason is not yet known.

Another (and less accurate) method of measuring noise figures is physically to change the temperature of the generator resistance R_g and to plot the over-all noise power as a function of temperature. The thermal noise from R_g should be linearly proportional to the temperature, whereas the excess noise contributing to $(F - 1)$ [see Eq. (7)] is independent of the temperature. The zero-temperature (extrapolated) noise is the excess noise power, which can be divided by the thermal noise at temperature T_0 to yield the quantity $(F - 1)$. An experimental plot showing noise power as a function of temperature is reproduced in Fig. 5·5. The data were taken by R. R. Nelson and J. L. Lawson at an intermediate frequency of 6 Mc/sec using a triode-connected 6AK5 at approximately optimum generator resistance [see Eq. (39)]. The noise figure determined by the plot is 1.07, which substantially agrees with the value of 1.06 determined by a diode measurement.

Pentode vs. Triode Amplifiers.—We have seen [Eq. (40)] that the best noise figure available depends upon several factors that are functions of the particular tube used. We may ask how these quantities differ in a triode and pentode; indeed, we may ask how the optimum noise figure depends upon operating a given tube as a pentode or as a triode. With a given tube the only quantity appearing in Eq. (40) that differs with pentode and triode connection is R_{eq}; the equivalent noise resistance is always higher in a pentode because of screen-grid partition noise. It is easy to calculate R_{eq} for a triode. We have seen from Eq. (4·50) that the shot-noise voltage fluctuation in the plate is exactly equivalent to a voltage fluctuation in the grid circuit (of a noiseless tube) equal to

$$G_V(f) \, \Delta f = \frac{\theta}{\sigma} \frac{4kT_c}{g_m} \Delta f, \tag{45}$$

which is also equal to the equivalent voltage generated by R_{eq}, i.e., $4kT_0 R_{eq} \, \Delta f$.   Therefore,

$$R_{eq} = \frac{\theta}{\sigma} \frac{T_c}{T_0} \frac{1}{g_m}. \tag{46}$$

If appropriate values for an oxide-coated cathode are assigned to θ, σ, and T_c, we obtain the simple formula

$$R_{eq} \approx \frac{2.5}{g_m}. \tag{47}$$

In a similar fashion the equivalent noise resistance R_{eq} can be calculated for a pentode connection,

$$R_{eq}(p) = \left(1 + 8.7\sigma \, \frac{I_g}{g_m} \, \frac{1000}{T_c}\right) R_{eq}(t), \tag{48}$$

where $R_{eq}(t)$ is the equivalent resistance of a triode-connected tube operating with identical space current.   It will be noticed that because

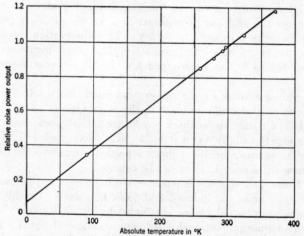

FIG. 5·5.—Relative noise power output.

of the screen-grid collector current I_g, the pentode noise *always exceeds* the triode noise.   For this reason amplifiers that are to have a very low noise figure should be constructed with an input triode stage.

Equations (47) and (48) are given, together with a number of other useful relations, by Harris.[1] He has verified them experimentally in a large number of cases.

Suppression of Induced Grid Noise.—It has been assumed hitherto in the discussion that the various sources of noise that have been considered are independent. This assumption, however, is not valid; the same electrons that produce fluctuations in anode current (shot noise) induce noise currents in the grid. It was shown in Sec. 4·10 from the form of the current pulses produced by a given electron at the grid and anode that the two noise contributions are substantially in quadrature, provided the effective load attached to the grid is resistive. In this case the noise powers from the two sources can be added as though they were independent. If the grid load is reactive, however, the grid-current pulse will produce a grid-voltage change having components in phase or out of phase with the anode-current pulse. It is natural to ask whether or not this circumstance can be used to cancel out part of the shot noise with part of the grid noise. From an analysis of the phases involved, this cancellation might be expected to occur when the grid reactance is capacitive or, in other words, when the resonant frequency of the grid circuit is lower than the intermediate frequency chosen for measurement. Experiments by R. R. Nelson and J. L. Lawson have shown that at 30 Mc/sec, the noise figure of a triode-connected 6AK5, measured with a fairly high-resistance generator (making induced grid noise evident) is best when the grid circuit is tuned to a somewhat lower frequency than the noise measurement frequency. This observation corroborates the cancellation picture. Unfortunately these experiments were discontinued before it was ascertained how much cancellation could be effected.

In a similar manner simple analysis indicated that reactive feedback from anode to grid could accomplish the same type of result. It was expected that inductive feedback would accomplish some cancellation; this was experimentally verified by R. R. Nelson and J. L. Lawson. However, more experimental evidence is needed to establish the degree to which these noise contributions can be canceled.

5·6. Noise Cancellation Schemes.—We have seen in two cases, i.e., local-oscillator noise and induced grid noise, how noise normally present in a receiver can be reduced or eliminated by circuit ingenuity without at the same time proportionally reducing the desired signal. It is of great importance to learn when noise cancellation is possible and when impossible.

The elimination of local-oscillator noise appears to be possible only

[1] W. A. Harris, "Fluctuations in Vacuum Tube Amplifiers and Input Systems," *RCA Rev.*, **5**, 4, April 1941.

because one can operate on the local-oscillator noise energy *independently* of the signal energy.   In other words, the *source* of noise does not cause it to appear initially on the same two terminals as the signal.   Likewise, in the case of induced grid noise, the noise behavior at grid and anode (from the same source) is substantially different from the signal contribution.

It seems, on the other hand, that cancellation is *not* possible if the extra noise is generated at the same terminals as is the signal.   In this case any noise cancellation scheme should also and to the same degree cancel the signal.   This consideration will apply, therefore, to signal-circuit losses, crystal-mixer losses, etc.   For these effects, the only hope for lower noise lies in improved methods of construction, lower temperatures, etc.

CHAPTER 6

EXTERNAL NOISE SOURCES; CLUTTER

6·1. Origin and Description of "Clutter."—The term "clutter" is used to describe signals reflected from such objects as rain, "window" or "chaff,"[1] vegetation, and the surface of the sea. The inclusion of clutter in a discussion of noise is justified by the similarity, though superficial, between the appearance of clutter on an A-scope and that of noise on an extended A-scope and by the close similarity of their mathematical treatment. The chief difference between clutter and noise is that whereas there is correlation in clutter received during a number of consecutive pulses, noise is completely independent from pulse to pulse.

The mathematical description of clutter is based on the assumption that it is caused by reflections from a large number of independent and independently moving scatterers, (e.g., strips of window, raindrops). With this model statistical predictions can be made of the power received as a function $I(r)$ of range[2] when the pulse travels through rain or window, etc. These considerations have led to predictions concerning the appearance of individual traces on the A-scope.[3] Furthermore, the power $I(t)$ returned from a region at fixed range can be considered as a random function of time. This function is actually observed only for a discrete set of values of the time variable, that is, once for each pulse. Experimentally the function $I(t)$ is obtained from these discrete observations by interpolation using a "boxcar" device (*cf.* Sec. 2·7) and a low-pass filter. With the commonly used PRF's the function $I(t)$ thus obtained is sufficiently well represented for comparison with the theoretical predictions.

Both $I(r)$ and $I(t)$ are random functions. Even if the average number and cross section of the scatterers do not depend on range, $I(r)$ fluctuates because the phase relations between the scatterers contributing to the return are different in different regions of space.

Fluctuations in $I(t)$ occur because the phase relations of one assembly

---

[1] These terms have been used to describe a large collection of thin metallic strips, used as a jamming device.

[2] Experimentally, the function of range is obtained as a function of time on a microsecond scale with range $= c/2 \times$ time.

[3] A. J. F. Siegert, "On the Appearance of the A-scope When a Pulse Travels through a Homogeneous Distribution of Scatterers," RL Report No. 466, Nov. 9, 1943.

of scatterers change with time because of the random motion of the scatterers. The changes of intensity arising from the statistical fluctuations of the number of scatterers can be neglected, since they are small compared with the fluctuations due to changing relative phases when the average number of scatterers contributing to the clutter is large. Clutter is therefore considered as the return from N scatterers where N is merely the average number of scatterers and not a random variable.[1] The r-f signal received from the kth individual scatterer is denoted by

$$x_k \cos 2\pi f_0 t + y_k \sin 2\pi f_0 t,$$

where f_0 is the carrier frequency.

The signal intensity $x_k^2 + y_k^2$ depends on the field strength at the scatterer and on the distance from the scatterer to the receiver. The total power received is given by $I(t) = X^2(t) + Y^2(t)$, where $X = \Sigma x_k$, and $Y = \Sigma y_k$. The phase $\tan^{-1}(y_k/x_k)$ depends mainly on the distance from the scatterer to the receiver. The x_k and y_k may be functions of time for the following reasons: (1) The field strength at the point where the scatterer is located may change, for example, if the scatterer moves out of the illuminated area; (2) the scatterer may change its cross section ("chaff," sea return); and (3) the distance between transmitter and scatterer may change. The first cause will be disregarded, since the number of scatterers entering and leaving the beam is usually small during a continuous series of observations (several thousand pulses). The second cause will also be neglected, since the rotating motion of the "chaff" is slow and does not affect the phase. In sea return, too little is known about the scatterers to make reasonable assumptions for the purposes of calculation. The third cause has been studied extensively as far as phase changes go. Intensity changes brought about by changes of distance are so small and so slow that they can be neglected.

Besides assuming N to be large, it will be essential to assume that the amplitudes received from the scatterers are independent of each other. This assumption will be discussed in more detail along with the derivations of the first two probability distributions $W_1(I)$ and $W_2(I_1,I_2,t)$.

6·2. Derivation of the First Two Probability Distributions.—To obtain the first probability distribution $W_1(I)$, the distribution $W_N(X,Y)$ is first calculated for the components

---

[1] For distances r from the transmitter that are large compared with the pulse length,

$$N = n\left(\frac{\pi r \theta}{2}\right)^2 \frac{c\tau}{2},$$

where n is the average number of scatterers per unit volume, θ the beam width, τ the pulse duration, and c the velocity of light.

$$X = \sum_{k=1}^{N} x_k, \qquad Y = \sum_{k=1}^{N} y_k$$

of the total field received from N scatterers, assuming a given probability distribution $w(x_k, y_k)$ for the field received from the kth scatterer. The assumption of one distribution for all scatterers can be justified, even if there are several classes of scatterers, e.g., raindrops of various sizes. It is assumed further that the return amplitudes from different scatterers are independent, that is, that the probability of receiving x_k, y_k from the kth scatterer and x_l, y_l from the lth scatterer is given by the expression

$$w(x_k, y_k) w(x_l, y_l).$$

This assumption is justified if the N scatterers represent a sample containing large numbers of scatterers of each class.[1]

It is clear that under these assumptions the problem of finding $W_N(X, Y)$ is nothing but the *two-dimensional random-walk problem*, treated in Sec. 3·6. With the additional assumption that $w(x, y)$ is isotropic, and hence

$$w(x, y)\, dx\, dy = \frac{1}{2\pi} f(r)\, dr\, d\phi,$$

we obtain, within an error of the order of magnitude $1/N$, the Rayleigh distribution

$$W_1(I)\, dI = \frac{dI}{I_0} e^{-\frac{I}{I_0}}, \tag{1}$$

where $I_0 = N\overline{r^2}$ is the average power returned by the N scatterers.

To derive the joint probability of obtaining return signals of power $I(t_1) = I_1$ and $I(t_2) = I_2$ a time $t = t_2 - t_1$ apart, the probability $W(X_1, Y_1, X_2, Y_2)$ is again first derived for the components of the total field received from all N scatterers at the times t_1 and t_2. It is assumed that the return signals from all N scatterers are received simultaneously at both instances of time. As long as I_1 and I_2 are observed at the same range and without turning the antenna, this assumption is justified, since the number of scatterers drifting into and out of the region from which the signals are received during the time t is small compared with N.

The probability of receiving amplitudes $x_1^{(k)}$, $y_1^{(k)}$ at time t_1 and $x_2^{(k)}$, $y_2^{(k)}$ at time t_2 from the kth scatterer is denoted by $\tau(x_1^{(k)}, y_1^{(k)}; x_2^{(k)}, y_2^{(k)})$.[2] The scatterers have been assumed to be independent; that is, the proba-

---

[1] If there were, for instance, only a few scatterers of large cross section among many of small cross section, the knowledge that the return signal from the kth scatterer is large would diminish the probability of observing a large signal from another scatterer.

[2] The probability $w(x_1^{(k)}, y_1^{(k)})$ used above is related to this function by

$$w(x_1^{(k)}, y_1^{(k)}) = \int\!\int \tau(x_1^{(k)}, y_1^{(k)}; x_2^{(k)}\, y_2^{(k)})\, dx_2^{(k)}\, dy x_2^{(k)}.$$

bility of receiving the field $x_1^{(k)}$, $y_1^{(k)}$; $x_2^{(k)}$, $y_2^{(k)}$ from the kth scatterer and $x_1^{(l)}$, $y_1^{(l)}$; $x_2^{(l)}$, $y_2^{(l)}$ from the lth scatterer is assumed to be $\tau(x_1^{(k)}, y_1^{(k)}; x_2^{(k)}, y_2^{(k)})$ $\tau(x_1^{(l)}, y_1^{(l)}; x_2^{(l)}, y_2^{(l)})$.

The fact that a whole cloud of chaff, for instance, may be carried by the wind so that the average velocity of the particles is the same does not contradict the assumption of independence.

The probability for the initial phase $\phi_1 = \tan^{-1}(y_1/x_1)$ is assumed to be independent of ϕ_1. The unconditional probability for $\phi_2 = \tan^{-1}(y_2/x_2)$ is also assumed independent of ϕ_2, whereas the conditional probability for ϕ_2, with given ϕ_1, depends on $\phi = \phi_2 - \phi_1$. The averages $\overline{x_1}$, $\overline{y_1}$, $\overline{x_2}$, $\overline{y_2}$ are therefore all equal to zero.

Assuming that u, the velocity component of the scatterers parallel to the line of sight, does not change during a time t, which in the experiments is less than about $\frac{1}{15}$ sec, we have $\phi = (4\pi/\lambda)ut$.

The absolute value of the field received at t_2, $r_2 = \sqrt{x_2^2 + y_2^2}$ is assumed[1] to be the same as the value for t_1, $r_1 = \sqrt{x_1^2 + y_1^2}$.

Under these assumptions the joint probability for the amplitudes may be found by the method explained in Sec. 3·6 or by Chandrasekhar;[2] and omitting terms vanishing for $N \to \infty$, we obtain[3]

$$W_2(X_1, Y_1, X_2, Y_2, t) = \frac{1}{(2\pi)^4} \int \int \int \int d\xi_1 \, d\eta_1 \, d\xi_2 \, d\eta_2$$

$$\exp\left[i(X_1\xi_1 + Y_1\eta_1 + X_2\xi_2 + Y_2\eta_2) - \frac{N}{2} \overline{(x_1\xi_1 + y_1\eta_1 + x_2\xi_2 + y_2\eta_2)^2} \right]$$

(2)

with

$$\overline{(x_1\xi_1 + y_1\eta_1 + x_2\xi_2 + y_2\eta_2)^2}$$
$$= \int \int \int \int dx_1 \, dy_1 \, dx_2 \, dy_2 \, (x_1\xi_1 + y_1\eta_1 + x_2\xi_2 + y_2\eta_2)^2$$
$$\tau(x_1, y_1, x_2, y_2) \quad (3)$$

[1] For window, these assumptions mean that changes of return power and phase caused by rotation of the strips during the time $t_2 - t_1$ have been neglected. According to the expressions derived by F. Bloch, M. Hamermesh, and M. Philips ("Return Cross Sections from Random Oriented Resonant Half-wave Length Chaff," RRL Report 411-TM-127, June 19, 1944), the phase of the returned field is actually independent of the orientation of the strip. Since the time intervals over which the experiments extend are small compared with the rotation time of window strips, neglect of the intensity changes brought about by changes of orientation during the time t is justified. The dependence of return power on the initial orientation is taken care of in the probability distribution, of course.

[2] S. Chandrasekhar, "Stochastic Problems in Physics and Astronomy," *Rev. Mod. Phys.* **15**, 1–89 (January 1943).

[3] For further details of the derivation see A. J. F. Siegert, "On the Fluctuations in Signals Returned by Many Independent Scatterers," RL Report No. 465, Nov. 12, 1943. The fact that assumptions made in this report are more special than those above does not affect the expression for W_2.

where

$$r(x_1,y_1,x_2,y_2)\, dx_1\, dy_1\, dx_2\, dy_2 = w(r_1,u)\, dr_1 \frac{\lambda}{4\pi t}\, d\phi\, \delta(r_1^2 - r_2^2) 2r_2\, dr_2 \frac{d\phi_1}{2\pi} \quad (4)$$

with $u = \frac{\lambda}{4\pi t}(\phi_2 - \phi_1)$. The ranges of the variables are

$$0 \leqq r_1, r_2 \leqq \infty, \qquad -\infty \leqq \phi \leqq +\infty, \qquad 0 \leqq \phi_1 \leqq 2\pi.$$

In the foregoing expression, $w(r_1,u)\, dr_1\, du$ is the probability that a scatterer returns a field between r_1 and $r_1 + dr_1$, and its velocity component away from the transmitter lies between u and $u + du$.

Straightforward calculation leads to the expression

$$W_2(X_1, Y_1, X_2, Y_2, t) = \frac{1}{\pi^2 I_0^2 (1 - g^2)}$$

$$\exp\left(- \frac{1}{I_0(1 - g^2)}\{X_1^2 + Y_1^2 + X_2^2 + Y_2^2 - 2g[X_1(X_2 \cos\psi + Y_2 \sin\psi) + Y_1(-X_2 \sin\psi + Y_2 \cos\psi)]\}\right), \quad (5)$$

with

$$I_0 = N\overline{r_1^2},$$

$$\overline{r_1^2} = \int_0^\infty r_1^2\, dr_1 \int_{-\infty}^\infty w(r_1,u)\, du,$$

$$ge^{i\psi} = \frac{1}{\overline{r_1^2}} \int_0^\infty r_1^2\, dr_1 \int_{-\infty}^\infty w(r_1,u) e^{4\pi i u t/\lambda}\, du,$$

where g is real and positive.

For the distribution of intensities $I_1 = X_1^2 + Y_1^2$, $I_2 = X_2^2 + Y_2^2$ we obtain

$$W_2(I_1, I_2, t)\, dI_1\, dI_2 = \frac{dI_1\, dI_2}{I_0^2(1 - g^2)} e^{-\frac{I_1 + I_2}{I_0(1 - g^2)}} J_0\left[\frac{2ig\sqrt{I_1 I_2}}{I_0(1 - g^2)}\right], \quad (6)$$

where g is given by

$$g = \frac{1}{\overline{r_1^2}}\left|\int_0^\infty r_1^2\, dr_1 \int_{-\infty}^\infty w(r_1, u) e^{4\pi i u t/\lambda}\, du\right| = \frac{\overline{r_1^2 e^{(4i/\lambda)ut}}}{\overline{r_1^2}}, \quad (7)$$

and J_0 is the Bessel function of zero order. It is noteworthy that g cannot become negative and that only g appears in the final result; the phase angle ψ has dropped out.

The relation between W_2 and W_1 is easily verified:

$$\int_0^\infty dI_2\, W_2(I_1, I_2, t) = W_1(I_1).$$

For the average product there is obtained

$$\overline{I_1 I_2} = \int_0^\infty \int_0^\infty W_2(I_1, I_2, t) I_1 I_2\, dI_1\, dI_2 = I_0^2(1 + g^2), \quad (8)$$

which, for $t = 0$, leads to the result $\overline{I^2} = 2I_0^2$ derived above, since $g(0) = 1$. The result for $\overline{I_1 I_2}$ can be used to determine g^2 experimentally from observed values of $I(t)$, since

$$g^2 = \frac{\overline{I_1 I_2} - I_0^2}{\overline{I^2} - I_0^2}. \tag{9}$$

The following special cases, though not realized experimentally, may give some insight into the qualitative behavior of the correlation function $g^2(t)$, especially into its dependence upon the velocity distribution of the scattering centers. If it is assumed that all scatterers return a field of the same absolute value $r_1 = p$, that all directions of motion are equally probable, and that the speed distribution is $q(v)\, dv$, Eq. (7) yields

$$g = \left|\overline{e^{(4\pi i/\lambda)u\tau}}\right| = \frac{1}{2}\left|\int_0^\infty q(v)\,dv \int_0^\pi \sin\theta\,d\theta\, e^{(4\pi it/\lambda)v\cos\theta}\right|$$

$$= \left|\int_0^\infty q(v)\,dv\, \frac{\sin\left(\dfrac{4\pi vt}{\lambda}\right)}{\left(\dfrac{4vt}{\lambda}\right)}\right|. \tag{10}$$

If all horizontal directions are equally probable, if the speed distribution is again $q(v)\, dv$, and if the radar cross section of a strip is not correlated with its direction of motion, we obtain

$$g = \frac{1}{2\pi}\left|\int_0^\infty q(v)\,dv \int_0^{2\pi} d\psi\, e^{(4\pi it/\lambda)v\cos\psi}\right|$$

$$= \left|\int_0^\infty q(v)\,dv\, J_0\left(\frac{4\pi vt}{\lambda}\right)\right|. \tag{10a}$$

If in addition all particles move with the same speed v_0, we get

$$g = \left|J_0\left(\frac{4\pi v_0 t}{\lambda}\right)\right|. \tag{10b}$$

Correlation between r_1 and u could occur, for example, if the strips glided through the air in a direction perpendicular to their long axes, since r_1 depends on the orientation of the strip. The correct formula for this dependence leads to a rather involved integral. It can be seen qualitatively, however, what will happen if the above hypothesis is correct: The particles moving in the line of sight contribute most, and the picture is essentially equivalent to two clouds, one moving away from and one moving toward the transmitter, with velocity distributions centered about $\pm v_0$. If an equal number of particles move in both directions, we may write $w(u) = \frac{1}{2}[f(u - v_0) + f(u + v_0)]$ and we obtain

$$g = \frac{1}{2} \left| \int_{-\infty}^{\infty} [f(u - v_0) + f(u + v_0)]e^{(4\pi i/\lambda)tu} \, du \right|$$

$$= \frac{1}{2} \left| (e^{(4\pi i/\lambda)v_0} + e^{-(4\pi i/\lambda)v_0}) \int_{-\infty}^{\infty} f(v)e^{(4\pi i/\lambda)vt} \, dv \right|,$$

$$g = \left| \cos \frac{4\pi v_0 t}{\lambda} \int_{-\infty}^{\infty} f(v)e^{4\pi i(vt/\lambda)} \, dv \right|. \tag{11}$$

The normalized spectrum $F(\omega)$ of $I - I_0$ is obtained from the Wiener-Kintchine relation

$$F(\omega) = \frac{2}{\pi} \int_0^{\infty} g^2 \cos \omega t \, dt.$$

It should be noted that for all values of ω,

$$F(\omega) \leqq F(0), \tag{12}$$

since $g^2(t)$ is always positive. This inequality does not exclude the possibility of $F(\omega)$ having maxima as long as these maxima are not larger than $F(0)$. The spectrum can also be expressed by means of $w(r,u)$ as follows:

$$F(\omega) = \frac{2}{\pi} \int_0^{\infty} g^2(t) \cos \omega t \, dt = \frac{1}{\pi} \int_{-\infty}^{\infty} g^2(t)e^{i\omega t} \, dt,$$

since g^2 is an even function. Substituting for g we find

$$F(\omega) = \frac{\lambda}{2\pi} \int_{-\infty}^{\infty} du \, S(u)S\left(u + \frac{\lambda\omega}{4\pi}\right), \tag{13}$$

where

$$S(u) = \frac{1}{\overline{r^2}} \int_0^{\infty} r^2 \, dr \, w(r,u) \tag{14}$$

and

$$\overline{r^2} = \int_{-\infty}^{\infty} du \int_0^{\infty} r^2 \, dr \, w(r,u).$$

Thus $S(u) \, du$ is that fraction of the received power that is returned by scatterers whose velocity component away from the transmitter lies between $u - (du/2)$ and $u + (du/2)$.

6·3. The Probability Distributions When a Constant Signal Is Present. Although the theory developed up to this point adequately describes the clutter caused by window and rain, it has to be modified for vegetation. Here there is usually a constant signal returned from motionless objects such as rocks, tree trunks, and cliffs together with the clutter from moving objects such as leaves and branches. This distinction is, of course, somewhat dependent on wind velocity, and the type of return received from the same wooded slope has been observed to vary from a nearly steady signal on a windless day to clutter with small constant signal on a stormy day.

In the presence of a constant return, the voltage in the r-f or i-f stage is given by $X_s \cos \Omega t + Y_s \sin \Omega t = (X + S) \cos \Omega t + Y \sin \Omega t$, where $S \cos \Omega t$ is the fixed signal, $X \cos \Omega t + Y \sin \Omega t$ the random signal, and X and Y are Gaussian random functions as described above. The probability distribution for the total amplitudes at a chosen time is, therefore, given by the expression

$$W(X_s, Y_s)\, dX_s\, dY_s = \frac{dX_s\, dY_s}{\pi I_0} e^{-\frac{(X_s - S)^2 + Y_s^2}{I_0}},$$

where I_0 is the average power of the clutter, $I_0 = \overline{X^2 + Y^2}$. By introducing polar coordinates $X_s = I_s \cos \phi$, $Y_s = I_s \sin \phi$ and integrating over the polar angle ϕ, we obtain, for the probability distribution of the power $I_s = X_s^2 + Y_s^2$,

$$W_1(I_s)\, dI_s = \frac{dI_s}{I_0} e^{-\frac{I_s + S^2}{I_0}} J_0\left(2i\, \frac{S\sqrt{I_s}}{I_0}\right). \tag{15}$$

The average power is given by

$$\begin{aligned}
\bar{I}_s &= \overline{(X + S)^2} + \overline{Y^2} = \overline{I + 2XS + S^2} \\
&= I_0 + S^2,
\end{aligned} \tag{16}$$

since $\bar{X} = 0$.

The joint probability distribution for the total amplitudes X_{s1}, Y_{s1}, X_{s2}, Y_{s2} observed at two instances t_1 and $t_2 = t_1 + t$ is given by the expression

$$W_2(X_{s1}, Y_{s1}; X_{s2}, Y_{s2}; i)\, dX_{s1}\, dX_{s2} = \frac{dX_{s1}\, dY_{s1}\, dX_{s2}\, dY_{s2}}{\pi I_0^2 (1 - g^2)} \exp$$
$$\left\{ -\frac{(X_{s1} - S)^2 + Y_{s1}^2 + (X_{s2} - S)^2 + Y_{s2}^2 - 2g[(X_{s1} - S)(X_{s2} - S) + Y_{s1}Y_{s2}]}{I_0(1 - g^2)} \right\}, \tag{17}$$

where g is the correlation function of the clutter amplitudes defined in the preceding section. The joint probability for the power $I_{s1} = I_s(t_1)$, $I_{s2} = I_s(t_2)$ has not been obtained in closed form. The average product $\overline{I_{s1}I_{s2}}$ can be found, however, without explicit integrations in the following manner: We have

$$\begin{aligned}
\overline{I_{s1}I_{s2}} &= \overline{(I_1 + 2X_1 S + S^2)(I_2 + 2X_2 S + S^2)} \\
&= (1 + g^2)I_0^2 + 2S(\overline{X_1 I_2} + \overline{X_2 I_1}) + 2I_0 S^2 + 2g I_0 S^2 + S^4,
\end{aligned}$$

since $\bar{X} = 0$, $\overline{X_1 X_2} = g I_0 / 2$. Since the clutter is symmetrical in time, we have $\overline{X_1 I_2} = \overline{X_2 I_1}$. We write

$$X_2 I_1 = [gX_1 + (X_2 - gX_1)][X_1^2 + Y_1^2]$$

and note that since $X_2 - gX_1$ is independent of X_1 and Y_1,

$$\overline{X_2 I_1} = g\overline{X_1^3} + g\overline{X_1 Y_1^2} \\ + \overline{(X_2 - gX_1)}\,\overline{X_1^2 + Y_1^2} = 0.$$

We therefore have

$$\overline{I_{s1} I_{s2}^{2}} = (1 + g^2)I_0^2 + 2(1 + g)I_0 S^2 + S^4.$$

For the special case that $t_1 = t_2$, this becomes

$$\overline{I_s^2} = 2I_0^2 + 4I_0 S^2 + S^4,$$

and the correlation coefficient is found to be

$$\frac{\overline{I_{s1} I_{s2}} - \overline{I}}{\overline{I_s^2} - \overline{I}_s^2} = \frac{g^2 I_0 + 2gS^2}{I_0 + 2S^2}. \tag{18}$$

when the signal-to-clutter ratio increases from 0 to ∞, the correlation coefficient increases from g^2 to g and not to unity as might at first be expected.

6·4. Experimental Techniques for Clutter Measurements.—The main features of clutter that are of interest are the spatial distribution of scatterers and the rate at which the total reflecting power of these scatterers varies. A technique for measuring these quantities by photographing successive sweeps on an A-scope has been used successfully by the Wave Propagation Group, Radiation Laboratory.[1] A photograph of a single trace on an A-scope yields information concerning the spatial reflection of objects provided a simple calibration of the deflection sensitivity of the A-scope is made. Successive photographs of sweeps that recur after short intervals show the time variation of reflected intensity at any point. Figure 6·1 reproduces a strip from a typical film showing sea echoes recorded on a 9.2-cm radar system. The interval between traces is 3 msec, and the sweep length is 1500 yd. For convenience in reference each frame area is provided with an identification number obtained by photographing a

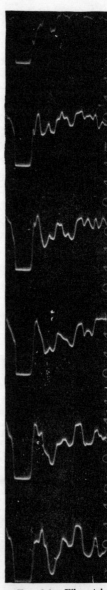

Fig. 6·1.—Film strip showing successive sea echoes.

[1] For complete details of this method see Vol. 13 of the Radiation Laboratory Series.

synchronized counter. The prominent pulse on the right is a saturated artificial echo pulse, 1 μsec long, obtained from a signal generator. Figure 6·2 shows some typical calibration curves for the A-scope deflection in percentage of saturation plotted logarithmically against signal level in decibels. The horizontal scale for each receiver gain setting has been shifted so that the values all coincide at deflections of 0.6 saturation. At high-gain settings the deflection calibration is influenced by noise; the

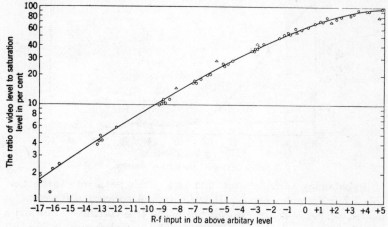

FIG. 6·2.—Deflection calibration curves.

convention has been made to measure the deflection to the *average value* of the echo (or signal) plus noise.

The *first probability* distribution is obtained by dividing the intensity scale into a number of adjoining intervals and recording the number of measurements falling within each interval. The *fluctuation rates* are obtained from the correlation function, which has been defined for an infinite sample as [*cf.* Eq. (9)]

$$\rho(\tau) = \frac{\overline{P(t)P(t + \tau)} - (\bar{P})^2}{\overline{P(t)^2} - (\bar{P})^2}. \tag{19a}$$

For a finite sample (N traces) an observed correlation function can be defined as

$$\rho_{\text{obs}}(n) = \frac{\dfrac{1}{N} \sum_{i=1}^{N} P_i P_{i+n} - \left(\dfrac{1}{N} \sum_{j=1}^{N} P_j\right)^2}{\dfrac{1}{N} \sum_{i=1}^{N} P_i^2 - \left(\dfrac{1}{N} \sum_{j=1}^{N} P_j\right)^2}, \tag{19b}$$

where the correlation time τ has been replaced by the more convenient experimental parameter n defined equal to τ/T, where T is the time interval between successive measurements (sweeps). It will be noticed that the evaluation of ρ_{obs} requires n measurements outside of the N samples; however, in a practical case these "excess" measurements can be made as small as a few per cent of N.

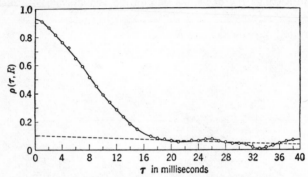

Fig. 6·3.—Typical correlation function.

In obtaining ρ_{obs} from actual film data certain peculiarities are noticeable. For example, Fig. 6·3 shows a typical correlation function ρ_{obs} plotted against τ or, equivalently, n. The true correlation function ρ should, of course, be identically unity for $\tau = 0$; however, in Fig. 6·3 extrapolation of the curve back to $\tau = 0$ gives a value substantially less than unity. This discontinuity at the origin is caused by the presence of a small amount of receiver noise, which of course is completely random from sweep to sweep. The effect of the noise is easily calculated. The first probability distributions for noise alone and for clutter alone are similar and are given by Eq. (1). If one remembers that the noise is uncorrelated, one can easily calculate the combined power and correlation functions of the clutter plus noise. These are

$$\bar{P}_{c+N} = \bar{P}_c + \bar{P}_N,$$

representing simple addition of power, and by Eq. (19a)

$$\rho_{c+N} = \rho_c \frac{(\bar{P}_c)^2}{(\bar{P}_c + \bar{P}_N)^2}.$$

The fact that the correlation function in the presence of noise is related to the correlation function in the absence of noise by a simple known factor makes the determination of the correct ρ_c extremely simple.

Another peculiarity of Fig. 6·3 is indicated by the very slow approach to zero for large values of τ. This indicates slow secular changes in the average power P_c. This fluctuation is nearly always very slow compared with the fast Doppler beat arising from the velocity distribution of the scatterers. A rigorous treatment of this case would appear to be quite difficult, since it is no longer a stationary process. However, a first approximation can be obtained as follows: Divide the sample of N values into groups each containing m measurements, each separated by a time interval τ. The quantity $m\tau$ is long compared with the periods of Doppler fluctuations but small compared with the period of the secular variation in power. We may now define correlation coefficients for the various subgroups; for example, by analogy with Eq. (19a),

$$(\rho_j)_{\text{obs}} = \frac{\dfrac{1}{m}\displaystyle\sum_{i=1}^{m} P_{i,j}P_{i+n,j} - \left(\dfrac{1}{m}\displaystyle\sum_{i=1}^{m} P_{i,j}\right)^2}{\dfrac{1}{m}\displaystyle\sum_{i=1}^{m} P_{i,j}^2 - \left(\dfrac{1}{m}\displaystyle\sum_{i=1}^{m} P_{i,j}\right)^2}.$$

These correlation coefficients are presumably independent of the average power and of the particular subgroup. The over-all ρ_{obs} can be computed by Eq. (19b); and if the Doppler fluctuations are Gaussian, one can relate the over-all ρ_{obs} to the $(\rho_j)_{\text{obs}}$ as follows:

$$\rho_{\text{obs}} = \frac{[1 + (\rho_j)_{\text{obs}}]\widetilde{P_0^2} - (\tilde{P}_0)^2}{2\widetilde{P_0^2} - (\tilde{P}_0)^2},$$

where the curly line denotes an average of the subgroup power $_{j0}$ over the various groups. It is seen that as ρ_j approaches zero, ρ_{obs} approaches a value different from zero, which can be written

$$\lim_{\tau \to \infty} \rho_{\text{obs}} = \frac{\delta^2}{1 + 2\delta^2},$$

where δ is the standard deviation of the distribution for P_0. It should be mentioned that in addition to the correlation function the first probability distribution will also be affected by the secular variation of P_0. The standard deviation for P is no longer unity but $\sqrt{1 + \delta^2}$.

Even though the corrections are made for receiver noise and secular clutter variations the observed corrected correlation coefficients usually fluctuate erratically for large values of τ. This difficulty is usually caused by statistical fluctuations produced by the finite size of the sample.

In order to tell if experimentally observed deviations from theoretical distributions are significant, it is important to know the magnitude of the experimental errors involved. Three types of errors may be distinguished: the fluctuations due to the finite size of the sample, the errors in reading the film, and the errors in calibration.

The fluctuations in the number of measurements falling within a given intensity range are distributed according to the well-known Poisson distribution. The rms fractional deviation is $1/\sqrt{n}$, where n is the expectation value of the number of measurements, providing n is small

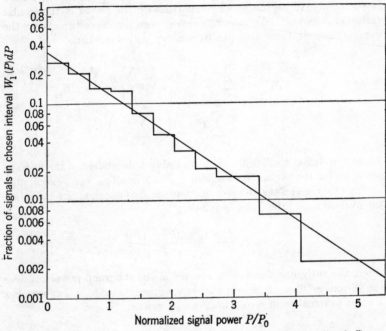

Fig. 6·4.—Experimental and theoretical first probability distributions (for chaff).

compared with the size of the sample N. It must be remembered that this assumes independent trials. Normally there is correlation between successive measurements, and n must be replaced by n', the number of independent measurements.

Errors in the reading of the film may be either systematic or random. It is difficult to estimate a systematic error. However, a known source of random error is usually present. Depending upon the computer and the nature of the trace, there is an error in measuring the deflection, ranging from 0.05 cm to several millimeters, but usually around 1 mm. Consider now an interval equal to the minimum measurable difference, centered about the deflection corresponding to the boundary between two deflection groups. Of the pulses falling in this interval zone, some, by chance, will be assigned to one group and some to the other. The rms fluctuation of the number in a group, due to such an "uncertainty zone" at one boundary, is given by $\frac{1}{2}\sqrt{m}$ where m is the total number of measurements falling in the uncertainty zone.[1] Note that m includes all measurements falling in the interval, since all trials are independent.

6·5. Experimental Results. *Chaff.*—Since chaff, or "window," is composed of a large number of randomly moving dipoles, it is ideal to use for comparing experiment with theory. Figure 6·4 compares a typical experimental first probability distribution, taken at a wavelength of 9 cm, with the theoretical exponential curve. The histogram represents the analysis of 1000 pulses, and the straight line corresponding to the theoretical curve uses the value of the measured average intensity of the sample analyzed. The deviations between the two plots are random and do not indicate any significant differences.

TABLE 6·1.—DEVIATIONS BETWEEN THEORETICAL AND EXPERIMENTAL FIRST PROBABILITY DISTRIBUTIONS

Chaff　　　$\lambda = 9.2$ cm　　　1000 pulses

Interval of $\dfrac{P}{P_0}$ (1)	No. of pulses in interval		Difference (4)	Expected rms due to finite sample (5)	Fluctuation in No. border error (6)
	Experimentally (2)	Theoretically (3)			
0　　−0.34	275	292	−17	14	3
0.34–0.68	205	206	− 1	13	4
0.68–1.01	143	146	− 3	11	4
1.01–1.35	136	103	+33	9	3
1.35–1.69	79	72	+ 7	8	3
1.69–2.03	47	54	− 7	7	3
2.03–2.36	32	37	− 5	6	2
2.36–2.70	21	26	− 5	5	2
2.70–3.38	35	31	+ 4	5	2
3.38–4.05	14	16	− 2	4	1
4.05–5.40	9	12	+ 3	3	1
5.40–8.43	4	4	0	2	1

Table 6·1 compares the magnitude of the deviations in each interval with the expected rms fluctuations due to the finite size of the sample and "border error" as discussed in Sec. 6·4. In Column 5 it has been assumed that all the measured pulses are independent of each other. Since there is actually considerable correlation between neighboring pulses, the

[1] The reasoning employed is as follows: It is equally likely that a measurement will be assigned to either group. The average number going to any one group is $m/2$. The rms fluctuation in this number is $\sqrt{m/2(1 - \frac{1}{2})} = \frac{1}{2}\sqrt{m}$.

figures in Column 5 represent minimum values. The "border error" calculation assumes that differences in the pulse height of less than 1 mm were not measurable, which is likewise a minimum figure. It is seen that the actual deviations are, with one exception, well inside the expected statistical fluctuations. Equally good results have been obtained in all measurements of chaff cut for $\lambda = 10$ cm and observed on $\lambda = 9.2$ and $\lambda = 3.2$ cm. The first probability distribution of the echo on 515 Mc/sec of chaff cut for the "Wurzburg" band ($\lambda \approx 50$ cm) has been measured at Radio Research Laboratory and good agreement was likewise obtained with theory.[1]

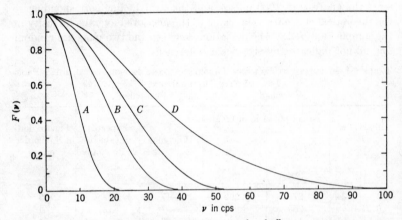

FIG. 6·5.—Frequency spectra for chaff.

The shapes of the frequency spectra of the fluctuations of chaff echo have always been found to be roughly similar, resembling error curves centered at the origin. The widths of the spectra, however, are quite variable even at one wavelength. For example, Fig. 6·5 shows the spectra for the echo of chaff cut for $\lambda = 10$ cm, as measured on $\lambda = 9.2$ cm on four occasions. It is significant that the widest spectrum D was obtained with gusty winds up to 25 mph while wind speed was 10 mph or less for the other cases. The width of the spectrum depends upon the relative velocity of the chaff dipoles, i.e., the so-called "horizontal dispersal rate," and it is to be expected that this rate depends on the speed and gustiness of the wind.

The narrowest spectrum, Curve A, was obtained with chaff of the same electrical properties as used for the other curves but with slightly different mechanical and aerodynamical properties. In addition the

[1] G. P Kuiper, "A Study of Chaff Echoes at 515 Mc," RRL Report 411-73, December 1943.

chaff was dispensed from a slow-moving blimp instead of into the relatively turbulent slip stream of an airplane.

It is not believed that there is any significant dependence of the spectrum on the "age" of the chaff, i.e., the length of time between the initial drop and the measurement. The ages for the four curves A, B, C, D of Fig. 6·5 are 3 min, 20 sec, 6 min, and 10 min, respectively.

If the fluctuation arises solely from the Doppler beats of the moving chaff dipoles, then it is seen from Sec. 6·2 that the correlation function is a function of the quantity v/λ, that is, the dispersal velocity divided by

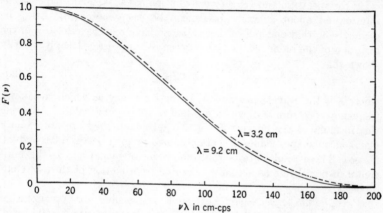

Fig. 6·6.—Spectrum of chaff for 2 wavelengths.

the wavelength. Hence the width of the frequency spectrum of the fluctuation should be proportional to the radar wavelength for the same velocity distribution. More exactly, if simultaneous measurements of the frequency spectra are made on several wavelengths, the curves should coincide when plotted as functions of the product of the fluctuation frequency and radar wavelength. Accordingly in Fig. 6·6 the experimental frequency spectra for chaff measured simultaneously on $\lambda = 3.2$ and 9.2 cm is plotted against the product of frequency and radar wavelength. The small discrepancy between the two curves is well within experimental error.

The frequency spectrum of chaff has also been measured at 515 Mc/sec[1], and the maximum frequency present to an appreciable extent was found to be 4 cps on horizontal polarization. When "scaled" to $\lambda = 9$ mm this value roughly corresponds to Curve A of Fig. 6·5. Considering that the chaff size was different, the wavelength dependence is at least qualitatively verified. (The frequency of fluctuation on

[1] *Ibid.*

vertical polarization was found to be somewhat slower, with a maximum of 3 cps, whereas all the microwave measurements were made with horizontal polarization.)

Mention must also be made of some results obtained in England on the frequency of fluctuation that are not in agreement with the above conclusions.[1]   Pulse-to-pulse photographs of chaff echoes were made on 212 and 3000 Mc/sec.   A statistical analysis was not carried out, but it is stated that there was qualitative evidence of fluctuation frequencies in the range 10 to 25 cps on both frequencies.

If the spectrum and velocity distribution have Gaussian shapes, some information about average speeds can be easily obtained.   Let $\bar{v}$ be defined such that one-half of the scatterers have relative velocities in the direction of the radar set that lie between $-\bar{v}$ and $+\bar{v}$.   Then it is easily shown that

$$\bar{v} = 0.2\lambda f_{\frac{1}{2}}, \tag{20}$$

where λ is the wavelength and $f_{\frac{1}{2}}$ is the frequency at which the power frequency spectrum is down to one-half of its original value.   Applying this formula to the curves of Fig. 6·5 (although they are not exactly Gaussian in shape) values of $\bar{v}$ are obtained ranging between 0.6 and 2.0 ft/sec.   These results are of the same order of magnitude as the horizontal dispersal rate as actually measured from motion pictures of chaff dipoles.

Precipitation Echo.—The scatterers responsible for precipitation echoes are undoubtedly either raindrops or water particles in solid form. One would therefore expect that the conditions for treating the target as an assembly of random scatterers are well satisfied.   Figure 6·7 shows a typical experimental first probability distribution as obtained from the analysis of 1000 pulses at $\lambda = 3.2$ cm of the echo from a shower.   The deviations of the histogram from the theoretical curve (plotted as a straight line on this scale) are random.   An analysis of the deviations, similar to that made for chaff echo, shows that they are within the expected statistical fluctuations.

Unfortunately, only a small amount of data is available on the frequency spectrum of the fluctuations of precipitation echo.   Three films were measured on $\lambda = 9.2$ cm, and one on $\lambda = 3.2$ cm, all for the echo from shower or thunderstorms.   The rate fluctuation appears to be several times that for chaff.   Figure 6·8 is a plot of the power frequency spectrum for the three cases measured on 9.2 cm.   The shapes of the spectra are roughly Gaussian except one case, where there is a pronounced tail above 80 cps.   It is doubtful, however, if this tail is significant.

[1] "Final Report on ADRDE Window Trials," ADRDE Report No. 250, April 1944.

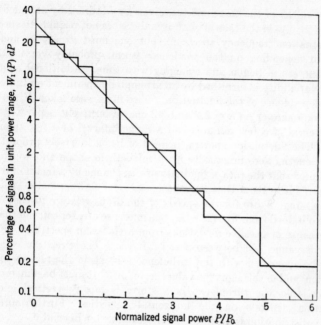

FIG. 6·7.—First probability distribution for precipitation echo.

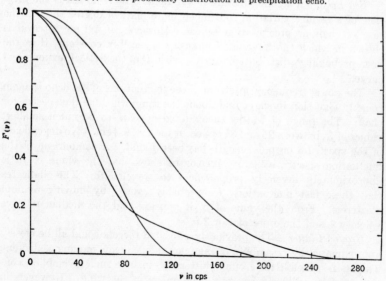

FIG. 6·8.—Frequency spectra for precipitation echo.

The widths of the three spectra, given by $f_{1/2}$, differ by as much as a factor of 2. As in the case of chaff it is therefore not possible to speak of the fluctuation frequency spectrum, but one must expect to find the spectrum depending on the particular storm, probably varying even within the storm region and changing with time. Additional evidence for this variability is furnished by an attempted experiment on the wavelength dependence of the fluctuation. Two films were taken of the echo from a rain shower on $\lambda = 9.2$ and 3.2 cm, respectively, separated by a time interval of a few minutes and a range interval of a few thousand yards. The fluctuation spectra, instead of being inversely proportional to wavelength, were practically identical both in shape and width. It is concluded that the rate of fluctuations can change by a factor of 3 even over short intervals of time and space.

An average figure for the speeds of the drops relative to each other may be obtained from Eq. (20), but one must use greater caution than for chaff because of possible deviations from a Gaussian spectrum. Figure 6·7 yields values of $\bar{v}$ between 3 and 5 ft/sec. These relative velocities should be connected with the turbulence existing in the regions of precipitation, and in this light the values seem low. It must be remembered, however, that the turbulence in a storm is mostly vertical and the fluctuation depends on the horizontal velocities. Furthermore the velocity distribution is quite broad and extends far beyond $\bar{v}$.

Sea Echo.—A striking feature of the radar echo from sea is the presence of a secular variation to a much more marked degree than in the case of chaff or precipitation echoes. However, if a time interval is chosen in which the "average" intensity is sensibly constant, then the first probability distribution agrees with the theoretical exponential curve.

The power frequency spectrum of the fluctuations of sea echo is again roughly Gaussian in shape and about the same width as the spectra for chaff. The range of widths encountered appears to be much smaller; values of $f_{1/2}$ between 25 and 35 cps occur for $\lambda = 9.2$ cm. No dependence of the spectrum on pulse length has been found. A comparison of the fluctuation spectra at two wavelengths show that the value of $f_{1/2}$ is approximately inversely proportional to wavelength. This indicates that these fast fluctuations are probably caused by moving random scatterers. From the value of $f_{1/2}$ it appears that the median relative velocity $\bar{v}$ is of the order of 1 or 2 ft/sec.

Ground Clutter.—The previously discussed targets could all be closely approximated by assemblies of random, independent, moving scatterers. Targets responsible for ground clutter also include such assemblies, consisting of leaves, branches, etc., that move in the wind. However, in addition there are scatterers with fixed phases, for example, tree trunks, rocks, etc. The total echo is the sum of the echoes from both classes of targets.

Several first probability distributions for ground clutter have been measured. They are found to agree with Eq. (15) if suitable values are inserted for the reflected power from the fixed and moving scatterers respectively. At a wavelength of 9.2 cm a heavily wooded hill subjected to gusty winds of 50 mph shows almost no fixed contribution, while a sparsely vegetated rocky terrain shows almost no random contribution. One would expect the ratio of fixed to random power to increase with wavelength; this has been qualitatively confirmed by experiment.

The shape of the spectrum appears to be roughly similar to those of the chaff or sea echo, although the differences from the Gaussian shape are somewhat more pronounced. The widths of the spectra, however, are smaller by an order of magnitude than those of the other clutter echoes. These widths naturally increase with wind speed and in addition depend to some extent on the terrain. They also appear to be essentially proportional to frequency. Representative values of $f_{\frac{1}{2}}$ for a wavelength of 10 cm are from 1 to 5 cps. This indicates very small relative velocities of the moving scatterers.

6·6. Classification of Interference.—Examples of electronic interference are legion. A common one is the static in radio reception. To understand the principles involved in the perception of signals in interference it is well to know the various types of electronic interference that may be encountered. Electronic interference reduces the desired signal visibility, either because of saturation within the receiver or because of unavoidable mixing of the interference with the desired signal. In the mixing process the identity of the signal will be destroyed if the electronic interference is sufficiently strong. In general, the interference is more serious when its characteristics correspond to those of the desired signal. This correspondence may consist of similarities in either power spectra or time distributions. Likewise, methods for reducing the deleterious effects of interference are based upon the differences between the desired signal and the interference. If the interference spectrum is similar to that of the desired signal, then, in general, the differences in time dependence are utilized. If, however, the time dependence is similar to that of the signal, it is often feasible to take advantage of differences in the spectra in finding suitable filters for the separation of the desired signal from the interference. These matters will be discussed in detail in Chap. 12.

It is important to note, however, that the power spectrum of the interference is not by itself an adequate criterion of its behavior. One can appreciate this fact by observing that the spectrum of thermal noise, such as was discussed in Chap. 4, is uniform throughout the frequency scale. The spectrum of a single, discrete, extremely short pulse is also uniform and continuous throughout the frequency scale. The time dependence of the thermal noise and the discrete pulse are entirely different, however, and it is obvious how one can utilize this difference to distinguish the two phenomena. True, if one uses the term "spectrum" in its exact sense, that is, including the phase factors between the various frequency components, then the spectrum will be an exact description of the phenomenon. It is usually customary, however, to speak of the "spectrum" in terms of the *power per unit frequency interval*. This neglects the phase factors, and therefore the spectrum is not a complete description of the phenomenon.

As was stated above, the electronic interference may mix with and cover up the desired signal. It is important to note, however, that the signal may be lost through still another mechanism. The interference, if sufficiently large, can cause the receiver to operate in such a region that it is essentially *saturated*. Under these conditions the signal will be suppressed just because the receiver no longer responds to incremental input voltages. A more complete discussion of the saturation characteristics of the receiver will be found in Chap. 12.

Interference may be variously classified, of course. For the purposes of this book electronic interference can be conveniently put into only two general categories. The first category comprises the simple forms of interference; the second, the complex forms. Of the simple forms of interference only two varieties will be discussed: c-w interference and pulsed interference, that is, interference caused by a succession of short r-f pulses similar to the radar pulses discussed in Chap. 2. There are obviously many types of complex interference, but only four gereral varieties will be treated here. Three of these are forms of noise-modulated r-f power, and the fourth variety is a series of "randomized" pulses, that is, pulses that occur at random time intervals. It is hoped that other types of interference can be understood by interpolation, superposition, and extension.

6·7. Simple Types of Interference. *Continuous-wave Interference.*— Continuous-wave r-f energy has a spectrum that is essentially monochromatic. Its characteristics are similar to those of the c-w signal described in Chap. 2, for example, a constant-amplitude r-f wave.

One reason for the deleterious effect of c-w r-f interference is that it mixes with the signal in random phase. This arbitrary phase relationship between the interference and the signal causes the signal contribution in the receiver to vary randomly in time. In addition to this phenomenon the c-w interference may possibly saturate the receiver in such a way that the response of the receiver to incremental signals is essentially zero.

Under this condition no signal will be seen in the receiver output regardless of the size of the input signal.

Pulsed Interference.—Because it is now easy to produce a series of intense r-f pulses, it is important to consider the interference effects they may produce. Any modern radar set usually causes interference of this type in near-by receiving equipment. One may assume that the interference consists of a series of very intense r-f pulses repeated at intervals corresponding to the PRF of the interfering set. The length of these pulses will be that commonly used in radar practice, perhaps a few microseconds; therefore, the spectrum of the interference will be similar to that described in Chap. 2 for pulse signals. Equation (2·24) shows that the main energy content will be contained within a frequency band approximately equal to twice the reciprocal of the interfering pulse length.

The deleterious effects of pulsed interference depend considerably upon the type of desired signal with which the interference competes. If the signal is a weak radar echo, the power spectrum of the pulsed interference will be similar to that of the desired signal; hence the interference is relatively serious. The intensity of the interference is generally considerably greater than the intensity of the radar signal. The chance that the interfering signal occurs at the same instant of time, i.e., at the same radar range, as the desired signal, however, is ordinarily very small. Because of this, the pulsed interference is not usually troublesome; the desired signal is simply seen during the time when the interfering pulses are not present. It is interesting to note that receiver saturation in the presence of pulsed interference *reduces* the deleterious effect of the interference whereas it *increases* the deleterious effect of c-w interference as previously discussed. Receiver saturation simply eliminates the major portion of the incoming pulsed interference as seen in the output of the receiver. Even though pulsed interference does not necessarily prevent the observation of the desired signal, it is nevertheless extremely fatiguing to an observer. Methods for its elimination have been developed and are discussed in Chap. 12.

6·8. Complex Types of Interference.—There are many ways in which interference may be made more complex. Almost all of these methods depend upon making some parameter of the interference random in time. Randomizing amounts to making the interference "noisy" in some respect.

Amplified R-f Noise.—It is possible to obtain "noisy" r-f energy by simply amplifying thermal noise. It is true that the total amplification must be enormous, but amplifiers for this purpose can easily be made. The spectrum and time distributions of the emitted radiation may, of course, be almost exactly like those of the thermal noise itself.   Thermal noise is discussed in Chaps. 4 and 5, where it is pointed out that its spectrum is uniform throughout the frequency range and no correlation exists between the voltages at one instant and the next.   The amplitude distribution of the r-f voltage is, of course, Gaussian.

The difficulties in the production of such amplified r-f noise appear if it is desired to obtain a wide band of r-f energy.   Although such devices are relatively easy and straightforward to construct, wideband amplifiers are clumsy, expensive, and consist of a great many components.   Where the noise bandwidth of the radio frequency must be large, one of the following alternative methods is desirable.

Continuous-wave Interference Amplitude-modulated by Noise.—It is possible to modulate a c-w carrier by audio or video noise.   The r-f output consists of a strong carrier and noise sidebands.   The total band of frequencies occupied by these noise sidebands is, in general, just twice the bandwidth of the modulating noise.   The effect of the carrier itself cannot be neglected; its action is similar to ordinary c-w interference.

The carrier can be modulated by several types of noise.   It is common to use a noise voltage derived from thermal noise in the video system itself.   In this case the video noise has a Gaussian amplitude distribution. One of the properties of this distribution is that it has no well-defined upper or lower limit.   It therefore follows that when this amplitude function is used to modulate the carrier, the upper or positive noise peaks will be *limited* at some point because of the finite power-handling capabilities of the transmitter.   Likewise the lower end will be limited at some point because of the original finite strength of the carrier itself. The original carrier amplitude is customarily located at one-half the maximum value that can be supplied by the transmitter.   In this fashion, the limiting, or "clipping," as it is sometimes called, is symmetrical for the positive and negative noise peaks.

The degree of clipping depends on the amplitude of the modulating video noise compared with the carrier level.   If the noise amplitude is small, the clipping will be relatively unimportant and the r-f sidebands due to the noise will be uniformly distributed on each side of the carrier up to frequency limits determined by the video bandwidth of the noise itself.   As the modulating noise amplitude is increased, clipping becomes more and more important, with the effect of slightly modifying the r-f noise spectrum.   This modification is discussed in Sec. 12·7.

The clipped noise in interference of this type differs from the unclipped noise in its relationship to signal visibility.   Clipping produces a ceiling to the interference, above which the signal may be easily seen and therefore always increases signal visibility for the same total noise power.   The ceiling effect will be more pronounced if the modulation percentage is high. It will also be more pronounced if the bandwidth of the receiver subject to the interference is large compared with the bandwidth of the modulating noise. Both these effects are brought out more clearly in Chap. 12.

Continuous-wave Interference Frequency-modulated by Noise.—If the video noise function is used to modulate the frequency of c-w radiation, the essential advantage to be gained by modulation of this form is that a relatively large r-f band can be covered by a given interfering station. In interference of this form, therefore, the total frequency excursion is customarily made several times as large as in the c-w a-m case. It is usual, however, to make the frequencies contained in the original video-modulating function similar to those of the case just discussed.

Effects of the f-m interference are somewhat different from those of a-m interference. The noise amplitude in the receiver is determined by the excursions of the interference signal across the r-f or i-f acceptance band of the receiver. If one assumes that the total frequency excursion is large compared with the bandwidth of the receiver but that the frequencies contained in the noise producing the modulation are small compared with the bandwidth of the receiver, then the receiver output will contain a number of pulses whose shape in time is similar to the shape of the i-f or r-f bandwidth in frequency and whose amplitudes are relatively constant. These pulses will be repeated at random times. Because of the relatively constant amplitude of these pulses, the effect of the interference is similar to that of highly limited, or clipped, a-m noise. A "ceiling" effect occurs but for quite a different reason from that in the a-m case.

The effectiveness of interference of this type clearly depends upon obtaining a noise function such that an excursion across the receiver band occurs within a time p approximately equal to the receiver response time, that is, a time equal to the reciprocal of its bandwidth. If such an excursion does not occur, the interference will lose its effectiveness because of the constant-amplitude pulses produced and because of the time spaces between them. Within these spaces the desired signal can be found without any accompanying interference.

In actual practice it is not usually possible to obtain either pure amplitude modulation or pure frequency modulation. The effectiveness of both types of interference, however, is about the same provided the bandwidths, excursion, and fractional modulation are properly apportioned. Therefore, if both phenomena occur, they can be treated by addition of the separate effects.

Random Pulses.—It is possible to obtain "noisy" r-f interference by a series of pulses that have constant amplitudes and pulse length but random occurrence. The "randomizing" itself can be done in a number of ways.   One possibility is to produce the pulses from the impulses generated by the disintegrations of a radioactive source.   If the average spacing between these pulses is long, interference of this type will clearly have exactly the effect of the simple pulsed interference discussed in Sec. 6·7.   If the average spacing between the pulses becomes of the order of magnitude of the reciprocal of the receiver bandwidth, however, the output of the receiver will contain a series of superimposed pulses in which the degree of overlapping is random.   The output of the receiver, therefore, contains random amplitude fluctuations, or noise, and this noise interferes with signal visibility in a way similar to that described for thermal noise.   Only the two extreme spacing conditions can usually be treated adequately: (1) when the spacing between pulses is very large and (2) when the average spacing between pulses becomes very short. Chapter 12 treats these questions in detail.

CHAPTER 7

THE DETECTABILITY OF SIGNALS IN THE PRESENCE OF NOISE

THEORETICAL INTRODUCTION

7·1. Definition of the Signal Threshold.—The problem of determining how far "noise" limits the detection of a "signal" is a complex one and is only partially amenable to a theoretical analysis. Since in the last analysis a human observer must judge, either visually or aurally, whether the signal is present or not, it is clear that some of the psychophysiological properties of the eye or the ear will influence the signal threshold. For instance, in the visual observation of a radar signal on an A-scope or PPI, enough light must be produced on the screen to make the display visible. In other words there is a *brightness* limit for the detection of a signal. Furthermore, the *contrast* between the image of the signal and that of the noise background must be great enough for the signal to be seen; hence there is also a contrast limitation for the detection of a signal. Such limitations are sometimes of practical importance, and some experimental studies (especially of contrast limitation) have been made.[1] It is obvious, however, that little can be said theoretically about these limitations. Only when the function of the observer is reduced to *measuring* or *counting* will the question of the minimum detectable signal become a definite statistical problem for which a theoretical analysis can be attempted.[2] The success of such an analysis has shown that for a rather wide range of experimental conditions, the essential limitation for the detectability of a signal is due to the statistical nature of the problem.[3] In this chapter the discussion will be restricted therefore to what may be called the statistical limit for the detection of a signal.

[1] J. Fairbairn and R. G. Hopkinson, "Visibility of PPI Traces on Cathode Ray Tubes. Traces on Uniform Backgrounds," Report No. 8506 of the Research Laboratories of the General Electric Company, Ltd., Wembley, Middlesex, England, July 7, 1944. For further remarks on contrast, see Sec. 8·8.

[2] Among the theoretical reports, see especially S. A. Goudsmit, "The Comparison between Signal and Noise," RL Report No. 43-21, January 1943; D. O. North, "Analysis of the Factors Which Determine Signal/Noise Discrimination in Radar," RCA Technical Report PTR 6-C, June 1943; J. H. van Vleck and D. Middleton, "Theory of the Visual vs. Aural or Meter Reception of Radar Signals in the Presence of Noise," RRL Report No. 411-86, May 1944.

[3] It should be emphasized that not *all* the experimental observations can be explained by the statistical theory. To explain the deviations, assumptions must be made about the human observer. For examples, see Secs. 8·7 and 8·9.

The first question that arises is how to define the minimum detectable signal, or the *signal threshold;* here it is important to emphasize that one can speak of a *minimum* detectable signal only (1) when the number of observations is limited or (2) when the time of observation is limited.

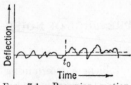

FIG. 7·1.—Brownian motion of a galvanometer mirror.

The simple case of the detection of a small current by means of a sensitive galvanometer may help explain this. Because of thermal agitation the mirror of the galvanometer will have an unavoidable Brownian motion around its equilibrium position. It might seem, therefore, that when a current or signal (introduced at $t = t_0$; see Fig. 7·1) produces a deflection small compared with the mean "jitter" of the mirror, such a current could not be detected. This is true, however, only when the number of observations is limited. When there is unlimited time, the *average* position and therefore also a *change* of the average position of the mirror can be determined as accurately as desired.

Strictly speaking, therefore, the noise or the thermal motion does not limit the detectability of a signal.[1] It is only when there is a *limited* observation time that for small signals one can make a guess or a bet as to whether the signal is present or not, and there is then a definite probability that the guess is right. Of course, for increasing signal strength this probability will rapidly increase and approach unity. A plot of the probability of success vs. signal strength will be referred to as the betting curve. The *minimum detectable signal* can then be defined as that signal strength for which the probability of guessing right is, let us say, 90 per cent; this means that, on the average, the guess will have proved right in nine out of ten cases. The minimum detectable signal defined in this manner will decrease when the observation time increases and, in principle, will approach zero when this time goes to infinity. It is not necessary, of course, that the time of observation be actually the time during which the human observer looks at or listens to the signal and remembers the results of his observations. It is often possible to let the detecting system perform automatically a great number of observations and present a suitable average to the human observer. North[2] calls this "integration of the signal before detection," in contrast to the effect of the human observation time, which he calls "integration after detection."[3] It is

---

[1] Excluded here are all *systematic* variations (for instance, of the zero position of the galvanometer), which in practice will always put a limit on the detectability of a signal.

[2] *Loc. cit.*

[3] Similarly a distinction will be made between the *integration time* of the detecting system and the *observation time*, which is the human integration time.

advisable to make this distinction because only the human observation, and not the recording apparatus, is influenced by physiological and psychological factors that often defy a strict theoretical analysis. In principle, however, the human element can always be reduced to a measuring or a counting, and then the distinction between the integration and the observation time will disappear.

The idea that the determination of the minimum detectable signal is essentially a game of chance (when only a finite time is available) is clearly recognized in the experiments carried out at the Radiation Laboratory by J. L. Lawson and coworkers. In these experiments, which will be discussed in detail in Chap. 8, a radar signal could be produced and shown on a A-scope at six different positions. The noise was usually visible all the time. Every 3 sec, let us say, the position of the signal was changed in a random fashion, and the observer had to guess where the signal was. The number of successes

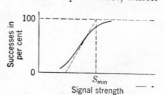

Fig. 7·2.—Schematic betting curve.

(above the number of pure chance successes) was recorded, and in this way, by varying the signal strength, there was obtained a betting curve (see Fig. 7·2) from which the signal threshold P_S could be defined.[1]

A careful study has been made of the dependence of P_S on all kinds of parameters (for an enumeration, see Sec. 8·4), and in Chap. 8 the experimental results will be discussed in detail. For the development of the theory it is first necessary to obtain some information about the probability distributions and about the spectrum of the output of a superheterodyne receiver when both signal and noise are present.

7·2. Probability Distributions and Spectra.—In Sec. 3·8 there was discussed the problem of finding the probability distributions and the spectra of Gaussian noise after it has gone through a linear or square-law detector. In this section the results of Sec. 3·8 will be extended to the case where a signal is also present.[2] The whole analysis will start from the i-f stage of the receiver. The convenient fiction will be used that

---

[1] It would be best to agree on a definite percentage (say 90 per cent) and define $P_{S_{90}}$ as the signal strength for which this percentage is reached. However, it is often more convenient to define P_S graphically, as indicated in Fig. 7·2 (see also Sec. 8·3).

[2] Only an outline of the calculations will be presented. The problem has been discussed often, and several methods have been used. Here the method of North will be used, which was explained in Sec. 3·8. For the so-called "direct method" and further references, see S. O. Rice, *Bell System Techn. J.*, **25**, 45 (1945), Part IV, and also W. R. Bennett, *J. Acoust. Soc. Am.*, **15**, 164 (1944). *Cf.* also the report of J. H. van Vleck and D. Middleton, "Theory of the Visual vs. Aural or Meter Reception of Radar Signals in the Presence of Noise," RRL Report No. 411-86, May 1944, *J. Applied Phys.*, **11**, 940 (1946).

the input of the i-f amplifier is connected to a signal generator and to a source of Gaussian noise that has a constant spectrum and given power per unit frequency interval.   The problem is to find the probability distributions and the spectrum *after* the signal-plus-noise has gone through the i-f amplifier and a linear or square-law detector.

Fourier Analysis of Signal and Noise.—The initial signal amplitude[1] will be represented by the formula

$$S_{in}(t) = \alpha_0(t) \cos 2\pi f_c t + \beta_0(t) \sin 2\pi f_c t, \tag{1}$$

where f_c is the i-f carrier.   The quantities α_0 and β_0 are either constant (for a c-w signal) or periodic functions of t (for a pulsed signal).   In the

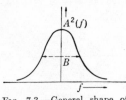

FIG. 7·3.—General shape of the i-f pass band.

latter case the periodicity interval is the pulse repetition period Θ_0, and $\alpha_0(t)$, $\beta_0(t)$ describe the shape of the pulse.   Usually the pulse will be assumed to be rectangular in shape and of duration τ.   When the pulse is not rectangular, the pulse length τ will always be defined as the distance between half-power points. Since the pulses ordinarily do not overlap, it is usually not necessary to take the periodicity

of the signal into account (but see Chap. 9), and $\alpha_0(t)$, $\beta_0(t)$ can represent *one* pulse, where t is measured from the middle of the pulse.

After the signal has gone through the i-f amplifier, it can easily be shown that the amplitude becomes

$$S(t) = \alpha(t) \cos 2\pi f_c t + \beta(t) \sin 2\pi f_c t, \tag{2}$$

where

$$\alpha - i\beta = \int_{-\infty}^{+\infty} df\, G_s(f) Z(f) e^{2\pi i f t}, \tag{3}$$

$$G_s(f) = \int_{-\infty}^{+\infty} dt\, (\alpha_0 - i\beta_0) e^{-2\pi i f_c t}, \tag{4}$$

and $Z(f)$ is the *system function* of the i-f amplifier.   The frequency f is always measured from the carrier frequency f_c.   The function $Z(f)$ will, of course, in general be complex; let us write

$$Z(f) = A(f) e^{-i\phi(f)}. \tag{5}$$

The quantity $A(f)$ represents the amplitude function, and $\phi(f)$ the phase function; $A^2(f)$ will usually[2] be an even function of f and will have a maximum at $f = 0$.   Then the i-f bandwidth B (see Fig. 7·3) will always

[1] In the following the terms "signal amplitude" and "noise amplitude" will be used.   To fix the physical interpretation of these quantities it will always be understood that these quantities have the physical dimensions of the *square root of power*.

[2] This is not always the case, but in what follows it will nevertheless always be assumed, since the formulas then become simpler.   Only in Chap. 13 will a case be met where $A^2(f)$ is *not* an even function of f.

mean the distance between half-power points, that is, points where $A^2(f)$ is half of the value at $f = 0$.

Let us now consider the noise amplitude. We may assume it to be periodic with a period Θ that is very long compared with all periods occurring in the system and that afterward we shall let approach infinity. Initially the noise amplitude can be developed in a Fourier series

$$N_{\text{in}}(t) = \sum_{k'=0}^{\infty} (a_{k'} \cos 2\pi f_{k'} t + b_{k'} \sin 2\pi f_{k'} t), \tag{6}$$

where $f_{k'} = k'/\Theta$. The quantities $a_{k'}$ and $b_{k'}$ are random variables, and it will be assumed, as in Sec. 3·7, that

1. $$\begin{aligned} \overline{a_{k'}} &= \overline{b_{k'}} = 0, \\ \overline{a_{k'}a_{l'}} &= \overline{b_{k'}b_{l'}} = \frac{\sigma^2}{\Theta} \delta_{k'l'}; \qquad \overline{a_{k'}b_{l'}} = 0. \end{aligned} \right\} \tag{7}$$

2. The $a_{k'}$ and $b_{k'}$ are Gaussianly distributed. The quantity σ^2 in Eq. (7) is a constant with the physical dimension of energy; in fact,

$$\sigma^2 = kTF, \tag{8}$$

where k is the Boltzmann constant, T the absolute (room) temperature, and F the over-all noise figure of the receiver (see Chap. 5).

After the noise amplitude [Eq. (6)] has gone through the i-f amplifier, the amplitude becomes

$$N(t) = \sum_{k'} A_{k'}[a_{k'} \cos (2\pi f_{k'} t - \phi_{k'}) + b_{k'} \sin (2\pi f_{k'} t - \phi_{k'})].$$

Since $A_{k'}$ will be a maximum for $f_{k'} = f_c$, it is convenient again to measure the frequencies from the carrier frequency f_c as zero point by putting

$$f_k = f_{k'} - f_c.$$

The sum of signal *and* noise amplitude can then be written in the form [*cf.* Eq. (2)]

$$S(t) + N(t) = X(t) \cos 2\pi f_c t + Y(t) \sin 2\pi f_c t, \tag{9}$$

where

$$\begin{aligned} X(t) &= \alpha(t) + \sum_{k=-\infty}^{+\infty} A_k[a_k \cos (2\pi f_k t - \phi_k) + b_k \sin (2\pi f_k t - \phi_k)], \\ Y(t) &= \beta(t) + \sum_{k=-\infty}^{+\infty} A_k[-a_k \sin (2\pi f_k t - \phi_k) + b_k \cos (2\pi f_k t - \phi_k)]. \end{aligned} \right\} \tag{10}$$

This amplitude is then applied to the second detector.

First Probability Distribution after the Second Detector.—With the input as given by Eq. (9), the detector output will be

$$r(t) = \sqrt{X^2(t) + Y^2(t)}$$

when the detector is *linear* and $r^2(t)$ when the detector is *quadratic*. The first question that arises is the probability distribution of r at a definite time instant t. This can be found by first determining the joint distribution for X and Y together. Since X and Y are linear functions of the random variables a_k and b_l [see Eq. (10)], which are Gaussianly distributed, it follows that X and Y are also Gaussianly distributed. Now it is easily found from Eqs. (7) and (10) that

$$\left. \begin{array}{c} \bar{X} = \alpha(t), \qquad \bar{Y} = \beta(t), \\[2mm] \overline{(X - \alpha)^2} = \overline{(Y - \beta)^2} = \dfrac{\sigma^2}{\theta} \displaystyle\sum_{k=-\infty}^{+\infty} A_k^2 \to \sigma^2 \int_{-\infty}^{+\infty} df\, A^2(f) = W, \\[2mm] \overline{(X - \alpha)(Y - \beta)} = 0. \end{array} \right\} \quad (11)$$

Therefore the distribution function for X and Y must be

$$P_1(X,Y)\, dX\, dY = \frac{dX\, dY}{2\pi W}\, e^{-[(X-\alpha)^2+(Y-\beta)^2]/2W}. \tag{12}$$

By introducing polar coordinates r and θ instead of X and Y, and by integrating over θ, there is finally found for the distribution of r

$$P_1(r)\, dr = \frac{r\, dr}{W}\, e^{-\frac{r^2+\alpha^2+\beta^2}{2W}} I_0\left(\frac{r}{W}\sqrt{\alpha^2 + \beta^2}\right), \tag{13a}$$

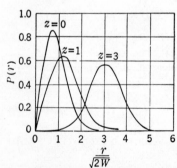

FIG. 7·4.—First probability distributions for different values of the signal-to-noise ratio.

where $I_0(x)$ is the Bessel function of zero order and purely imaginary argument.

A rough graph of $P_1(r)$ for different values of z, where

$$z = (\alpha^2 + \beta^2)/2W,$$

is shown in Fig. 7·4. For large values of z, the form of $P_1(r)$ becomes nearly Gaussian and may then be approximated by

$$P_1(r) \approx \frac{1}{\sqrt{2\pi W}}\, e^{-\frac{(r-\sqrt{\alpha^2+\beta^2})^2}{2W}}. \tag{13b}$$

From Eq. (13b) the average values can be calculated[1]

[1] *Cf.* Sec. 7·6, where will also be found some of the properties of the confluent hypergeometric function $F(a,b;z)$ that occurs in Eq. (14a).

$$\bar{r} = \int_0^\infty r P_1(r)\, dr = \sqrt{\frac{\pi W}{2}}\, F\left(-\frac{1}{2}, 1; -\frac{\alpha^2 + \beta^2}{2W}\right), \quad (14a)$$

$$\overline{r^2} = \int_0^\infty r^2 P(r)\, dr = \alpha^2 + \beta^2 + 2W. \quad (14b)$$

Equation (14b) also follows immediately from Eq. (11); it shows that with regard to mean-square values, the signal and the noise are simply additive (see Fig. 7·5); $2W$ is the constant noise power, and $\alpha^2 + \beta^2$ has the shape of the pulse after it has gone through the i-f amplifier.

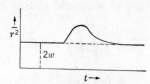

Fig. 7·5.—Mean-square deflection as a function of the time.

Second Probability Distribution.—To find the spectrum of $r(t)$ and $r^2(t)$, there must first be calculated the average values $\overline{r_1 r_2}$ and $\overline{r_1^2 r_2^2}$, where the subscripts 1 and 2 refer to two time instants t_1 and t_2. For this, we need the joint probability of finding X and Y between X_1 and $X_1 + dX_1$ and Y_1 and $Y_1 + dY_1$ at time t_1 *and* between X_2 and $X_2 + dX_2$ and Y_2 and $Y_2 + dY_2$ at time t_2. Since X_1, Y_1, X_2, Y_2 are all linear functions of the random variables a_k, b_l [see Eq. (10)], the probability distribution $P_2(X_1, Y_1; X_2, Y_2)$ will be a four-dimensional Gaussian distribution, which can be written in the form

$$P_2(X_1, Y_1; X_2, Y_2)\, dX_1\, dY_1\, dX_2\, dY_2$$

$$= \frac{dX_1\, dY_1\, dX_2\, dY_2}{4\pi^2 W(1 - \rho^2)} \exp\left(-\frac{1}{2W(1 - \rho^2)} \{[(X_1 - \alpha_1)^2 + (Y_1 - \beta_1)^2 + (X_2 - \alpha_2)^2 + (Y_2 - \beta_2)^2] - 2\rho[(X_1 - \alpha_1)(X_2 - \alpha_2) + (Y_1 - \beta_1)(Y_2 - \beta_2)]\}\right). \quad (15)$$

In Eq. (15) the subscripts on α and β again refer to the two times t_1 and t_2; ρ is a function of $\tau = t_2 - t_1$, defined by

$$\rho(\tau) \equiv \frac{\int_{-\infty}^{+\infty} A^2(f) \cos 2\pi f\tau\, df}{\int_{-\infty}^{+\infty} A^2(f)\, df}, \quad (16)$$

and it may be called the *normalized correlation function of the noise alone*.

For the *quadratic* detector we must calculate $\overline{r_1^2 r_2^2}$; using Eq. (15) we easily find

$$\overline{r_1^2 r_2^2} = \int\!\!\int\!\!\int\!\!\int_{-\infty}^{+\infty} dX_1\, dY_1\, dX_2\, dY_2\, (X_1^2 + Y_1^2)(X_2^2 + Y_2^2) P_2(X_1, Y_1; X_2, Y_2)$$

$$= (\alpha_1^2 + \beta_1^2 + 2W)(\alpha_2^2 + \beta_2^2 + 2W) + 4W\rho(\alpha_1\alpha_2 + \beta_1\beta_2) + 4W^2\rho^2. \quad (17)$$

For the *linear* detector we have to find the average value $\overline{r_1 r_2}$. This cannot be calculated exactly; however, for most purposes it is sufficient to find an approximate value by developing Eq. (15) in powers of ρ [from Eq. (16) we see that $\rho \leqq 1$] up to ρ^2.[1] The successive terms can then be integrated and we find

$$\overline{r_1 r_2} = \int\!\!\!\int\limits_{-\infty}^{+\infty}\!\!\!\int\!\!\!\int dX_1\, dY_1\, dX_2\, dY_2\, \sqrt{(X_1^2+Y_1^2)(X_2^2+Y_2^2)}\, P_2(X_1, Y_1; X_2, Y_2)$$

$$\approx I_1(1)I_2(1) + \frac{\rho}{W}\{[I_1(X) - \alpha_1 I_1(1)][I_2(X) - \alpha_2 I_2(1)]$$

$$+ [I_1(Y) - \beta_1 I_1(1)][I_2(Y) - \beta_2 I_2(1)]\} + \frac{\rho^2}{2W^2}\{[I_1(X^2) - 2\alpha_1 I_1(X)$$

$$+ (\alpha_1^2 - W)I_1(1)][I_2(X^2) - 2\alpha_2 I_2(X) + (\alpha_2^2 - W)I_2(1)] + [I_1(Y^2) - 2\beta_1 I_1(Y)$$

$$+ (\beta_1^2 - W)I_1(1)][I_2(Y^2) - 2\beta_2 I_2(Y) + (\beta_2^2 - W)I_2(1)] + 2[I_1(XY)$$

$$+ \alpha_1\beta_1 I_1(1) - \alpha_1 I_1(X) - \beta_1 I_1(Y)][I_2(XY) + \alpha_2\beta_2 I_2(1) - \alpha_2 I_2(X)$$

$$- \beta_2 I_2(Y)]\}, \quad (18)$$

where $I(\phi)$ is defined by the integral

$$I(\phi) = \frac{e^{-\frac{\alpha^2+\beta^2}{2W}}}{2\pi W} \int_0^\infty r^2 e^{-\frac{r^2}{2W}}\, dr \int_0^{2\pi} e^{\pi/W(\alpha\cos\theta+\beta\sin\theta)}\, d\theta\, \phi(r_1\theta). \quad (19)$$

In particular, we find ($X = r\cos\theta$, $Y = r\sin\theta$)

$$\left.\begin{aligned}
I(1) &= \sqrt{\frac{\pi W}{2}}\, F\left(-\frac{1}{2}, 1; -z\right), \\[4pt]
\left.\begin{aligned} I(X) \\ I(Y) \end{aligned}\right\} &= \left.\begin{aligned} \alpha \\ \beta \end{aligned}\right\} \frac{3}{2}\sqrt{\frac{\pi W}{2}}\, F\left(-\frac{1}{2}, 2; -z\right), \\[4pt]
\left.\begin{aligned} I(X^2) \\ I(Y^2) \end{aligned}\right\} &= \frac{3}{2}\sqrt{\frac{\pi W}{2}}\left[WF\left(-\frac{3}{2}, 1; -z\right) \pm \frac{5}{8}(\alpha^2-\beta^2)\, F\left(-\frac{1}{2}, 3; -z\right)\right], \\[4pt]
I(XY) &= \frac{15}{8}\sqrt{\frac{\pi W}{2}}\,\alpha\beta F\left(-\frac{1}{2}, 3; -z\right),
\end{aligned}\right\} \quad (20)$$

with $z = (\alpha^2 + \beta^2)/2W$. The subscripts 1 and 2 on the I's in Eq. (18) indicate that the α and β involved should have the corresponding subscripts (for some of the integrals involved, see Sec. 7·6). The result is

----

[1] When there is *no* signal, $\overline{r_1 r_2}$ can be computed exactly in terms of the complete elliptic integrals $E(\rho)$ and $K(\rho)$, as was mentioned in Sec. 3·8:

$$\overline{r_1 r_2} = W[2E(\rho) - (1 - \rho^2)K(\rho)]$$
$$= \frac{\pi W}{2}\left(1 + \frac{\rho^2}{4} + \frac{\rho^4}{64} + \cdots\right).$$

This shows that at least in this case the series development in powers of ρ converges rapidly.

still so complicated that for the further discussion, it is convenient to consider separately the cases where $z \ll 1$ and $z \gg 1$. Using the developments for the confluent hypergeometric functions F (see Sec. 7·6) we then find for *small signal-to-noise ratios*

$$\overline{r_1 r_2} \approx \frac{\pi}{32W} [(\alpha_1^2 + \beta_1^2 + 4W)(\alpha_2^2 + \beta_2^2 + 4W) + 4W\rho(\alpha_1\alpha_2 + \beta_1\beta_2) + 4W^2\rho^2], \quad (20a)$$

which has practically the same form as Eq. (17), the latter being the exact expression for the quadratic detector; and for *large signal-to-noise ratios*

$$\overline{r_1 r_2} \approx [(\alpha_1^2 + \beta_1^2)(\alpha_2^2 + \beta_2^2)]^{1/2} + W\rho \frac{\alpha_1\alpha_2 + \beta_1\beta_2}{[(\alpha_1^2 + \beta_1^2)(\alpha_2^2 + \beta_2^2)]^{1/2}} + \frac{W^2\rho^2}{2} \frac{(\alpha_1\alpha_2 + \beta_1\beta_2)^2}{[(\alpha_1^2 + \beta_1^2)(\alpha_2^2 + \beta_2^2)]^{3/2}}. \quad (20b)$$

Determination of the Spectrum—Example.—The average values $\overline{r_1^2 r_2^2}$ and $\overline{r_1 r_2}$ as given by Eqs. (17) and (18) are still functions of the two time instants t_1 and t_2; or with $\tau = t_2 - t_1$, they may be considered functions of t_1 and τ. To obtain the spectrum we must still average over t_1.[1] From the resulting functions $R_Q(\tau)$ and $R_L(\tau)$ we then find the spectrum $G(f)$ by the relation

$$G(f) = 4 \int_0^\infty R(\tau) \cos 2\pi f \tau \, d\tau. \quad (21)$$

An example will demonstrate this procedure. Instead of a pulsed signal, let us take an *a-m c-w signal*

$$S(t) = (S + S_0 \cos 2\pi f_0 t) \cos 2\pi f_c t. \quad (22)$$

The pass band of the i-f amplifier will be taken to be rectangular of width B; hence

$$Z(f) \begin{cases} = 1 & \text{for } |f| < \tfrac{1}{2}B, \\ = 0 & \text{for } |f| > \tfrac{1}{2}B. \end{cases} \quad (23)$$

We then obtain [see Eqs. (3) and (11)]

$$\alpha(t) = S + S_0 \cos 2\pi f_0 t, \qquad \beta(t) = 0, \qquad W = \sigma^2 B. \quad (24)$$

Substituting these values in Eq. (17) and averaging over t_1, we obtain

---

[1] *Cf.* Sec. 3·3. The signal and noise together form a *nonstationary* random process; and in order to obtain the correlation function, we have to perform both an ensemble and a time average. At this point we should remember that the signal functions $\alpha(t)$ and $\beta(t)$ are periodic functions of t.

$$R_Q(\tau) = \left(S^2 + \frac{S_0^2}{2} + 2\sigma^2 B\right)^2 + 2S^2 S_0^2 \cos 2\pi f_0 \tau + \frac{S_0^4}{8} \cos 4\pi f_0 \tau$$

$$+ 4\sigma^2 B \rho(\tau) \left(S^2 + \frac{S_0^2}{2} \cos 2\pi f_0 \tau\right) + 4\sigma^4 B^2 \rho^2(\tau). \quad (25)$$

In Eq. (25) $\rho(\tau)$ is, of course, completely determined by Eq. (23); in fact we find from Eqs. (17) and (23) that

$$\rho(\tau) = \frac{2}{B\tau} \sin \frac{B\tau}{2}.$$

However, in determining the spectrum from $R_Q(\tau)$ by means of the basic Eq. (21), it is not necessary to first calculate $\rho(\tau)$. We can make use of the following general equations [cf. Eqs. (3·25) and (3·75)]:

$$\left.\begin{array}{l} 2 \displaystyle\int_0^\infty d\tau \cos 2\pi f \tau = \delta(f), \\[2mm] 4 \displaystyle\int_0^\infty d\tau \cos 2\pi f \tau \cos 2\pi f_1 \tau = \delta(f - f_1), \\[2mm] 4 \displaystyle\int_0^\infty d\tau \rho(\tau) \cos 2\pi f \tau = 2Q(f), \\[2mm] 4 \displaystyle\int_0^\infty d\tau \rho^2(\tau) \cos 2\pi f \tau = 2 \displaystyle\int_{-\infty}^{+\infty} Q(f_1) Q(f + f_1) \, df_1, \end{array}\right\} \quad (26)$$

where $Q(f)$ is the normalized i-f spectrum; hence

$$Q(f) = \frac{A^2(f)}{\displaystyle\int_{-\infty}^{+\infty} df \, A^2(f)}. \quad (27)$$

Using these results there is finally obtained for the spectrum, in the case of the *quadratic detector*,

$$G_Q(f) = 2\left(S^2 + \frac{S_0^2}{2} + 2\sigma^2 B\right)^2 \delta(f) + 2S^2 S_0^2 \delta(f - f_0) + \frac{S_0^4}{8} \delta(f - 2f_0)$$

$$+ 8\sigma^2 \begin{cases} \left(S^2 + \dfrac{S_0^2}{2}\right), & \text{for } 0 < f < \dfrac{B}{2} - f_0, \\[2mm] S^2 + \dfrac{S_0^2}{4}, & \text{for } \dfrac{B}{2} - f_0 < f < \dfrac{B}{2}, \\[2mm] \dfrac{S_0^2}{4}, & \text{for } \dfrac{B}{2} < f < \dfrac{B}{2} + f_0, \\[2mm] 0, & \text{for } f > \dfrac{B}{2} + f_0, \end{cases}$$

$$+ 8\sigma^4 \begin{cases} (B - f), & \text{for } 0 < f < B, \\ 0, & \text{for } f > B. \end{cases} \quad (28)$$

This result is shown in Fig. 7·6 and can be understood in simple terms. The spectrum consists of four parts:

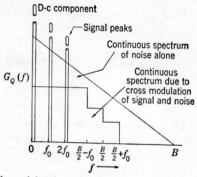

Fig. 7·6.—Spectrum of a modulated c-w signal plus noise after a square-law second detector.

1. *Direct-current term*, shown by the peak at $f = 0$. Both the signal and the noise contribute to this term. The signal part is simply the square of the mean signal power; the noise part is $4\sigma^4 B^2$ or $4W^2$, which, according to Eq. (14b), is just $(\overline{r^2})^2$ for noise alone; finally there is a cross term, which represents the average value of the beats between the signal and the noise.

2. *Signal peaks.* They are self-evident; that with the single modulating frequency f_0 we get two peaks (at f_0 and $2f_0$) is, of course, a consequence of the fact that we have a quadratic detector.

3. *Continuous spectrum due to cross modulation of signal and noise.* The beats between the three discrete frequencies f_c, $f_c \pm f_0$, which are contained in the signal before the second detector, with all the noise frequencies in the band B will lead clearly to a continuous spectrum, which consists of three blocks between the frequencies $(0, B/2)$, $[0, (B/2) - f_0]$, $[0, (B/2) + f_0]$. It is also easily seen that the height of the first block will be proportional to $S^2\sigma^2$, whereas for the other two it will be proportional to $\frac{1}{4}S_0^2\sigma^2$. Adding the three blocks leads, then, to the complete continuous spectrum as shown in Fig. 7·6.

4. *Continuous spectrum of noise alone.* This spectrum is caused by the beats between any two noise frequencies. Since the number of pairs of noise components with a certain frequency difference will decrease as the difference increases, it is clear that the spectrum will decrease with increasing f, and for a rectangular i-f pass band it is easy to see that the triangle will be as shown in Fig. 7·6 (*cf.* also Sec. 3·8).

For the *linear detector* there are some important differences in the spectrum. To understand these it is best to consider separately the cases of a small and a large signal.

Using the formula of Eq. (20a), substituting Eq. (24) and averaging over t_1, we obtain for *small signal-to-noise ratios*

$$R_L(\tau) = \frac{\pi}{32\sigma^2 B}\left[\left(S^2 + \frac{S_0^2}{2} + 4\sigma^2 B\right)^2 + 2S^2 S_0^2 \cos 2\pi f_0 \tau \right.$$
$$\left. + \frac{S_0^4}{8}\cos 4\pi f_0 \tau + 4\sigma^4 B^2 \rho^2\right]. \quad (29a)$$

The term that is proportional to ρ may be neglected, since the continuous spectrum due to the cross modulation of signal and noise will now be negligible compared with the pure noise spectrum. Equation (29a) leads to the spectrum

$$G_L(f) \approx \frac{\pi}{32\sigma^2 B}\left[\left(S^2 + \frac{S_0^2}{2} + 4\sigma^2 B\right)^2 \delta(f) + 2S^2 S_0^2 \delta(f - f_0)\right.$$
$$\left. + \frac{S_0^4}{8}\delta(f - 2f_0) + 8\sigma^4(B - f)\right], \quad 0 < f < B. \quad (29b)$$

This result is similar to the case of the quadratic detector; it should be noted especially that although the detector is linear, we still get the double frequency $2f_0$ in the discrete spectrum. The continuous spectrum is still triangular in this approximation, but the height of the triangle (which for the quadratic detector was $8\sigma^4 B$) is now $(\pi/4)\sigma^2$ and, therefore independent of the bandwidth.

Starting from Eq. (23b) and now neglecting the term proportional to ρ^2, we obtain for *large signal-to-noise ratios*

$$R_L(\tau) \approx S^2 + \frac{S_0^2}{2}\cos 2\pi f_0 \tau + \sigma^2 B \rho, \quad (30a)$$

$$G_L(f) \approx S^2\delta(f) + \frac{S_0^2}{2}\delta(f - f_0) + \begin{cases} 2\sigma^2, & \text{for } 0 < f < \dfrac{B}{2}, \\ 0, & \text{for } f > \dfrac{B}{2}. \end{cases} \quad (30b)$$

Now one gets only a signal peak at f_0 and the continuous spectrum consists of one block between $f = 0$ and $f = B/2$.

General Discussion of the Spectrum.—In the general case the results will be similar. One always starts from Eq. (17) or (18). The signal function $\alpha^2 + \beta^2$ must be developed in a Fourier series, and we must average over the time t_1. The parts in Eqs. (17) and (18) that are independent of ρ will give terms of the form $C_k \cos 2\pi f_k \tau$, and these will lead to the d-c part and the signal peaks in the spectrum. Of course, for a pulsed signal with repetition period Θ, the peaks will be spaced $1/\Theta$ apart. The parts in Eqs. (17) and (18) that are proportional to ρ lead to the continuous cross-modulation spectra, whereas those which are proportional to ρ^2 lead to the pure noise spectra. The shapes of these spectra will, in general, not be so simple as in Fig. 7·6; the noise spectrum, for instance, will be triangular only for a rectangular i-f pass band. It remains true, however, that for a quadratic detector the initial value of the noise spectrum is proportional to B and the area is proportional to B^2, whereas for a linear detector the initial value is independent of B and the area is proportional to B.

7·3. Detectability Criteria. *The Deflection Criterion.*—Let us return now to the problem of determining the signal threshold. Most of the theoretical analysis available at present is based on a more or less plausible, but in principle arbitrary, choice of a *detectability criterion*. For instance, let us consider again the simple example of measuring a small current with a galvanometer (see Fig. 7·1) and suppose that only *one* measurement can be made of the deflection r. The average value of the deflection will be a little different when the current (or signal) is present, and it is plausible to assume that in one measurement the current is just detectable if the shift of the average value is of the same order of magnitude as the standard deviation of r (whether with or without current makes little difference, since the currents to be detected are small). Or in a formula

$$\frac{\bar{r}_{S+N} - \bar{r}_N}{[\overline{r_N^2} - (\bar{r}_N)^2]^{1/2}} = k, \tag{31a}$$

where the subscripts S and N refer to signal and noise and where k is a constant that is of the order of magnitude of 1 if only one observation is made. The criterion [Eq. (31a)] will be called the "deflection criterion." It can also be used for the visual detection of one radar signal pulse on an A-scope in the presence of noise; in this way the dependence of the signal threshold on parameters like pulse length, i-f and video bandwidths can be satisfactorily explained. A detailed discussion will be found in Chap. 8 (especially Secs. 8·6 and 8·7); here only the following more general observations are made.

1. The detectability criterion [Eq. (31a)] might be generalized to

$$\frac{\bar{f}_{S+N} - \bar{f}_N}{[\overline{f_N^2} - (\overline{f_N})^2]^{1/2}} = k, \tag{31b}$$

where $f(r)$ is some function of the deflection still at our disposal. By choosing the proper function $f(r)$ we can try to make the signal threshold as small as possible. Or by choosing a function $f(r)$

that emphasizes the *large* deflections, we can try to express the tendency of some observers to look mainly at the tops of the noise fluctuations.   The simplest and most natural choice, however, is to take for $f(r)$ the *actual* deflection on the A-scope; hence, with the notation of Sec. 7·2, $f(r) = r$ if a linear detector is used, and $f(r) = r^2$ if a square-law detector is used.   The signal threshold will then depend on the kind of second detector used.   It turns out, however, that for small signal-to-noise ratios, the difference in threshold between a linear and quadratic detector is so small that it is unobservable.[1]   Therefore, the usual practice will be to take $f(r) = r^2$, since all formulas are then simpler.   It is unprofitable to speculate on what feature of the fluctuating A-scope picture the observer bases his judgment.   Only for a so-called "ideal" observer (see Sec. 7·5) does the question of the choice of the function $f(r)$ have a precise sense.

2. The deflection criterion [Eq. (31a) or (31b)] applied to the detection of a radar signal pulse considers only the deflection produced by the pulse at *one* instant of time.   This time point is chosen, of course, to be the time corresponding to the *maximum* of the pulse after it has passed through the i-f and video amplifiers.   The shape of the pulse is *not* taken into account except in so far as it affects the maximum value.   In the evaluation of the average values occurring in the detectability criterion [Eq. (31a) or (31b)] only the first probability distribution of the random process describing the signal and noise is required.   The theory based on this criterion may therefore be called a *one-point theory*.   It is not difficult to devise criteria in which the deflection at two time points would enter and that would lead to a *two-point theory;* the latter would use the *second* probability distribution and would be more sensitive to the shape of the pulse.   And in this way we can go on.   It seems, however, that most of the experimental observations can be understood on the basis of the simple one-point theory, and therefore the more refined two- or n-point theories will not be considered.

3. The influence of the time of observation or of the total number of observations, the importance of which was stressed in Sec. 7·1, can be taken into account by the following simple and natural generalization of the deflection criterion [Eq. (31a) or (31b)].   Let us suppose that instead of one observation, N independent observa-

---

[1] The reason is that for small signal-to-noise ratios the linear and square-law detectors act in about the same way, as we see from the correlation functions and spectra [cf. Eqs. (28) and (29b)].   For the proof, see Van Vleck and Middleton, "Theory of the Visual vs. Aural or Meter Reception of Radar Signals in the Presence of Noise," RRL Report No. 411-86, May 1944, and Sec. 8·6.

tions[1] are made with the signal and N observations without the signal.

It seems natural, then, to use in the detectability criterion, not the deflection r or $f(r)$, but the average value

$$y = \frac{1}{N} \sum_{i=1}^{N} f(r_i), \tag{32}$$

where $r_1, r_2, \ldots, r_N$ are the N observations of the deflection. We shall therefore assume that the signal is just detectable if the shift of the average value of y due to the signal is of the same order of magnitude as the standard deviation of y when only noise is present. Or in a formula[2]

$$\frac{\bar{y}_{s+N} - \bar{y}_N}{[\overline{y_N^2} - (\bar{y}_N)^2]^{1/2}} = k. \tag{33}$$

Now it follows easily from Eq. (32) that, if the r_i's are independent,

$$\bar{y} = \bar{f}, \qquad \overline{y^2} = \frac{1}{N^2} [N\overline{f^2} + N(N-1)(\bar{f})^2].$$

Hence,

$$\left. \begin{array}{l} \bar{y}_{s+N} - \bar{y}_N = \bar{f}_{s+N} - \bar{f}_N, \\[2mm] \overline{y_N^2} - (\bar{y}_N)^2 = \frac{1}{N} [\overline{f_N^2} - (\overline{f_N})^2]. \end{array} \right\} \tag{34}$$

The shift of the average value is, therefore, the same as before, whereas the fluctuation decreases and goes to zero for $N \to \infty$. The signal will therefore be the more easily detectable the larger N is. Substituting Eq. (34) into Eq. (33) we obtain

$$\frac{\bar{f}_{s+N} - \bar{f}_N}{[\overline{f_N^2} - (\overline{f_N})^2]^{1/2}} = \frac{k}{\sqrt{N}}. \tag{35}$$

This equation is the generalization of the deflection criterion [Eq. (31b)] for the case of N observations. (For further discussion and for the comparison with experiment, see Secs. 8·8 and 8·9.)

The Power Criterion.—In connection with other methods of observing a radar signal it is sometimes simpler to use a different type of detectability criterion. Let us consider, for instance, the so-called "aural

---

[1] In the example of the measurement of a small current with a galvanometer, "independent" means that the time intervals between the observations must be large compared with the correlation time. For radar signal pulses this independence is always assured, since the repetition period is always large compared with the correlation time of the noise.

[2] The subscript N (for "noise") should not be confused with N the number of observations.

method" of detection.   In Sec. 7·2 it was mentioned that the spectrum of the output of the video amplifier consists of a continuous part and a series of discrete "signal" peaks.   These discrete frequencies represent the power spectrum of the periodic series of signal pulses and are therefore spaced $1/\Theta_0$ apart if Θ_0 is the pulse repetition period.   By using a filter with a bandwidth that is small compared with $1/\Theta_0$, one of the discrete frequencies (for instance, the fundamental frequency $1/\Theta_0$) can be isolated, and we can try to listen to the output of the filter with an earphone. This is the aural method of detection.   It is clear that the power in the signal peak has to compete with the power in the section of the continuous noise spectrum that is cut out by the filter.   Therefore it is natural to assume that the signal peak is detectable if its power P_S is of the same order of magnitude as the power P_N in the segment of the continuous noise band.   Or in a formula

$$\frac{P_S}{P_N} = k', \tag{36}$$

where k' is of the order of unity.   This criterion will be called the *power criterion*.

On the basis of the power criterion [Eq. (36)], Van Vleck and Middleton[1] have analyzed the aural and also the meter method of detection.   A short account of their work will be given in Chap. 9.   The main point to be emphasized here is that the analysis of these methods of detection gives essentially the same result for the signal threshold.   By the word "essentially" is meant that in the different methods, the dependence of the signal threshold on the parameters of the signal, such as pulse length, PRF, and total number of pulses, will be the same.   They can still differ numerically, which may sometimes be significant, but the difference *cannot* be made so large as one pleases by changing some parameter of the signal.   This fact will be discussed in detail in Chap. 9; the main distinction between the different methods is fundamentally a difference of the ratio of *integration* time to *observation* time.   Or in other words, we let the detecting system do more or less integration before the human observation begins.

Of course, the different methods of detection are equivalent *only* if each method is pushed to the limit of its capacity.   In practice this will almost never be done, and therefore the different methods will usually give different signal thresholds.   Furthermore, in actual practice it will make a lot of difference at which point the human observation begins and whether it is visual or aural.

[1] *Loc. cit.*   In the meter method of detection the output of the filter that selects the signal peak is rectified and recorded by some kind of meter.   The change of the average value of the meter deflection when the signal is present provides the method for detecting the signal.

The power criterion [Eq. (36)] is also used in the analysis of the noise limitation in *communication systems*. The following distinction can be made between a detection and a communication system. In a detection system only the presence or absence of a signal has to be determined; therefore a c-w signal or a series of constant pulses can be used. In a communication system more than just a yes-or-no answer is required, and some sort of modulation must therefore be applied to the c-w signal or to the series of pulses. The frequencies and amplitudes of this modulation of the signal are the quantities to be detected. These will appear as a discrete line spectrum superposed on the spectrum of the noise and the unmodulated signal. For a sinusoidal modulation there will be only one such peak, and the detectability of this peak will depend on the ratio of its power to the continuous noise power with which it has to compete. The power criterion [Eq. (36)] is again applicable, and the theory is therefore similar to the theory for the aural method of detecting a radar signal. There is one important difference, however. The main result of the theory now will *not* be the determination of the minimum detectable signal power, but the dependence of the minimum detectable modulation ϵ_{min} on the ratio z of the unmodulated signal power to the noise power. It is clear that ϵ_{min} will be a monotonic decreasing function of z, and it can be shown that for large z, $\epsilon_{min} \approx 1/z$, whereas for small z, $\epsilon_{min} \approx 1/z^2$. Explicit expressions for ϵ_{min} as a function of z will be derived in Chap. 10 for some pulse modulation schemes and in Chap. 13 for the well-known a-m and f-m communication systems.

7·4. What Is the Best Method for Detecting a Radar Signal.—In the previous section we mentioned that the visual and the aural methods of detection are essentially equivalent if each method is pushed to the limit of its capacity. The question arises whether or not with these methods of detection an absolute limit has been reached. In this section we shall show that this is *not* the case, so that there is still room for an essential improvement of the present detection methods.

Suppose that one has a train of signal pulses which persists over a time θ. Let the repetition period again be Θ_0, so that there are altogether $N = \theta/\Theta_0$ pulses. Now it can be shown that under the best possible circumstances an average signal power $\bar{P}_{min}$ can be detected, given by the formula

$$\bar{P}_{min} = \frac{k}{\sqrt{\theta\Theta_0}} \sigma^2. \tag{37}$$

Here k is a numerical factor of order of magnitude 1, and σ^2 is the average noise *energy* before the i-f amplifier. This noise energy is due to many causes but can always be considered as thermal noise with an effective temperature T^*, so that $\sigma^2 = kT^*$, where k is the Boltzmann constant.

For the derivation of Eq. (37) we refer to Sec. 8·6 (visual observation method) and Sec. 9·6 (aural and meter detection methods). Here we only want to point out that Eq. (37) follows from the fact that the detectability of the signal depends for small signal strengths on the *square of the signal amplitude*. With the deflection criterion [Eq. (31b)], for instance, the detectability of the signal depends on the shift of the average value of some function $f(r)$ of the deflection r, which is caused by the signal. From the probability distribution of the deflection [Eq. (13)] it follows immediately that for small signals the shift of $\overline{f(r)}$ will be proportional to S^2 if S is the signal amplitude. As a consequence one obtains from the deflection criterion for the signal threshold an equation of the form

$$\frac{S^2}{W} = \frac{\text{const.}}{\sqrt{N}}, \tag{38}$$

where the constant is of the order of unity and depends slightly on the type of second detector and on the shapes of the pulse and i-f pass band; W is the noise power after the i-f amplifier. Since $\bar{P}_{\min} \propto S^2\tau/\Theta_0$, $W \propto B\sigma^2$, $N = \theta/\Theta_0$ and since for best performance $B\tau$ must be of order unity,[1] Eq. (37) follows immediately from Eq. (38).

From Eq. (37) follows that the minimum detectable energy of the whole train of signal pulses is given by

$$E_{\min} = \Theta \bar{P}_{\min} = k\sigma^2 \sqrt{\frac{\theta}{\Theta_0}} = k\sigma^2 \sqrt{N}. \tag{39}$$

Clearly $E_{\min}$ is usually *much* larger than $\sigma^2 = kT^*$, since N is usually a large number. It seems unlikely that this is the best one can do. The detection system may be considered as an energy-measuring device, which has itself an uncertainty in energy of the order kT^*. The detection of the whole train of signal pulses can now be considered as *one* observation of the energy E, and one must expect that the detection can be done with almost certainty as soon as E is a few times kT^*. This gives a limit for E that is much lower than Eq. (3) and in the authors' opinion the absolute limit which one may ever hope to reach.

The reason why with the present detection systems this absolute limit has not been reached can be traced to the fact that the present methods do *not* measure the total energy of the noise and of the series of pulses. To the authors' knowledge only one system of detection has so far been proposed that really measures the received energy. Emslie[2] has shown how this can be done in principle by letting the signal beat with a continuous wave, which is introduced into the receiver at the same

---

[1] *Cf.* Sec. 8·6.

[2] A. G. Emslie, "Coherent Integration," RL Report No. 103-5, May 16, 1944.

time as the signal pulses and which has always the same phase relation with the successive signal pulses.[1] If the amplitude of the coherent continuous wave is large compared with the rms noise amplitude, then the probability distribution of the deflection r will be Gaussian [Eq. (13b)] with a variance $2W$ and with an average value

$$\bar{r} = (S^2 + C^2 + 2SC \cos \phi)^{1/2}, \tag{40}$$

where C is the amplitude of the coherent continuous wave and ϕ the constant phase angle between the continuous wave and the signal. Of course, $C \gg S$, and therefore it is clear that the shift of the average value which is caused by the signal is porportional to the *signal amplitude*. In fact, from Eq. (40) follows

$$\bar{r}_{S+N} - \bar{r}_N \approx S \cos \phi. \tag{41}$$

In contrast to Eq. (38) we now obtain from the deflection criterion for the signal threshold the equation

$$\frac{S \cos \phi}{\sqrt{2W}} = \frac{\text{const.}}{\sqrt{N}}. \tag{42}$$

Clearly, if the phase angle ϕ can be kept constant and equal to zero, Eq. (6) leads to a minimum detectable energy of the pulse train that is of the order kT^*.

7·5. Theory of the Ideal Observer.—The theoretical analysis based on the detectability criteria discussed in Sec. 7·3 leads to a formula for the signal threshold that contains a numerical factor k of order of magnitude unity which has to be found from experiment. The reason for this indeterminacy is, of course, that the minimum detectable signal is not defined strictly on the basis of a "betting curve." It seems desirable therefore to try to formulate a more fundamental theory, which will remove the ambiguity of the choice of detectability criterion and which will explain the betting curve and in this way determine the value of the numerical constant k.

Referring again to our galvanometer example (Sec. 7·1), suppose that we know the probability distribution of the deflection r both when the current is present and when there is noise alone. Suppose, furthermore, that we do not know whether there is a current present or not and that we have to decide this question on the basis of N observations. The question then arises how to make use of these observations in the best possible way, so that the conclusion we draw from these observations, namely, whether the current is present or not, will have the best chance

[1] For further details about the coherent continuous wave, which forms an essential feature of the so-called MTI system, *cf.* Chap. 12.

to be right. We shall say that *the ideal observer* always makes use of the observations in this way, and we shall speak of *the ideal observer criterion.* Of course, even the ideal observer can make only a bet, but it is the best possible bet that can be made. The betting curve for the ideal observer will be completely determined by the probability distributions for the deflection r, so that the numerical value of the constant k can be determined. To illustrate this we shall now consider a few examples.[1]

The "Off-on" Experiment.—Suppose that in a long series of trials a signal of given strength is presented to the observer on the average during half of the time. The observer does not know for any given trial whether the signal is present or not, and he has to decide this on the basis of N observations, which he is allowed to make during each trial. We shall assume that the time intervals between the observations are long enough to make the N observations of the deflection $r_1, r_2, \ldots, r_N$ independent of each other. The problem is to find the criterion that in the long run will lead to the smallest number of errors.

Let $P(o,r)$ and $P(s,r)$ be the probability distributions for a deflection r without and with the signal. The functions $P(o,r)$ and $P(s,r)$ are supposed to be known. The set of N observations $r_1, r_2, \ldots, r_N$ during one trial may be represented by one point in a N-dimensional "observation space." Since the observations are independent, the probability of finding a definite set $r_1, r_2, \ldots, r_N$ is given by

$$P(o,r_1)P(o,r_2) \cdots P(o,r_N) \tag{43a}$$

or

$$P(s,r_1)P(s,r_2) \cdots P(s,r_N), \tag{43b}$$

depending on whether the signal is off or on. A detectability criterion is a division of the N-dimensional observation space in two regions, which may be called the off-region and the on-region. If the point representing the N observations in one trial falls in the off-region, the observer will decide that no signal is present; whereas if the point falls in the on-region, he will make the opposite decision. Clearly the probability for obtaining the right answer is given by

$$W_1(s) = \tfrac{1}{2}\left[\int \cdots \int_{(on)} dr_1 \cdots dr_N \, P(s,r_1) \cdots P(s,r_N) \right.$$
$$\left. + \int \cdots \int_{(off)} dr_1 \cdots dr_N \, P(o,r_1) \cdots P(o,r_N)\right] \tag{44}$$

[1] It should be pointed out that the ideal observer theory is practically identical with the Neyman-Pearson theory of the best criterion for testing a statistical hypothesis. *Cf.*, for instance, J. Neyman, "Basic Ideas and Theory of Testing Statistical Hypotheses," *J. Roy. Stat. Soc.*, **105**, 292 (1942).

where the symbols (on) and (off) under the integral signs mean that the integrations are to be taken over the on- and off- region. The factor $\frac{1}{2}$ is the a priori probability, which represents the fact that the observer knows that in half of the total number of trials the signal is present. The ideal observer will choose the off- and on-regions in such a way that the probability W_1 is a maximum. Writing Eq. (44) in the form:

$$W_1(s) = \frac{1}{2} \int_0^\infty \cdots \int \prod_{k=1}^N P(o,r_k)\, dr_k \left\{ \begin{array}{ll} \displaystyle\prod_{i=1}^N \frac{P(s,r_i)}{P(o,r_i)} & \text{in on-region} \\[2ex] 1 & \text{in off-region} \end{array} \right\} \qquad (45)$$

One sees that since the common factor $\prod_k P(o,r_k)$ is positive W_1 will be a maximum if in the on–region $\prod_i P(s,r_i)/P(o,r_i) > 1$ and in the off-region $\prod_i P(s,r_i)/P(o,r_i) < 1$. Or in other words, for the ideal observer criterion the surface in the observation space, which divides the off-region from the on-region, is given by the equation

$$\prod_{i=1}^N \frac{P(s,r_i)}{P(o,r_i)} = 1. \qquad (46)$$

Introducing the functions,

$$\left. \begin{array}{l} \displaystyle Q(s,y) = \int_0^\infty \cdots \int \prod_{k=1}^N P(s_1 r_k)\, dr_k\, \delta\left[y - \sum_{i=1}^N \log \frac{P(s,r_i)}{P(o,r_i)} \right], \\[3ex] \displaystyle R(s,y) = \int_0^\infty \cdots \int \prod_{k=1}^N P(o,r_k)\, dr_k\, \delta\left[y - \sum_{i=1}^N \log \frac{P(s,r_i)}{P(o,r_i)} \right], \end{array} \right\} \qquad (47)$$

where $\delta(x)$ is again the Dirac δ-function, the probability of success for the ideal observer can be written in the form

$$W_{1,\max}(s) = \frac{1}{2} \left[\int_0^\infty dy\, Q(s,y) + \int_{-\infty}^0 dy\, R(s,y) \right]. \qquad (48)$$

We shall postpone the further evaluations of this expression until we have considered some other examples. Clearly

$$\left. \begin{array}{c} \displaystyle \int_{-\infty}^{+\infty} dy\, Q(s,y) = \int_{-\infty}^{+\infty} dy\, R(s,y) = 1, \\[2ex] Q(o,y) = R(o,y). \end{array} \right\} \qquad (49)$$

For $s = 0$, $W_{1,\,max}(s)$ is therefore equal to $\frac{1}{2}$ as it should be. For $s \to \infty$, $Q(s,y)$ will be different from zero only for large positive y, where as $R(s,y)$ will only have appreciable values for large negative values of y. For $s \to \infty$ the integrals in Eq. (6) can therefore be extended to the complete range from $-\infty$ to $+\infty$; and because of Eq. (49) $W_{1\,max}(s)$ will then become 1.

The "Two-positions" Experiment.—Suppose that in a long series of trials a signal of given strength is presented to the observer on either of two positions with equal a priori probability.[1] For any given trial the observer does not know in which position the signal is, and he has to decide this on the basis of the observations that he is allowed to make during each trial. Call the two positions a and b, and suppose that the observer makes N observations of the deflection at each position. A detectability criterion is a division of the $2N$-dimensional observation space in an (a)- and (b)-region. If the point representing the $2N$ observations $r_{a1}, r_{a2}, \ldots, r_{aN}, r_{b1}, r_{b2}, \ldots, r_{bN}$ falls in the (a)-region, the observer will decide that the signal was in the position a; whereas if the point falls in the (b)-region, he will decide in favor of position b. Since all observations are supposed to be independent, it can easily be seen that the probability for obtaining the right answer is given by

$$W_2(s) = \frac{1}{2} \int_0^\infty \cdots \int \prod_{K=1}^N P(o,r_{ak})P(o,r_{bk})$$

$$\times\, dr_{ak}\, dr_{bk} \left\{ \begin{array}{ll} \displaystyle\prod_{i=1}^N \frac{P(s,r_{ai})}{P(o,r_{ai})} & \text{for region } (a) \\[2ex] \displaystyle\prod_{i=1}^N \frac{P(s,r_{bi})}{P(o,r_{bi})} & \text{for region } (b) \end{array} \right\} \qquad (50)$$

The ideal observer will choose the (a)- and (b)-regions in such a way that W_2 is a maximum. From Eq. (8) it follows that this can be done by taking

$$\prod_{i=1}^{N} \frac{P(s,r_{ai})}{P(o,r_{ai})} = \prod_{i=1}^N \frac{P(s,r_{bi})}{P(o,r_{bi})}$$

as the equation of the surface, which divides the (a)- from the (b)-region, and the probability of success for the ideal observer can then be written in the form

$$W_{2,\,max}(s) = \int_{-\infty}^{+\infty} dy\, Q(s,y) \int_{-\infty}^{y} dy_1\, R(s,y_1), \qquad (51)$$

[1] This means of course that in the average the signal appears an equal number of times on either of the two positions.

where the functions Q and R are defined by Eq. (47). For $s = 0$, $R(o,y) = Q(o,y)$; putting

$$\beta = \int_0^y dy_1\, R(s,y_1),$$

Eq. (51) becomes

$$W_{2,\,\mathrm{max}}(o) = \int_0^1 d\beta\, \beta = \frac{1}{2}$$

as it should. For $s \to \infty$ the upper limit y in Eq. (9) can be replaced by $+\infty$, and because of Eq. (49) it is clear that for $s \to \infty$, $W_{2,\,\mathrm{max}}(s)$ approaches unity.

The "m-positions" Experiment.—If the signal can appear on any one of m positions with equal a priori probability, an easy generalization of the reasoning for the two-positions experiment leads to the equation

$$W_{m,\,\mathrm{max}}(s) = \int_{-\infty}^{+\infty} dy\, Q(s,y) \left[\int_{-\infty}^y dy_1\, R(s,y_1) \right]^{m-1} \tag{52}$$

for the probability of success for the ideal observer. It can be easily seen that for $s \to \infty$, $W_{m,\,\mathrm{max}}$ approaches unity; whereas for $s \to o$, $W_{m,\,\mathrm{max}} \to 1/m$, which is the a priori probability for finding the signal on any one of the m positions.

Calculation of the Betting Curve.—For the further evaluation of the functions $W_{m,\,\mathrm{max}}(s)$, which represent the betting curves for the ideal observer in the different experiments, the functions $R(s,y)$ and $Q(s,y)$ must first be calculated. According to Eq. (13) one has[1]

$$\left. \begin{aligned} P(s,r) &= \frac{r}{W}\, e^{-\frac{r^2+S^2}{2W}}\, I_0\!\left(\frac{rS}{W}\right), \\ P(o,r) &= \frac{r}{W}\, e^{-\frac{r^2}{2W}}. \end{aligned} \right\} \tag{53}$$

With these functions it does not seem feasible to calculate Q and R from Eq. (47) exactly. However, since we are mainly interested in the part of the betting curve for which the signal is small compared with noise, we can put

$$I_0\!\left(\frac{rS}{W}\right) \approx 1 + \frac{r^2 S^2}{4W^2} \approx e^{r^2 S^2/4W^2}.$$

Therefore

$$y = \sum_{i=1}^N \log \frac{P(s,r_i)}{P(o,r_i)} \approx -\frac{NS^2}{2W} + \frac{S^2}{4W^2} \sum_{i=1}^N r_i^2. \tag{54}$$

[1] $S^2 = \alpha^2 + \beta^2$. The time chosen must correspond, of course, to the maximum of the deformed pulse. The shape of the pulse is not taken into account. Equation (52) refers to the one-point ideal observer theory (Sec. 7·3).

Calling

$$q = 2W + \frac{4W^2}{NS^2} y,$$

Eq. (47) can be written

$$\left. \begin{array}{l} Q(s,q) \, dq = dq \int_0^\infty \cdots \int \prod_{k=1}^N P(s,r_k) \, dr_k \, \delta\left(q - \frac{1}{N}\sum_{i=1}^N r_i^2\right), \\[2mm] R(q) \, dq = dq \int_0^\infty \cdots \int \prod_{k=1}^N P(o,r_k) \, dr_k \, \delta\left(q - \frac{1}{N}\sum_{i=1}^N r_i^2\right) \\[2mm] \qquad\qquad\qquad\qquad\qquad\qquad\qquad\qquad\qquad = Q(o,q) \, dq. \end{array} \right\} \quad (55)$$

In this approximation the ideal observer bases his judgment therefore on the distribution functions of the mean-square values of the N deflections $r_1, r_2, \ldots, r_N$ with and without the signal. Using Eqs. (53) the integrals in (55) can be calculated exactly, and one obtains

$$\left. \begin{array}{l} Q(s,q) = \frac{N}{2W} e^{-\frac{NS^2 + Nq}{2W}} \left(\frac{q}{S^2}\right)^{(N-1)/2} I_{N-1}\left(\frac{NSq^{1/2}}{W}\right), \\[3mm] R(q) = \frac{1}{(N-1)!} \left(\frac{Nq}{2W}\right)^{N-1} \frac{N}{2W} e^{-\frac{Nq}{2W}}, \end{array} \right\} \quad (56)$$

from which follows

$$\left. \begin{array}{l} \bar{q} = \int_0^\infty dq \, Q(s,q) = S^2 + 2W, \\[3mm] \overline{(q - \bar{q})^2} = \int_0^\infty dq \, (q - \bar{q})^2 Q(s,q) = \frac{4W}{N}(S^2 + W). \end{array} \right\} \quad (57)$$

If N is sufficiently large, $Q(s,q)$ can be replaced by a Gaussian distribution with the mean value and variance given by Eq. (57), and the integrals involved in the expressions (48), (51), and (52) for the betting curves in the different experiments can then be expressed in terms of the error function

$$\text{Erf}(x) = \frac{2}{\sqrt{\pi}} \int_0^x dt \, e^{-t^2}.$$

The final results are ($z = S^2/2W$):

1. Off-on experiment:

$$W_{1,\max}(z) = \frac{1}{2}\left[1 + \text{Erf}\left(\frac{\sqrt{N}}{2\sqrt{2}} z\right)\right]. \quad (58a)$$

2. Two-positions experiment:

$$W_{2,\max}(z) = \frac{1}{2}\left[1 + \text{Erf}\left(\frac{\sqrt{N}}{2} z\right)\right]. \quad (58b)$$

3. m-positions experiment:

$$W_{m,\,\text{max}}(z) = \frac{1}{2^{m-1}\sqrt{\pi}} \int_{-\infty}^{+\infty} dx\, e^{-x^2} \left[1 + \text{Erf}\left(x + \frac{1}{2}\, z\, \sqrt{N} \right) \right]^{m-1} \quad (58c)$$

These expressions may be compared with the experimental betting curves. In these curves the quantity plotted against the signal strength is usually *not* $W_{m,\,\text{max}}$ but

$$P_m(z) = \frac{1}{m-1}\,(mW_{m,\,\text{max}} - 1). \quad (59)$$

Clearly $P_m(z)$ will be zero for $z = 0$ and approach unity for $z \to \infty$. Defining the minimum detectable signal as the signal strength for the 90 per cent point on the betting curve $P_m(z)$, it is clear from Eqs. (58) that

$$z_{90} = \left(\frac{S^2}{2W} \right)_{90} = \frac{C_m}{\sqrt{N}}. \quad (60)$$

The signal threshold is therefore inversely proportional to the square root of the number of observations. The constant c_m increases slightly with the number of positions. Since each point on the betting curve decreases in the same way with increasing N, it is clear that the *width* of the betting curve which can be measured by the ratio of the z values corresponding to the 90 and the 10 per cent point will be independent of the number of observations. The width depends on the number of positions; it decreases if m increases, or in other words the betting curve becomes steeper if the number of positions increases. For a more detailed comparison with the experimental betting curves, compare Sec. 8·9. It should be emphasized that Eqs. (58) and their consequences hold only if the two approximations (a, $z \ll 1$, even at the 90 per cent point of the betting curve, and b, N sufficiently large, so that the Gaussian distribution can be used) are valid. Especially the $\sqrt{N}$-law expressed by Eq. (60) depends essentially on the Gaussian approximation. For the two-positions experiment we have made a detailed investigation of the errors caused by the two approximations. For N greater than 20 we found that the error in the signal threshold (defined by the 90 per cent point on the betting curve) is probably less than 10 per cent, so that under usual circumstances the error will be inappreciable.

7·6. Mathematical Appendix.—We shall collect here a number of mathematical results, which are needed in different places throughout the book.

The integrals occurring in Sec. 7·2 can all be performed by means of the general formula

$$\int_0^{2\pi} d\theta \cos n\theta\, e^{-a\cos\theta} = 2\pi(-1)^n I_n(a), \quad (61)$$

$$\int_0^\infty dt\, t^{\mu-1} I_\nu(at) e^{-p^2 t^2}$$

$$= \frac{\Gamma\left(\dfrac{\mu+\nu}{2}\right)\left(\dfrac{a}{2p}\right)^\nu}{2p^\mu \Gamma(\nu+1)}\, e^{a^2/4p^2} F\left(\frac{\nu-\mu}{2}+1,\ \nu+1;\ -\frac{a^2}{4p^2}\right). \quad (62)$$

Here $I_n(z)$ is the Bessel function of purely imaginary argument, and $F(a, b; z)$ is the confluent hypergeometric function,[1] which is defined by

$$F(a, b; z) = 1 + \frac{a}{b} z + \frac{a(a+1)}{b(b+1)} \frac{z^2}{2!} + \frac{a(a+1)(a+2)}{b(b+1)(b+2)} \frac{z^3}{3!} + \cdots \quad (63)$$

The asymptotic series for $F(a, b; z)$ for large *negative* values of z is

$$F(a, b; z) \approx \frac{\Gamma(b)}{\Gamma(b-a)} (-z)^{-a} \left[1 - \frac{a(a-b+1)}{z} \right.$$
$$\left. + \frac{a(a+1)(a-b+1)(a-b+2)}{z^2} + \cdots \right] \quad (64)$$

Often needed are the relations

$$e^{-z} F(a, b; z) = F(b-a, b; -z), \quad (65)$$

$$\frac{d}{dz} F(a, b; z) = \frac{a}{b} F(a+1, b+1; z), \quad (66)$$

and the recurrence relations

$$\left.\begin{aligned}
zF_{1,1} &= bF_{1,0} - bF_{0,0}, \\
aF_{1,1} &= (a-b)F_{0,1} + bF_{0,0}, \\
abF_{1,0} &= b(a+z)F_{0,0} - z(b-a)F_{0,1}, \\
aF_{1,0} &= (z+2a-b)F_{0,0} + (b-a)F_{-1,0}, \\
(b-a)zF_{0,1} &= b(z+b-1)F_{0,0} + b(1-b)F_{0,-1},
\end{aligned}\right\} \quad (67)$$

where the symbol $F_{k,l}$ is an abbreviation defined by

$$F_{k,l} = F(a+k, b+l; z).$$

If a is a negative integer, $F(a, b; z)$ reduces to a polynomial in z. If both a and b are positive integers, $F(a, b; z)$ can be expressed in exponential functions and polynomials in z. If a is a half integer and b is an integer, $F(a, b; z)$ can be expressed in Bessel functions $I_n(z)$ and exponential functions of z. Since in the literature the results are often expressed in this way, we shall give here a list of some of these identities:

[1] The usual notation is $_1F_1(a, b; z)$. For the integral (62) see G. N. Watson, *Theory of Bessel Functions*, Cambridge University Press, 1944, p. 394.

$$F\left(\frac{1}{2}, 1; -z\right) = e^{-\frac{z}{2}} I_0\left(\frac{z}{2}\right),$$

$$F\left(\frac{1}{2}, 2; -z\right) = e^{-\frac{z}{2}}\left[I_0\left(\frac{z}{2}\right) + I_1\left(\frac{z}{2}\right)\right],$$

$$F\left(\frac{3}{2}, 1; -z\right) = e^{-\frac{z}{2}}\left[(1-z)I_0\left(\frac{z}{2}\right) + I_1\left(\frac{z}{2}\right)\right],$$

$$F\left(\frac{3}{2}, 2; -z\right) = e^{-\frac{z}{2}}\left[I_0\left(\frac{z}{2}\right) - I_1\left(\frac{z}{2}\right)\right],$$

$$F\left(-\frac{1}{2}, 1; -z\right) = e^{-\frac{z}{2}}\left[(1+z)I_0\left(\frac{z}{2}\right) + zI_1\left(\frac{z}{2}\right)\right],$$

$$F\left(-\frac{3}{2}, 1; -z\right) = e^{-\frac{z}{2}}\left[\left(\frac{2}{3}z^2 + 2z + 1\right)I_0\left(\frac{z}{2}\right) + \left(\frac{2}{3}z^2 + \frac{4}{3}z\right)I_1\left(\frac{z}{2}\right)\right].$$

Tables of $F(a, b; z)$ for half-integer values of a and integer values of b can be found in the Report of the British Association for the Advancement of Science, 1927.

CHAPTER 8

PULSE TRAINS IN INTERNAL NOISE

This chapter will present experimental and theoretical results dealing with the determination of threshold power for a signal consisting of a train of pulses. A superheterodyne receiver will be assumed in which the noise is of the variety discussed in Chaps. 4 and 5; for threshold signals in external noise the reader is referred to Chaps. 11 and 12. Furthermore, in the interests of simplicity, only the results obtained in using a deflection-modulated, or type A, oscilloscope will be considered here. The intensity-modulated display is discussed in Chap. 9.

8·1. Standards for the Measurement of Signal Power.—The comparison between signal and noise power is most conveniently drawn in the i-f amplifier after the restriction in i-f bandwidth is made. At this point, the signal-to-noise power ratio is affected by both the i-f bandwidth and the noise figure of the receiver; therefore, both these quantities must be accurately known in order to calculate the input power ratio. This calculation, however, is very simple. As pointed out in Sec. 5·1 the noise power P_N in the receiver at any point is given by the relation

$$P_N = GF_T kT \, \Delta f, \tag{1}$$

where G is the total power gain of the receiver up to the point in question, F_T is the noise figure of the receiver expressed for a particular temperature T, and k is Boltzmann's constant. Although G is a function of the frequency, a mid-frequency value will suffice here. To be absolutely correct, the bandwidth Δf must be measured in a particular way; it is, in fact, calculated from the relation

$$\Delta f = \int_0^\infty A_f^2 \, df, \tag{2}$$

also see p. 101

where A_f is the amplitude response of the receiver at a particular frequency f, normalized to unity at midband. Equation (2) is introduced because the various noise components in the receiver are independent, hence add in power or in the squares of the amplitude functions. This assumes (nearly always validly) that the original noise is uniformly distributed throughout the frequency range.

The measurement of bandwidth by means of Eq. (2) is tedious and usually difficult. It is much more convenient to measure the bandwidth simply by the frequency interval between points at which the receiver power response is one-half its maximum value or its amplitude response is $\sqrt{2}/2$ times its maximum value; this half-power bandwidth is denoted by B. The difference between B and Δf depends upon the shape of the response curve; this in turn depends upon the type of receiver and type of interstage coupling. Because of the linear relationship between r-f and i-f voltages in the superheterodyne receiver (see Sec. 2·2) we may assume the bandwidth limitation to occur in either the r-f or i-f amplifier. It is customary in either case to use a number of simple networks that restrict the bandwidth; these networks are usually *single-tuned*, that is, a single inductance-capacitance-resistance mesh, or they are *multiply tuned*, that is, a number of coupled resonant meshes. The coupling adjustment on multiply tuned circuits is often made so that the response is constant to the highest possible order in the neighborhood of midband; this has several advantages besides giving a reproducible and calculable response curve. For a number of arrangements the differences between half-power bandwidths B and bandwidths Δf determined from Eq. (2) are shown in Table 8·1, taken from Stone's report.[1]

TABLE 8·1.—COMPARISON OF NOISE BANDWIDTHS AND 3-DB BANDWIDTHS

Type of coupling circuit	No. of stages	Noise band-width Δf	3-db band-width W	Ratio, db
Singly tuned	1	3.14	2.000*	1.95
	2	1.57	1.286	0.85
	3	1.18	1.02	0.64
	4	0.985	0.868	0.55
Doubly tuned	1	2.221	2.000*	0.46
	2	1.67	1.604	0.2
Triply tuned	1	2.096	2.000*	0.2
Quadruply tuned	1	2.038	2.000*	0.08
Quintuply tuned	1	2.020	2.000*	0.04

* Taken by definition.

It can be seen that the two types of bandwidth determinations are nearly alike. Since the half-power bandwidth is so much easier to measure, only the half-power bandwidths B will be used in this chapter.

Throughout the following discussion one further assumption will be made regarding the bandwidth B, namely, that it applies equally well to both signal and noise. This assumption is completely justified if the

[1] A. M. Stone, RL Report No. 708, June 22, 1945.

filter that is substantially responsible for B *follows* the source of noise. This condition prevails in nearly all microwave receivers and in nearly all well-designed receivers employing r-f amplification. For receivers in which this is not true, i.e., where the signal bandwidth is less than the noise bandwidth, a reduction in noise, without an accompanying loss in signal response, can be brought about by the use of a final i-f filter. For best results this final filter should be made to restrict the noise bandwidth to the same value as the signal bandwidth.

If we now measure the signal-to-noise power at some point in the receiver, we can calculate the input noise power by means of Eq. (1), noting first that the gain G is the ratio of signal power P_S in the receiver to the available input signal power $P_{S_{in}}$. Thus,

$$P_{S_{in}} = \frac{P_S}{P_N} F_T kT \, \Delta f; \tag{3}$$

and as before, Δf can be replaced by the approximate half-power bandwidth B.

The advantage in using Eq. (3) to calculate input signal power is considerable. The noise figure is measurable by methods that do not involve large amounts of attenuation; one of these methods, which is quite accurate, simply compares receiver noise with noise of known power generated by a diode (see Chap. 5). The measurement of receiver bandwidth is straightforward; the comparison of signal and noise power is also usually straightforward, although certain precautions may be necessary. These precautions will be discussed when a complete experimental system for determining threshold signals is presented. The input power can thus be measured with good accuracy even though it is in the neighborhood of 10^{-15} watt; this measurement would be difficult to make directly by means of a signal generator and a long-range calibrated attenuator. Furthermore, the ratio P_S/P_N, together with the bandwidth, determines the signal perceptibility. Two receivers having the same bandwidth and same shape response curves but different noise figures will have different signal threshold powers measured at their input terminals but, in the threshold condition, will show the same values of P_S/P_N. Therefore, in order that results may be universally applicable to all receivers, it is desirable to express threshold signals in terms of noise power in the receiver after the bandwidth restriction has occurred.

Up to this point a method has been outlined whereby the threshold signal power may be computed from the receiver noise figure, bandwidth, and a universal parameter, which is, in fact, the signal-to-noise power ratio. It has been tacitly assumed that the signal is a train of pulses, which is finite in length because of the limited time in which an observation must be made or because of scanning limitations. Scanning has been discussed in Chap. 2 and is of special importance when the intensity-modulated display is used. It has not yet been stated, however, how the signal power can be measured or, more important, how it can be compared with receiver noise power. Furthermore, it has not yet been pointed out how the signal power can be adjusted to correspond to the threshold condition. These questions will be answered in the following sections.

8·2. A (Synthetic) System for Experimental Purposes.—Since it will be useful in the discussion of experimental results to be presented in the following sections, a block diagram of a (synthetic) system is shown in Fig. 8·1. This system has been used at one time or another by Stone[1] and Ashby, Meijer, Stone, Sydoriak, and Lawson[2] to investigate the factors involved in signal discernibility for an A-scope display. It contains a pulse generator and synchronization circuit so that a series of pulses of controllable length, spacing, and number can be produced and the pulse power can be accurately compared with receiver noise power. In addition, the receiver, though a conventional superheterodyne, is arranged so that the i-f bandwidth is variable (in steps) over a wide range. A description of the various components and their functions follows.

The production of a series of r-f pulses having all the characteristics of a mathematically perfect series of pulses is a goal yet to be achieved. Usually the emitted r-f energy has frequency modulation associated with it, and the pulse shape is not rectangular. Furthermore, it is usually found that the r-f pulse power is affected by the duty ratio or fraction of time during which the oscillator is energized, even though the voltages of the oscillator power supply are held constant. This effect is usually due to internal heating of the oscillator elements; variations in average heat cause variations in electrode spacing with consequent change in oscillator efficiency. The difficulty of frequency modulation mentioned above can be solved by taking extreme care with the shape of the modulator pulse used to excite the oscillator; the difficulty regarding the duty ratio was solved in the system shown in Fig. 8·1 by actually maintaining the duty ratio of the oscillator itself constant. This condition is achieved essentially by operating the signal generator at the highest PRF that is to be used and by operating the A-scope sweep at an equal or lower repetition frequency. Thus the information presented on the A-scope recurs at any desired sweep repetition frequency, or SRF; at the same time it is certain that the pulse power from the signal generator is independent of the SRF. The variation in duty ratio brought about by a change in pulse length, however, still exists in this system; hence for each

[1] A. M. Stone, RL Report No. 708, June 22, 1945.
[2] Unpublished.

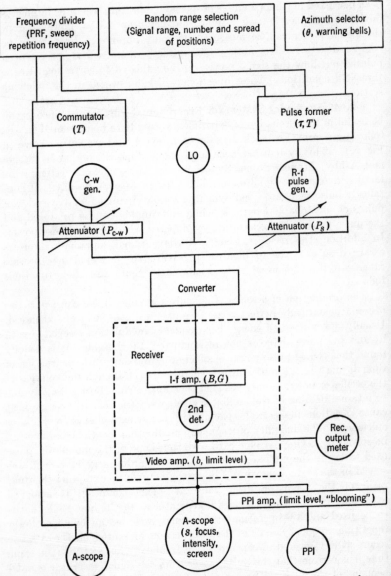

FIG. 8·1.—Block diagram of synthetic system. The parameters controlled in each component are shown in parentheses.

pulse length a calibration between pulse power and receiver noise power must be made. The independent control of the PRF and SRF has the additional advantage that for some experiments it is useful to operate the A-scope sweep *more* often than the signal pulse. In this way the pulse may appear on every other, every fourth, etc., sweep. This form of operation is useful in determining one of the effects of mixing the video signals of two or more systems. More will be said about this point later. There is therefore found in the top left-hand corner of Fig. 8·1 a synchronization unit that produces timing pulses determining both the PRF and SRF; these frequencies must be harmonically related to fulfill the functions described above. For convenience, the unit actually built for tests contains a 100-kc/sec crystal oscillator to provide initial stable pulses. A series of frequency-dividing stages is then used to halve each successive frequency. The resulting unit has available output trigger pulses with repetition frequencies from about 1 cps up to 100 kc/sec; all these frequencies are harmonically related and can be used independently to form the PRF and the SRF.

It has been noted that the signal is to consist of a finite train of pulses; the length of the train is determined by various factors, often chiefly connected with scanning. As we shall see in the following sections, the length of the pulse train, which will be called the signal presentation time θ, has a profound influence on signal threshold power; therefore, for experimental purposes it must be controllable over a considerable range of values. To prevent the oscillator duty ratio from being affected by θ the following scheme was devised. The signal position, or range, on the A-scope is adjusted so that the signal normally does not appear; i.e., it is displaced outside the limits of the A-scope sweep. During the interval θ the signal range is changed to bring it into the visible region on the A-scope. This procedure does not affect the duty ratio yet presents the signal on the A-scope only during the desired interval. The apparent signal range is, of course, fixed by the time delay between the timing pulse operating the A-scope sweep and the timing pulse operating the signal generator. The device controlling the signal presentation time is shown in the upper right-hand corner of Fig. 8·1. In addition to controlling this parameter it also functions, if desired, to provide a warning signal to the observer just prior to the signal presentation interval θ. Since the function of this unit is to set the length of a train of pulses, accomplished in a scanning system by azimuth selection caused by the rotating antenna beam width, the unit is labeled "azimuth selector." Indeed, for experiments with the PPI, to be discussed in Chap. 9, it becomes an actual azimuth selector.

In addition to presenting the signal on the A-scope for an interval θ it is desirable to present it at one of a number of defined range positions.

This is a necessary part of the method by which threshold signals are determined. It has been pointed out in Chap. 7 that a theoretical "betting" curve exists; there is also an experimental betting curve with similar characteristics. To determine this experimental betting curve it has been found most desirable to obtain correlation results between the observer's estimate of signal range and the actual signal range. So that the observer may be unaware of the actual signal position, it is necessary for the signal to occur at one of several designated range positions. The chosen position must be independent of previous selections and must be selected by chance. More will be said about this procedure below, but it is pertinent to remark here that a synchronization unit is necessary to perform this random range selection and that control of the number and spacing of the positions is also required. This unit is shown in schematic notation at the top of Fig. 8·1.

One other synchronization unit shown near the top left-hand corner of Fig. 8·1 needs explanation. It has been found that, when very small values of θ are used, the total number of A-scope sweeps of noise, with which the signal competes, extends beyond the interval θ. To test this point a commutator was used that allows the A-scope to be triggered only during the given interval θ; under these conditions the signal presentation time is still θ, and only during this interval is anything shown on the A-scope. The significance of this commutator will be discussed in subsequent sections.

The receiver used in the system of Fig. 8·1 is a conventional microwave superheterodyne using a crystal converter. To the r-f input terminals of this converter are coupled the output of the local oscillator, the pulsed signal generator, and a c-w r-f generator, which is used in the comparison of pulsed signal and noise power by a method to be described below. The c-w generator and pulsed signal generator have associated with them respective attenuators in their output lines. These attenuators, of the waveguide-beyond-cutoff variety, have extremely good relative accuracy, but the absolute values of the attenuation are not easily measurable. Both the signal and c-w generators are well shielded; this precaution is essential in making any measurements at levels approaching receiver noise. The part of the receiver following the converter is of the greatest importance in the experimental work; it is here that there are many parameters to adjust in the determination of optimum design. Some of the receiver parameters that may be expected to have an effect on signal threshold power are

1. I-f bandwidth.
2. Shape of i-f bandwidth.
3. Type of second detector.
4. Video bandwidth.

5. Shape of video bandwidth.

6. Video nonlinearity such as that caused by saturation or limiting.

Presumably only the most important of these variables were, for simplicity's sake, investigated. It was expected that the shapes of i-f and video bandwidths would not greatly affect threshold signals, provided the shapes were those characterized by properly adjusted filters. Therefore, in the receiver shown in block-diagram form in Fig. 8·1, the i-f and video bandwidths were determined by filters of types that are commonly used but are intermediate in complexity between the simple single-tuned circuit and the highly complicated multiply tuned circuits. The i-f bandwidth is determined essentially by a single double-tuned stage,[1] whereas the video bandwidth is determined by a single shunt-peaked section. In addition to fixing these parameters a *type* of second detector was chosen and not thereafter varied. It is of the linear, or *envelope*, type, which in receivers is almost universally used to the exclusion of other types. Occasionally a parabolic, or square-law, detector is found; however, there is now some evidence that the type of second detector has only a slight effect on the signal threshold power. This will be brought out in Sec. 8·7. Therefore, in summary, the receiver consists of a converter, an i-f amplifier whose gain and bandwidth are controllable, a linear second detector with an output meter to record the average video level, and a video amplifier whose bandwidth and limit level are controllable. The output line of the video amplifier is connected directly to the A-scope or, for intensity-modulated measurements, through an additional limiting stage to the PPI. The additional limiting stage is desirable so that the A-scope and PPI can be operated at different limit levels.

The description of the (synthetic) system is now complete except that the method by which the signal power is compared with noise power has not yet been explained. It might be thought that the signal power could be measured relative to noise by the contribution each makes in the output of the second detector, account being taken of the signal duty ratio. This is not the usual case; where the duty ratio is small, the contribution of a signal compared with that of the noise is unnoticeable. As the signal is increased in size to produce a measurable contribution, the signal pulses in the i-f amplifier become large enough to saturate the amplifier, thereby invalidating any measurement of the power. To overcome this difficulty the system shown in Fig. 8·1 was devised; the pulsed signal is first compared in power with a c-w generator, which, in turn, is compared with receiver noise. This latter comparison is easily made because the duty ratio of the c-w generator is unity. The pro-

---

[1] A. M. Stone and J. L. Lawson, "Theory and Design of Double-tuned Circuits," *Electronic Ind.*, April 1946, p. 62.

cedure is to adjust the receiver gain so that the second-detector output meter reads some fiducial value due to receiver noise only. The c-w generator attenuator is next adjusted so that the output meter increases its reading to $\sqrt{2}$ times the fiducial reading. At this point the power in the i-f amplifier, produced by the c-w generator, is just equal to the noise power in the i-f amplifier. The factor[1] $\sqrt{2}$ comes about because of the linear detector; a doubling of input *power* results in a change in output *amplitude* of $\sqrt{2}$. This procedure is valid only when there is a really linear second detector; this point can be checked experimentally by calibration against the attenuator associated with the c-w generator. To make the determination valid, receiver noise is made negligible by reducing the gain of the i-f amplifier.

The method by which the c-w generator power is made equal to receiver noise power has just been outlined, but the way in which the c-w power is compared with the signal power has not yet been mentioned. This comparison can be made by the following procedure. With the receiver gain reduced to the point that noise is negligible the signal is adjusted to an easily measurable amplitude on the A-scope. The c-w generator power (tuned to the mid-frequency of the signal) is then increased slowly until a flutter or "beating" effect in the signal is observed. This phenomenon is due to the addition of signal and c-w voltages in random phase from pulse to pulse. When the c-w and pulse voltages are in phase, the resulting video signals "beat" up to the maximum value; when they are out of phase, the video signals beat down to their lowest value. As the c-w power is increased, the signal on the A-scope is observed to beat lower and lower until it just beats down to the baseline. The c-w power that just produces this effect is easily reproducible, since the visual extension of the baseline can be estimated with great accuracy. A c-w power greater than this critical value causes the signal to beat below the baseline. This statement may seem surprising at first, but it must be remembered that the baseline does not represent zero video voltage but actually represents the steady rectified voltage produced by the c-w generator. Let us, therefore, examine the conditions under which the signal "beats" just to the baseline; this is clearly a

---

[1] Strictly speaking, this factor is not entirely correct because of the difference in the probability distributions of the amplitudes of noise and c-w signal. The output of the linear detector records the average rectified amplitude, which is proportional to the square root of power only for voltages that have similar amplitude distributions. The $\sqrt{2}$ factor would apply strictly only to the case where rms voltages are recorded; therefore a correction factor should be applied that comes in because of the difference between rms and average voltages. For noise, this factor has been evaluated; to equalize c-w and noise power the fiducial reading of the output meter should be increased by a factor of 1.45 with the addition of c-w power instead of by the stated factor of $\sqrt{2}$.

condition in which the difference between signal and c-w voltage during the pulse is just equal to the c-w voltage represented by the A-scope baseline.   This observation leads to the obvious conclusion that the signal pulse voltage is just twice the c-w voltage or that the signal power is just four times the c-w power.   This condition, incidentally, is independent of the detector linearity; it requires only that the detector response be independent of i-f signal phase.   The procedure, therefore, affords a high-precision method by which the signal power can be compared with the c-w generator power.   In the use of the beating technique one important precaution must be observed, however.   The i-f and video amplifier must have adequate bandwidth, enough properly to delineate the signal; otherwise the transient effect at the beginning and end of the signal arising from inevitable phase changes in the i-f voltage will cause a false reading.   This effect is unimportant as soon as the i-f bandwidth is larger than about twice the reciprocal of the pulse length; the video bandwidth should likewise be correspondingly large.   Therefore, in the comparison reading between signal and c-w voltages only the wide-band i-f amplifier connection should be used.

8·3. The Determination of Threshold-signal Setting.—A system has been described in which, once the attenuator setting is chosen for a threshold signal, the signal power can be measured in convenient units. This process is straightforward and requires no further refinements. However, the procedure by which the threshold signal is established is one in which considerable latitude exists; each investigator has usually seen fit to use a new procedure that generally has yielded slightly different results.   Apparently the process first used was to ask a number of observers to estimate the minimum detectable signal; the threshold signal was then assumed to be the average of their answers.   It was found that the individual estimates differed by large factors, indeed so large that it was nearly impossible to obtain reliable averages.   Furthermore, a given observer would usually change his estimate considerably from day to day, depending on such factors as A-scope trace intensity, focus conditions, and his own state of mind.   His estimate of minimum detectable signal would also be greatly affected by such factors as his previous training and by the degree of certainty that was required of his answer.   Because of this sort of difficulty a method was sought that did not depend on the observer's opinion.   The type of answer required of the observer and the consistency with which his determinations were found to be repeated at a subsequent date indicate that the procedure outlined here constitutes such an objective method.   Furthermore, different observers, when properly trained, all obtain virtually the same results.   The method is essentially one in which the observers' answers are correlated with some desired parameter of the signal.   In the case of the A-scope such a parameter is the range position of the signal; in the case of the PPI azimuth position could also be used.   In the former case the signal is made to appear at one of several definite range positions, and the observer is asked to guess the correct position.   His guesses are then correlated with the actual known positions in order to find out whether or not the signal is perceptible.   This procedure minimizes the judgment required from the observer; he is not required to judge whether or not the signal is visible but only which of several given positions is most likely to contain the signal.   Since this type of correlation is statistical in nature, a number of observations must be made; in order that each guess be independent of preceding observations, the range position of the signal must be randomly selected.   It is expected theoretically, and found experimentally, that the signal threshold power depends upon the number and spacing of these range positions.   A large number of positions increases the threshold power slightly; a small number of positions complicates the analysis because of chance lucky guesses.   For most of the experiments to be described in the next two sections six positions have been used; where the effect of number of positions is studied, however, this restriction obviously does not apply.

It is found experimentally that there is a "twilight" region where the signal can be detected only part of the time.   The fraction of time in which the signal is seen can be obtained from the correlation between guessed position and actual position as outlined above; this fraction increases continuously with increasing signal.   The result is analogous to the "betting" curve of the theoretically ideal observer described in Chap. 7 and indeed appears to differ from it in only two respects; viz., the actual observer appears to require a slightly higher value of signal power than the ideal observer, and the betting curve seems to have a different width (where the width is defined by the relative signal power change from 10 to 90 per cent correlation).   The width of the twilight region is usually smaller than that of the ideal observer, although if conditions of severe video limiting are experienced, the experimental twilight zone becomes very large.   These two general observations are not at all surprising.   For example, the first amounts to saying that a human observer is not so efficient as the theoretically ideal observer.   The second observation is expected when due allowance is made for the effects of contrast limitation in the human observer and for saturation effects in the video system.   These points will be considered in later sections.

A typical experimental betting curve is shown in Fig. 8·2 in which the correlation fraction, after the theoretical number of chance lucky guesses is subtracted, is plotted against relative signal power.   The signal power is expressed in decibels relative to the noise power in the receiver with a 1.0-Mc/sec i-f bandwidth; and as can be seen, the conditions in the experiment were chosen so that the entire betting curve occurs for signals smaller than noise power. Each experimental point on the curve was obtained from 20 observations (guesses); hence there is still considerable statistical scatter in the points. A reasonably smooth curve, however, can be drawn through the points, and it is not difficult to specify the signal power for a given correlation fraction. This specification can be made to within 1 or possibly 0.5 db in relative signal power. As can be seen from Fig. 8·2, however, such a specification requires about 100 individual observations; unfortunately this is the price that must be paid to achieve a quantitative measurement of threshold signal. The total time spent in obtaining experimental data for threshold

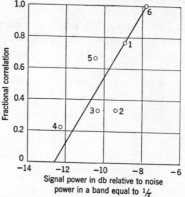

Fig. 8·2.—Experimental "betting" curve.

signals is therefore considerable; yet it is felt that the final results can be trusted only when such pains are taken.

So that the reader can appreciate the type of measurement just described, a series of photographs typical of an actual experiment have been made of an A-scope with six possible signal range positions. These are shown in Fig. 8·3 with the six possible positions shown below each picture as a row of tiny white dots. The conditions under which these photographs were made are unimportant in the present discussion. In Fig. 8·3a one photograph is shown where the signal occurs at randomly selected positions but in which the signal-to-noise power ratio was set at 6 db. In Fig. 8·3b the same conditions apply except that the signal-to-noise power ratio was set at 0 db. Likewise, for each of the series shown in Fig. 8·3 a different signal power was used. It can be seen that as the signal is reduced in size, more and more difficulty is experienced in locating it. The reader is invited to try his hand at guessing the correct positions for all the photographs in order to construct a betting curve; the correct answers are given on page 188.[1] A sample betting curve, derived from Fig. 8·3, is shown in Fig. 8·4, in which the correct number in each category is plotted against the relative signal power. This number is plotted directly, without first subtracting the chance lucky guesses; the procedure gives a slightly distorted betting curve but is simpler to use in illustrating the results. The coded points shown in this figure are those obtained by four independent skilled observers.

[1] Signal position answers to Fig. 8·3:

Because of the existence of a twilight region for signal threshold power it is not possible to speak of a threshold signal without referring to the entire betting curve. This is an extremely tedious procedure; it is ordinarily sufficient to refer to some characteristic region of the betting curve. As an example we may refer to the signal power required to give a correlation of 50 per cent; this can be used as a criterion of threshold

Photograph	Position	Photograph	Position	Photograph	Position
8.3a	6	8.3d 1	4	8.3f 1	1
8.3b 1	4	8.3d 2	3	8.3f 2	4
8.3b 2	5	8.3d 3	6	8.3f 3	5
8.3b 3	1	8.3d 4	5	8.3f 4	2
8.3b 4	2	8.3d 5	3	8.3f 5	3
8.3b 5	4	8.3e 1	1	8.3g 1	3
8.3c 1	5	8.3e 2	6	8.3g 2	5
8.3c 2	4	8.3e 3	2	8.3g 3	2
8.3c 3	1	8.3e 4	5	8.3g 4	2
8.3c 4	3	8.3e 5	4	8.3g 5	6
8.3c 5	1				

power. An objection to the use of the 50 per cent point, however, is that it is far from the point at which the observer *thinks* he can see the signal; the latter signal strength is probably nearer the one operationally useful. For this reason it is usually more desirable to specify the signal required

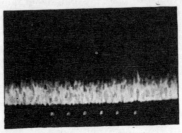

(a) Signal = noise + 6 db
Fig. 8·3.—Oscilloscope photographs with signal in random positions.

to give a large correlation; a figure of 100 per cent would be nearly ideal were it not for the extreme difficulty of finding it. It seems from Fig. 8·2 that a correlation of 100 per cent is reached rather abruptly, yet the shape of the betting curve between 80 and 100 per cent correlation is not well defined by the experimental points; indeed the statistical fluctuations in this neighborhood are so large that the shape of the curve as drawn is not necessarily correct. Strictly speaking, it is likely that a correlation of 100 per cent is never quite achieved, analogous to the situation in the

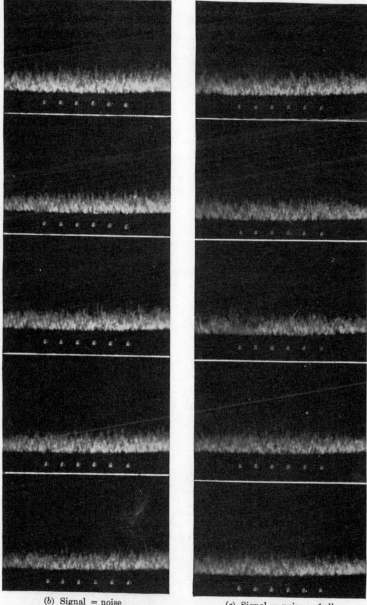

(b) Signal = noise

(c) Signal = noise − 1 db

Fig. 8·3.—Oscilloscope photographs with signal in random positions.   (Continued.)

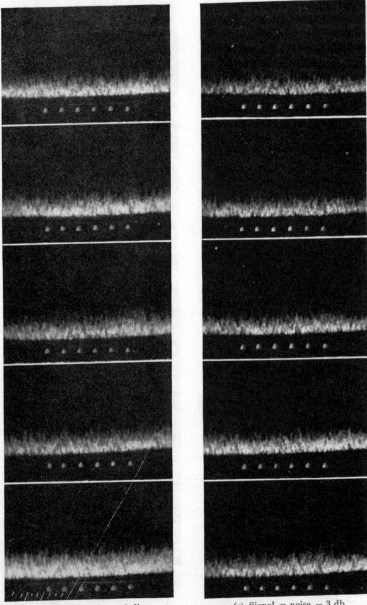

(d) Signal = noise − 2 db   (e) Signal = noise − 3 db
FIG. 8·3.—Oscilloscope photographs with signal in random positions.   (Continued.)

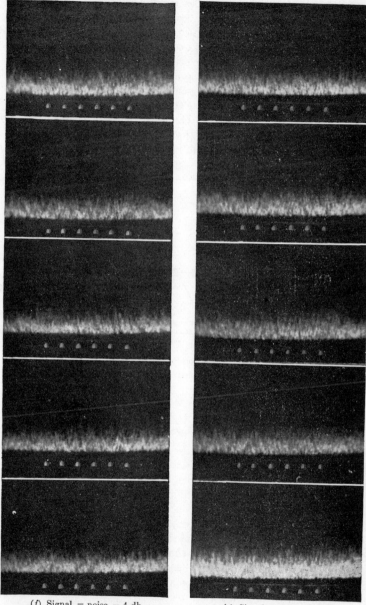

(f) Signal = noise − 4 db

(g) Signal = noise − 5 db

Fig. 8·3.—Oscilloscope photographs with signal in random positions.   (Continued.)

betting curve of the ideal observer described in Sec. 7·4. For all practical purposes, however, the correlation becomes 100 per cent very abruptly. Nevertheless, because of the statistical difficulty of determining a practical 100 per cent point, it is felt that a correlation of 90 per cent represents a more useful figure. At this correlation a skilled observer can feel that he really *sees* the signal at least a significant part of the time. It will be convenient to refer to the signal power required to yield 90 per cent correlation as $P_{S_{90}}$, which will also be considered to be the *threshold signal* unless explicitly stated otherwise. The second subscript will always refer to the percentage correlation, so that if other correlation criteria are temporarily used, their meaning will be obvious.

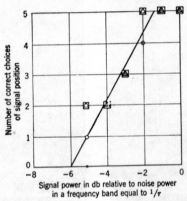

FIG. 8·4.—Sample betting curve derived from photographs of Fig. 8·3.

System parameters:

$B\tau = 1.1$

$s\tau$ = approximately optimum

PRF = 400 pps

Exposure time = 0.1 sec.

Key:
△ Observer *A*
□ Observer *B*
○ Observer *C*
● Observer *D*

It is desirable at this time to reiterate the point of view that is taken in setting up the procedure for determining threshold signals. The aim is to establish accurate criteria by which the effect of various system parameters on threshold signal can be studied. It is *not* desired to study the observer himself, especially as to methods of training or methods that would make his job easier or less tiring. It is true, however, that certain characteristics of the observer become inextricably entangled with parameters of the system, and these characteristics can be most readily studied by means of the suggested correlation technique. Most important of all, no real attempt has been made to study the observer's reactions to different situations. We must recognize that an observer searching for a weak signal will not report such a signal unless he is psychologically sure of its existence. The strength of signal required for psychological certainty depends upon many factors.   Some of them are (1) the importance of correctly reporting the signal, (2) the number of mistakes that have been previously made, (3) the observer's state of alertness, (4) previous amount and type of training and practice, etc.   These factors are extremely important in any operational situation; however, they are not pertinent to a discussion of the *system parameters* that affect threshold signals.

8·4. System Parameters and Scaling.—Let us list the various system parameters that are expected to have an effect on signal threshold power. It is not intended to be a complete list, but it probably contains most of the important quantities that pertain to a relatively straightforward receiving system containing an A-scope indicator.   For more complicated systems, such as the MTI system described in Sec. 11·5, it is obvious that additional parameters will be introduced.   In Table 8·2 there is listed beside some of the parameters a symbol that will represent that parameter.   The variables are listed in groups, each group generally being associated with some part of the receiving system.

The scanning variable is of special importance in the discussion of intensity-modulated indicators presented in Chap. 9.   For the A-scope, however, matters will be simplified by neglecting the shaping of the pulse train resulting from the antenna beam pattern.   The pulse train will be assumed to be of constant amplitude but of length θ as is listed in Item 5 of Table 8·2.

A blind investigation of the effect of each variable for various conditions of all the other parameters would assume prodigious proportions indeed, but a rough estimate of the number of observations required to complete the problem can be made.   Assuming that each parameter is to be set to each of five values and that a single determination for threshold signal requires about 100 observations (see Fig. 8·2), we arrive at the astonishing result that about 10^{16} observations need to be made.   This fact is convincing evidence that every effort must be made to simplify the problem and to investigate only those parameters which are expected to have a relatively pronounced effect on threshold signals.   This simplification will be carried on to a large extent, and the justification for such simplification is indicated below.   The numbers preceding the following paragraphs correspond to items in Table 8·2.

1. The pulse power P_s is, in fact, the dependent variable that we wish to find.   It is affected, of course, by the definition of threshold signal made in the preceding section as well as by all the other system parameters.

3. The pulse shape is relatively unimportant.   Almost all pulses in common use have a rectangular shape; for this reason other shapes will not be considered.

6. The receiver noise figure F has been disposed of in Sec. 8·1, although a knowledge of its value is required to compute final signal threshold power in absolute units.

8. The shape of the i-f bandpass curve has already been discussed in Sec. 8·2; it is believed that its effect is minor as long as it arises from an "approved" type of i-f coupling circuit.

TABLE 8·2.—PARAMETERS AFFECTING SIGNAL VISIBILITY

Parameter	Symbol	Remarks
The signal:		
1. Pulse power.................	P_S	
2. Pulse length.................	τ	
3. Shape of pulse		
4. Pulse repetition frequency.....	f_r	Abbreviated PRF
5. Duration of pulse train........	θ	Signal presentation time
The receiver:		
6. Noise figure.................	F	Abbreviated NF
7. I-f bandwidth...............	B	
8. Shape of i-f bandpass curve		
9. Type of second detector.......	......	Linear, quadratic, etc.
10. Video bandwidth............	b	
11. Shape of video bandpass curve		
12. Video limiting or saturation		
13. Receiver power gain..........	G	Affects output noise (and signal) level
The indicator:		
14. Trace brightness		
15. Focus conditions		
16. Direction of sweep...........	......	Vertical or horizontal
17. Sweep rate or speed..........	s	
18. Deflection sensitivity.........	......	Measured perpendicular to sweep
19. Screen material..............	P1, P7	Rate of decay—P1 fast (or instantaneous), P7 slow (few seconds)
20. Number of possible signal positions		
21. Spacing of signal positions		
The human observer................	......	No properties listed here, although they will be stated and discussed later
Video mixing......................	......	No specific property listed here, although the outputs of several systems can be mixed in various ways; this has an effect on threshold signals in each system
Scanning.........................	......	It is assumed the pulse train is of constant amplitude for a duration θ. Scanning actually causes a variation in pulse amplitude during the pulse train

9. The type of second detector also has been mentioned in Sec. 8·2; only the linear detector was experimentally investigated, although in this chapter the quadratic detector is considered from the theoretical point of view. If the signal is smaller than noise power—a condition generally experienced in threshold determinations—the linear and quadratic detectors are very nearly alike in signal perception sensitivity.

11. Analogous to the case of the i-f bandpass curve shape, it is expected that the shape of video bandpass curve has little effect on threshold signals. To be explicit, the shape of the video bandpass curve will be assumed to be that of a single shunt-peaked stage. This means a power-response law proportional to $1/(1 + f^4)$, where f is the frequency.

Of the remaining quantities it is possible to combine terms 6, 12, 13, and 18 into two useful and suitable variables. The noise figure (6), receiver gain (13), and video limiting voltage (12) essentially fix the fraction of the video noise distribution that is lost in the limiting process. It is therefore more useful to express the limit level directly in terms of the average noise voltage (before limiting); this ratio will be denoted by the symbol L.

Limiting is important only when a substantial fraction of the noise probability distribution is affected. Such limiting needs to be introduced only when an intensity-modulated display, such as the PPI, is used; it is necessary to prevent defocusing of the beam spot on the tube face for large noise fluctuations. For this reason the discussion of limiting will be deferred until the next chapter, which deals with results obtained from intensity-modulated display systems.

The noise figure (6), receiver gain (13), and A-scope deflection sensitivity (18) fix the average amplitude of noise as seen on the A-scope. It is more convenient to refer directly to this parameter than to the combination of system characteristics from which it is derived.

Let us consider a particular set of conditions where we examine in detail the geometrical picture on the face of the A-scope. This geometrical picture is composed of a number of overlaid traces; each trace for the purpose of visual inspection may be considered "laid onto" the screen instantaneously. There is a certain noise fluctuation in each trace whose spatial appearance is influenced by the receiver bandwidths B and b, by the average noise deflection, and by the A-scope sweep speed s. The actual appearance of the signal may be regarded as caused by pulse length τ, the receiver bandwidths B and b, and the signal-to-noise power ratio. Now let us consider the effect of an increase in pulse length by a factor β and inquire if there are similar changes that can be made in other parameters so that the geometrical picture on the A-scope may be left essentially unchanged.

If the pulse shape as viewed on the A-scope is to remain unchanged, the receiver bandwidths must be scaled *down* by a factor β and the sweep speed must also be scaled down by β. Since the total i-f noise power in the receiver is proportional to the i-f bandwidth, the receiver gain G must be increased by the factor β. This reasoning leads to the conclusion that for a given signal deflection the input signal power must be reduced by β. There is in addition one minor change that is necessary to keep the total trace intensity constant; because of the reduced sweep speed a reduction in the cathode-ray-tube beam current must be made, again by a factor β. It is clear that, when all these scale changes are made, the appearance of the A-scope face will be unchanged. We may write the old and the new

TABLE 8·3.—VARIOUS SCALING PARAMETERS

Old parameter	Scaled parameter	Invariant parameter
Pulse length τ	$\beta\tau$	
I-f bandwidth B	B/β	$B\tau$
Video bandwidth b	b/β	$b\tau$
Sweep speed s	s/β	$s\tau$
Threshold signal power $P_{S_{90}}$	$P_{S_{90}}/\beta$	$P_{S_{90}}\tau$ or $P_{S_{90}}/B$

scaled parameters as shown in Table 8·3. Also shown in this table is a list of combinations of the scaled parameters that are *invariant* to the scaling; these quantities are therefore much more suitable for ultimate use. The quantities $B\tau$ and $b\tau$ are dimensionless and usually have values within one or two orders of magnitude of unity. The quantity $s\tau$ is simply the geometrical length of the signal as it appears on the A-scope, and $P_{S_{90}}\tau$ is the threshold signal *energy*. It will be noticed that only four variables now exist in place of five; this reduction has been effected by the scaling argument. We are therefore left with the following parameters:

1. Trace brightness, average noise deflection; sweep parameters.
2. Product of i-f bandwidth and pulse length $B\tau$.
3. Product of video bandwidth and pulse length $b\tau$, product of sweep speed and pulse length $s\tau$, focus.
4. Pulse repetition frequency, PRF; sweep repetition frequency SRF.
5. Signal presentation time θ, screen material.
6. Attention interval θ_A, number and spacing of possible signal positions.
7. Video mixing.

These parameters are discussed in the following sections, where both experimental results and corresponding theoretical considerations are presented together.

8·5. Influence of Trace Brightness, Average Noise Deflection, Sweep Direction.—Before proceeding with the discussion, it is necessary to describe how the results are to be interpreted. When we speak of the effect of a single variable, we should like to mean the effect upon signal threshold power of changes in that variable when all other parameters are fixed at their most suitable values. The difficulty is now apparent—just how are we to know a priori the most suitable values of these parameters?

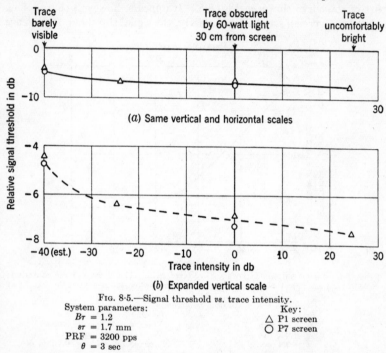

Fig. 8·5.—Signal threshold *vs.* trace intensity.

System parameters:

$B\tau = 1.2$

$s\tau = 1.7$ mm

PRF $= 3200$ pps

$\theta = 3$ sec

Key:

△ P1 screen

○ P7 screen

Fortunately this question is not vital, since it is found that the effect of one variable is not strongly dependent upon the values of the other parameters. In some cases the "most suitable" value of a parameter will not always be its value for maximum signal sensitivity; this situation arises when the desired operating conditions prevent the use of the most sensitive value of the parameter. Throughout the following discussion, therefore, parameters will generally be fixed at values that have been found through experience to be reasonably close to the most useful ones.

Dependence on Trace Brightness.—An experiment has been performed in which the trace intensity was varied over a factor of 10^6. Only a slight change in threshold signal was observed over the entire range. The results are shown in Fig. 8·5, and the pertinent system parameters are stated in the figure legend.   Unfortunately no absolute measure of trace intensity was available, but indicated on the abscissa are marks denoting the observer's reaction.   It is obvious that the effect of trace intensity is minor, although one remark of importance should be made.   This experiment was performed in a darkened room; it is expected that the effect of background illumination will greatly disturb the low-intensity part of the curve shown in Fig. 8·5.   It appears, however, that as long as the observer can see the trace clearly, the signal threshold dependence

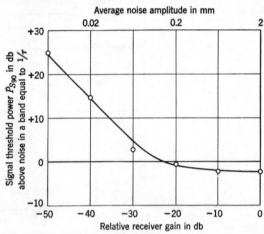

Fig. 8·6.—Signal threshold power *vs.* receiver gain.   The average noise amplitude is based on an estimate that this amplitude was 2 mm when the receiver gain was set at 0 db.

System parameters

$B\tau = 1.2$	Screen $= P1$
$s\tau = 0.7$ mm	Viewing distance $= 30$ cm
PRF $= 200$ pps	Vertical dimension
$\theta = 3.4$ sec	of focused spot $= 0.5$ mm

on trace brightness is nil.   This applies to both the P1 (short persistence) and P7 (long afterglow) screens.   The ordinate scale shown in this figure may seem confusing; it represents the signal threshold power expressed in decibels relative to the noise power.   Since the noise power is a function of the i-f bandwidth, it is evaluated for a particular bandwidth; i.e., $B = 1/\tau$.

Dependence on Average Noise Deflection.—This dependence has been established by specifically determining the signal threshold power as a function of the relative receiver gain.   The results are shown in Fig. 8·6, where the ordinate again represents signal power in decibels relative to the noise power in a band equal to $1/\tau$.   The abscissa represents relative receiver gain in decibels above an arbitrary level. For a relative receiver gain of 0 db, the estimated average noise deflection on the A-scope is 2 mm; since the second detector is linear, the average noise deflection for other gain settings can be calculated; this is shown on the top abscissa scale.

The pertinent system parameters for this experiment are indicated in the figure legend. As long as the average noise deflection exceeds about 0.5 mm, the signal threshold power is independent of the average deflection. As the noise deflection becomes smaller, the signal threshold power rises; for very small deflections the signal threshold power is inversely proportional to the receiver gain. This is the result expected if we assume that in this region a given video signal deflection is required, independent of noise power. This assumption is certainly reasonable in view of the negligible amplitude of noise.

Dependence on Direction of Sweep.—It has been reported in various places that the direction of the A-scope sweep influences the threshold signal; one of these reports indicated a difference of as much as 4 db in threshold signal. The experiment has been repeated by Sydoriak, Ashby, and Lawson[1] using the six-position correlation method of evaluation. The results show that the vertical sweep requires a signal substantially the same as that for the horizontal sweep. The observers felt, however, that the longer experience obtained in viewing the horizontal trace had created greater psychological difficulty in viewing signals on the vertical trace. Lack of adequate training on the vertical sweep can easily cause a difference of several decibels in the threshold signal. We may now be assured, however, that there is no fundamental difference in signal perception on A-scopes that have different trace directions.

8·6. Dependence on the Product of I-f Bandwidth and Pulse Length.— It is illuminating to look somewhat ahead and discuss qualitatively some features that are to be expected as a result of limitation of i-f and video bandwidths. The effect of i-f bandwidth limitation is somewhat different from the effect of video bandwidth limitation; this fact may seem surprising in view of the linear relationship between the modulation voltage of the i-f carrier and the video voltage. As has often been remarked, however, the linear detector records only the *absolute value* of the i-f envelope function; hence, with receiver noise that contains no carrier, cross-modulation terms develop. Video noise, then, even in a linear detector, is caused by the interaction of i-f noise components. The spectrum differs from the i-f noise spectrum. Hence the effect of reduction of video bandwidth differs from that of reduction of i-f bandwidth. The highest important video frequency produced by the second detector is numerically equal to the i-f bandwidth B, since this highest frequency

[1] Unpublished.

is the result of the interaction of the noise components at the two edges of the i-f band. Therefore once the video bandwidth b is larger than B, no effect of further widening the video bandwidth will be observable; this is a desirable condition for an experiment in which the effect of the i-f bandwidth is investigated.

We are not so fortunate in fixing other parameters at appropriate values. Therefore in the results that are to be presented a family of curves will be shown; each member of the family will represent different fixed conditions of other parameters.

It has been remarked in Sec. 8·1 that the total noise power in the i-f amplifier is proportional to B. This fact led to Eq. (3), which will now be rewritten in a more suitable form. A new parameter has been chosen for the signal threshold criterion because of its invariance to scaling, namely, the input threshold signal pulse energy $\tau P_{S_{in}}$. If we substitute B for Δf in Eq. (3), we may write

$$\tau P_{S_{in}} = \frac{P_S}{P_N} B\tau F_T kT. \tag{4}$$

Therefore, a measure of input signal threshold energy, which is independent of B, is the ratio of signal power to the noise power, the latter being evaluated where $B\tau = 1$ (in other words, for a bandwidth equal to $1/\tau$). This is the quantity which has already been plotted on the ordinate scales of Figs. 8·5 and 8·6 and which will be used throughout the following discussion of experimental results.

Experimental Results.—The results, from a series of experiments by Sydoriak, Ashby, and Lawson, are shown in Fig. 8·7. The abscissa represents $B\tau$ on a logarithmic scale, although the results were actually obtained with a fixed pulse length τ of 1.0×10^{-6} sec, by varying B in steps from approximately 10^5 to 10^7 cps. The ordinate represents the signal threshold power $P_{S_{90}}$ expressed in decibels relative to the noise power in a band equal to $1/\tau$. Several experimental curves are shown on the diagram; they were obtained for different values of the PRF and the signal presentation time θ. The bottom curve shown was obtained for a PRF of 3200 pps and a signal presentation time θ of 3 sec; the other two curves in ascending order were taken for a PRF of 200 pps and 12.5 pps, respectively, with θ fixed at 3 sec for both curves. The top curve is the result obtained for only a single trace on the A-scope. Also shown on the diagram is a line of 45° slope; this line represents the actual receiver i-f noise power on the same ordinate scale. Other pertinent system parameters are stated in the figure legend.

The experimental points were obtained by the three observers mentioned; the results for each observer are coded. Each point on the diagram represents the average over several trials. The results of about

10,000 individual observations are shown on this diagram. It is easy to see that the total spread of experimental points for a given condition is surprisingly small. Even more striking is the small difference between observers not only in the shape of the final curve but in its absolute value. This is good evidence that the six-position correlation method of evalu-

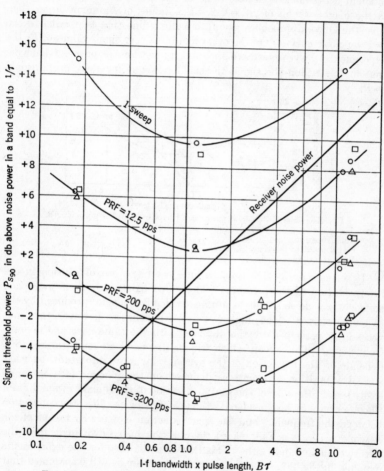

Fig. 8·7.—Signal threshold power *vs.* i-f bandwidth times pulse length.

System parameters

		Observers
Pulse length............................$\tau = 1\ \mu\text{sec}$		$\bigcirc$ R.A.
Pulse length on screen................$s\tau = 1.7$ mm		$\triangle$ J.L.
Video bandwidth........................$b = 10$ Mc/sec		$\square$ S.S.
Signal presentation time..............$\theta = 3$ sec		
Oscilloscope screen....................$= \text{P1}$		

ating threshold signals used in these experiments removes the necessity of nearly all psychological judgment on the part of the observer.

The general form of the curve seems to be relatively unaffected by the different values of PRF and θ, but its absolute value is considerably altered. The significance of this will be brought out later. For the moment it is sufficient to note that the curve has a broad, flat minimum in the neighborhood of $B\tau = 1.2$. For values of $B\tau$ much larger than this, the curve approaches asymptotically a line that is parallel to the receiver-noise curve. On the other hand, for very small values of $B\tau$ the experimental curve appears to approach a line whose slope is -1, showing that in this region the signal threshold power is inversely proportional to $B\tau$.

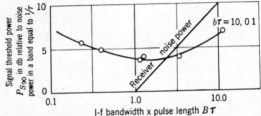

FIG. 8·8.—Signal threshold power *vs.* i-f bandwidth times pulse length.

System parameters

Pulse repetition frequency........................... PRF = 200 pps
Signal presentation time................................. θ = 3 sec
Pulse length on screen.................................. $s\tau$ = 0.05 mm

It seems wise at this time to interject one word of caution in the interpretation of these results. The video bandwidth itself was made sufficiently wide so as not to suppress video frequencies produced by the second detector. The higher video frequencies, however, are not necessarily perceived by the observer with the same ease as the lower frequencies. This effect, which will be discussed at length in Sec. 8·7, depends on the resolution of the eye and, far more important, on what spatial separation of events as depicted on the A-scope face are most easily seen. Because of the spatial selection of the human eye and brain the observer may be considered as a type of *frequency filter;* the connection between the frequency and the space function is made by means of the A-scope sweep. In this regard the observer may unwittingly limit the effective video bandwidth. This is indeed the case for the experiments depicted in Fig. 8·7. For the moment, therefore, it will be assumed that the results are valid only for the value of $s\tau$ shown; i.e., $s\tau$ = 1.7 mm. To show how the curve looks for a widely different value of $s\tau$ the signal threshold power was measured as a function of $B\tau$ when the pulse length on the oscilloscope $s\tau$ was set at 0.05 mm. The result is shown in Fig. 8·8, where all parameters other than $s\tau$ are the same as those for the curve

of PRF = 200 pps in Fig. 8·7. It
can be seen that for a small value for
$s\tau$ the effect is to raise the curve in
absolute magnitude and to flatten it
somewhat. The curve does not appear to approach the 45° line as
rapidly for large values of $B\tau$; this
effect will be shown in Sec. 8·7 to be
analogous to the effect expected by
a restriction in video bandwidth,
which from the above reasoning
arises from the spatial discrimination
of the observer's eye and brain.

These curves demonstrate that
the effects of i-f bandwidth B and
video bandwidth b become inextricably entangled. It is really not
possible to speak of the effect of one
of these parameters without bringing
in the other. For this reason when
we come to the discussion of video
bandwidth and also of sweep speed,
we shall find it convenient to study
the effects of these quantities by
curves of the type shown in Figs.
8·7 and 8·8.

The series of photographs shown
in Fig. 8·9 has been prepared to give
an impression of just what the observer sees when the i-f bandwidth
is varied. In each photograph A-
scope sweeps are shown with two signals appearing, one at position 1 and
the other at position 6. The only
difference between successive photographs is the value of $B\tau$. As can be

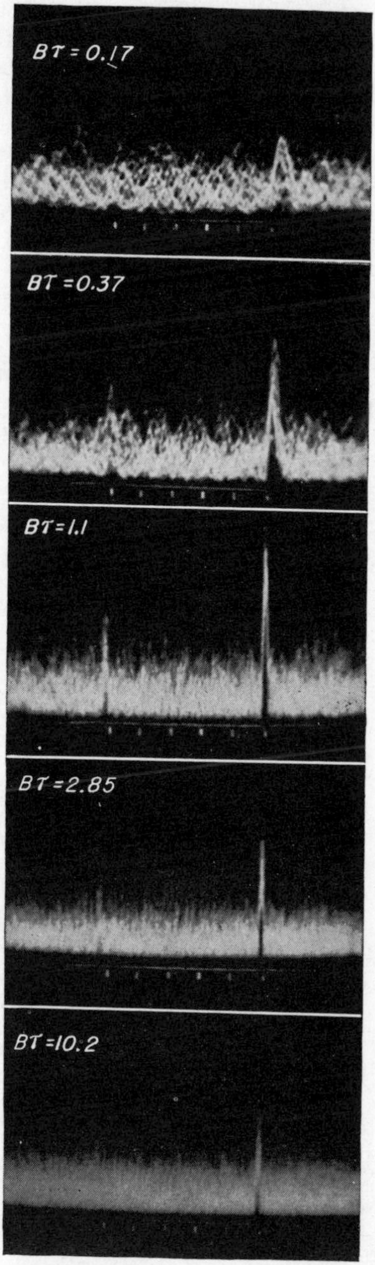

Fig. 8·9.—A-scope photographs illustrating the effect of i-f bandwidth. The signal
at position 1 is 5 db above noise power in a
receiver of bandwidth $1/\tau$. The signal at
position 6 is 11 db above the same level.
System parameters
$\tau = 1\ \mu\text{sec}$ $s\tau = 1\ \text{mm}$
PRF $= 200$ pps $\theta = 0.2$ sec

seen, the optimum value of $B\tau$ is in the neighborhood of unity.   The noise changes greatly in character over the series of photographs.   This is the result expected because of the change in video noise spectrum.   The l-f noise has a much coarser and grainier appearance than h-f noise.

Theoretical Interpretation.—Use will be made of the deflection criterion discussed in Sec. 7·3.   For a *square-law* second detector there must first be calculated the shift of the average value $\overline{r_{S+N}^2} - \overline{r_N^2}$ caused by the presence of a signal and the variance $\overline{r_N^4} - (\overline{r_N^2})^2$ for the noise alone.   From Eq. (7·14b) derived in Sec. 7·2 it follows that the signal threshold is determined by

$$\frac{(\alpha^2 + \beta^2)_{t=t_0}}{2W} = C, \tag{5}$$

where C is a constant.[1]   The numerator, as a function of time, represents the shape of the pulse after it has gone through the i-f amplifier.   It is easy to see that the maximum value (occurring, say, at time $t = t_0$) will

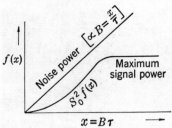

FIG. 8·10.—Signal and noise response *vs.* $B\tau$.

be of the form $S_0^2 f(x)$, where S_0^2 is the signal power *before* the i-f amplifier and $f(x)$ is a function of $x = B\tau$ which, for large x, becomes unity and which, for small x, is proportional to x^2 (see Fig. 8·10).   In fact, large x means that $B \gg 1/\tau$; hence the pulse is not deformed by the i-f channel, and the signal pulse power thus remains equal to S_0^2.   For small x or $B \ll 1/\tau$, the incoming signal *energy* ($\alpha\, S_0^2\tau$) will be reduced by the ratio $B/(1/\tau)$ after passing through the i-f section, and the pulse length will then become of the order of $1/B$.   Therefore, if S_1 denotes the *average* signal *amplitude* after the i-f amplifier, we have

$$S_0^2\tau\, \frac{B}{\dfrac{1}{\tau}} = S_1^2\, \frac{1}{B}$$

or

$$S_1^2 = S_0^2(B\tau)^2 = S_0^2 x^2.$$

The denominator in Eq. (5) represents the total fluctuating noise power; it is proportional to W and, therefore, to B.   According to the detect-

----

[1] *Cf.* Eq. (7·14b); in addition we require that $\overline{r_N^4} = 8W^2$, which follows from the distribution function $\left(\dfrac{r}{W}\right) e^{-\frac{r^2}{2W}}$ for noise alone.   The constant C still depends on the number of observations (see Sec. 7·3) and is therefore *not* of the order of unity but is usually much less than 1.

ability criterion, the maximum signal power *after* the i-f narrowing must be a certain fraction of the fluctuating noise power for the signal to be detected. This condition leads therefore to a formula for the minimum detectable signal energy[1] of the form

$$S_0^2 \tau = \text{const.} \frac{x}{f(x)},\qquad(6)$$

where the constant has the dimension of energy and is proportional to kT. The function $x/f(x)$ is proportional to x for large x and is proportional to $1/x$ for small x; hence it must have a minimum for some intermediate value of x; this minimum value will turn out to be of the order of unity.

For a *linear* second detector and for weak signals, we obtain,[2] instead of Eq. (5),

$$\frac{(\alpha^2 + \beta^2)_{t=t_0}}{2W} = 2\sqrt{\frac{4 - \pi}{\pi}}\, C = 1.045C.\qquad(7)$$

The signal threshold is therefore slightly higher than for a square-law detector, but the difference is only about 0.2 db, which is hardly observable.

The exact form of the function $f(x)$ in Eq. (6) will depend, of course, on the shape of the pulse and on the shape of the i-f pass band. Using the notation of Sec. 7·2, we can easily derive[3] from Eq. (5)

$$\frac{S_0^2 \left| \int_{-\infty}^{+\infty} df\, G(f)Z(f)e^{2\pi i f t_0} \right|^2}{2\sigma^2 \int_{-\infty}^{+\infty} |Z(f)|^2\, df} = C.\qquad(8)$$

---

[1] The threshold signal power Ps, used earlier in this chapter, is the same as S_0^2. Since with the deflection criterion, the signal threshold is not defined in relation to a betting curve, the percentage of the number of successes is not specified; it would affect only the value of the constant in Eq. (6).

[2] Using Eq. (7·14a), we get for the shift of the average value of r caused by the signal

$$\overline{r_{S+N}} - \overline{r_N} = \sqrt{\frac{\pi W}{2}}\left[F\left(-\frac{1}{2}, 1; -z\right) - 1 \right] \approx \sqrt{\frac{\pi W}{2}} \cdot \frac{z}{2},$$

for small values of $z = (\alpha^2 + \beta^2)/2W$. For the variance of r for noise alone we obtain

$$\overline{r_N^2} - (\overline{r_N})^2 = 2W - \frac{\pi W}{2}.$$

Equation (7) then follows from the deflection criterion [Eqs. (7·31)].

[3] Since the shape of the pulse *before* the i-f amplifier is symmetrical around the mid-point, $\beta_0(t) = 0$ can be put in Eq. (7·1). In Eq. (8) there has also been introduced

$$\alpha_0(t) = S_0 F(t).$$

The quantity $S_0^2/2$ is therefore the initial pulse power in watts: $G(f)$ is the Fourier transform of the initial pulse shape $F(t)$.

This result will be written in terms of the *minimum detectable average signal power* $\bar{P}_{\min}$[1] [instead of minimum detectable signal energy as in Eq. (6)]; since

$$\bar{P} = \frac{S_0^2}{\Theta_0} \int_{-\infty}^{+\infty} F^2(t)\, dt,$$

where Θ_0 is again the pulse repetition period, it follows from Eq. (8) that

$$\bar{P}_{\min} = \frac{2\sigma^2 C}{\Theta_0} \frac{\int_{-\infty}^{+\infty} dt\, F^2(t) \int_{-\infty}^{+\infty} df\, |Z(f)|^2}{\left| \int_{-\infty}^{+\infty} df\, G(f) Z(f) e^{2\pi i f t_0} \right|^2}. \tag{9}$$

To make the dependence on the bandwidth B and pulse length τ more evident [in order to get the result in a form analogous to Eq. (6)] we write

$$F(t) = F_1\left(\frac{t}{\tau}\right), \qquad Z(f) = Z_1\left(\frac{f}{B}\right). \tag{10}$$

The functions $F_1(z)$ and $Z_1(u)$, respectively, characterize, therefore, the shape of the pulse and of the i-f pass band. It is easy to show then that Eq. (9) can be written in the form

$$\bar{P}_{\min} = \frac{2\sigma^2 C}{\Theta_0} \eta\gamma \frac{x}{f(x)}, \tag{11}$$

where

$$\eta = \int_{-\infty}^{+\infty} |Z_1(u)|^2\, du, \qquad \gamma = \int_{-\infty}^{+\infty} F_1^2(z)\, dz,$$

$$f(x) = x^2 \left| \int_{-\infty}^{+\infty} G_1(ux) Z_1(u) e^{2\pi i u x \theta}\, du \right|^2,$$

$$G_1(\zeta) = \int_{-\infty}^{+\infty} dz\, F_1(z) e^{-2\pi i z \zeta},$$

$$x = B\tau, \qquad \theta = \frac{t_0}{\tau}.$$

Let us now consider a few examples.[2]

1. Gaussian pulse and Gaussian i-f pass band. Then[3]

$$F_1(z) = e^{-a^2 z^2}, \qquad Z_1(u) = e^{-a_1^2 u^2}.$$

---

[1] Usually the pulse shape is rectangular; hence $\bar{P}_{\min} = S_0^2 \tau / \Theta_0 = P_S \tau / \Theta_0$; see also footnote on p. 205.

[2] All these examples are somewhat academic, since for all of them the system function $Z(f)$ cannot be strictly realized. For all of them the shape of the deformed pulse will be symmetric around the maximum value, which occurs for $t_0 = 0$.

[3] The numerical values of the constants a and a_1 depend on the way one defines the pulse length and the i-f bandwidth. Defining them as the length and width at the half-power points gives $a = a_1 = 1.18$.

All integrals can be easily evaluated, and we get

$$\bar{P}_{min} = \frac{2\sigma^2 C}{\Theta_0} \frac{\pi}{2aa_1} \frac{x^2 + \left(\dfrac{aa_1}{\pi}\right)^2}{x}. \tag{12a}$$

The right-hand side is a minimum for $x = aa_1/\pi = 0.44$ (with $a = a_1 = 1.18$), and the value of $\bar{P}_{min}$ at this point is

$$(\bar{P}_{min})_{min} = \frac{2\sigma^2 C}{\Theta_0}. \tag{12b}$$

2. Gaussian pulse and rectangular i-f pass band.[1] Then

$$F_1(z) = e^{-a^2 z^2}, \qquad Z_1(u) \begin{cases} = 1 & \text{for } |u| < \tfrac{1}{2}, \\ = 0 & \text{for } |u| > \tfrac{1}{2}. \end{cases}$$

We obtain

$$\bar{P}_{min} = \frac{2\sigma^2 C}{\Theta_0} \sqrt{\frac{2}{\pi}} \cdot \frac{\left(\dfrac{\pi x}{2a}\right)}{\text{Erf}^2\left(\dfrac{\pi x}{2a}\right)}, \tag{13a}$$

where $\text{Erf}(z) = 2/\sqrt{\pi} \int_0^z dt\, e^{-t^2}$ is the error function. The right-hand side is a minimum for $x = 1.95a/\pi = 0.72$ (with $a = 1.18$), and the value at the minimum is

$$(\bar{P}_{min})_{min} = 1.12 \frac{2\sigma^2 C}{\Theta_0}. \tag{13b}$$

3. Rectangular pulse and rectangular i-f pass band. We find

$$\bar{P}_{min} = \frac{2\sigma^2 C}{\Theta_0} \frac{\pi}{2} \frac{\left(\dfrac{\pi x}{2}\right)}{Si^2\left(\dfrac{\pi x}{2}\right)}, \tag{14a}$$

where $Si(z) = \int_0^z dt\,(\sin t/t)$. The right-hand side has a minimum for $x = 1.37$, and

$$(\bar{P}_{min})_{min} = 1.10 \frac{2\sigma^2 C}{\Theta_0}. \tag{14b}$$

Graphs of $\Theta_0 P_{min}/2\sigma^2 C$ as a function of $x = B\tau$ and as given by Eqs. (12a), (13a), and (14a) are shown in Fig. 8·11.

In the experiments described in the beginning of this section, the

[1] The *same* result is obtained for the case of a rectangular pulse and a Gaussian i-f pass band.

pulse shape was practically rectangular. A double-tuned transitionally coupled i-f amplifier was used, which has the system function

$$Z(f) = \frac{1}{1 - \left(\dfrac{2f}{B}\right)^2 + i\,\sqrt{2}\left(\dfrac{2f}{B}\right)};$$

hence the shape of the i-f pass band is

$$|Z(f)|^2 = \frac{1}{1 + \left(\dfrac{2f}{B}\right)^4}.$$

Figure 8·12 shows, for different values of the bandwidth B, the shapes of an initially rectangular pulse after it has gone through the i-f amplifier.

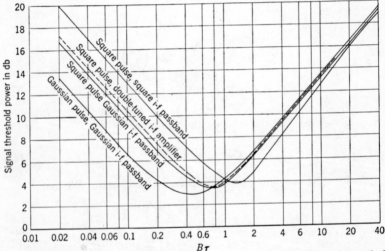

Fig. 8·11.—Signal threshold power $0P_{min}/\sigma^2C$ *vs.* $B\tau$ for different shapes of pulses and of i-f pass band.

From these curves the maximum value of the deformed pulse can be determined for different values of B; and by the application of the deflection criterion [Eq. (5)], the signal threshold as a function of $B\tau$ can be found.[1] The result is shown by the dotted curve in Fig. 8·11, from which it is seen that it differs very slightly from the case of a rectangular pulse and Gaussian i-f pass band. Since the calculations for a Gaussian i-f pass band are much simpler, from now on the double-tuned transi-

---

[1] In the calculations the overshoot shown in two of the curves of Fig. 8·12 was not taken into account; for these bandwidths the pulse was taken to be undeformed.

tionally coupled amplifier will always be approximated by a Gaussian amplifier with the corresponding bandwidth.

Figure 8·13 shows the comparison with experiment. The constant C was so chosen that the theoretical curve was an approximate fit to the experimental points for small x. The agreement is not very good; theoretically, the minimum occurs at about $x = 0.7$ instead of at $x \approx 1.2$, as indicated by the experiments. The curve is, however, fairly flat around the minimum; hence this discrepancy is probably not significant. More serious is the disagreement for large values of x. For large x the

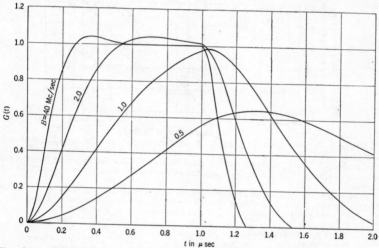

FIG. 8·12.—Shape of square pulse after passing through a double-tuned, transitionally coupled i-f amplifier with different values of the bandwidth.

theoretical curve is much steeper than the experimental data would indicate. This discrepancy is probably caused by the *influence of the sweep speed*. As will be explained in the next section, for a given sweep speed the finite resolving power of the eye is equivalent to a certain video bandwidth. If this "video bandwidth of the eye" is smaller than B and $Bτ \gg 1$, then the detectability of the signal will be improved or the signal threshold will be lowered. From the influence of the sweep speed on the signal threshold the apparent video bandwidth of the eye can be estimated, and the sweep-speed correction can then be calculated. The result is shown in Fig. 8·13; evidently the correction removes to a great extent the disagreement between theory and experiment.

This section is concluded with a remarkable theorem discovered by Wiener, Hansen, North, and Van Vleck independently. The theorem states that the best signal-to-noise ratio (or the lowest signal threshold) is obtained if the shape of the i-f pass band is the Fourier transform of the pulse shape. Van Vleck then says that "the i-f is matched to the pulse shape." When "matched" the value of the signal-to-noise ratio is then independent of the pulse shape.[1] This theorem is illustrated by the results obtained in Examples 1 and 2. At the minimum point for x the Gaussian pulse and Gaussian i-f pass band matched, since the Fourier

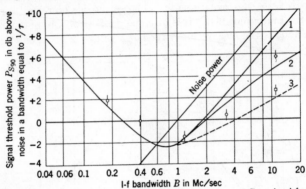

FIG. 8·13.—Signal threshold power *vs.* $B\tau$ for square pulses and Gaussian i-f pass band, comparison with experiment. Curve 1, infinite video bandwidth before correcting for sweep speed ($b = \infty$). Curve 2, infinite video bandwidth after correcting for sweep speed ($b = 2.2$ Mc/sec). Curve 3, corrected for finite video bandwidth and sweep speed ($b = 0.5$ Mc/sec).

The circles are experimental values obtained with $b = 10$ Mc/sec, and the square, for $b = 0.5$ Mc/sec. The vertical lines through the points show the experimental uncertainty.

Pulse repetition frequency	PRF = 200 pps
Pulse length	$\tau = 1$ μsec
Signal presentation time	$\theta = 3$ sec
Sweep speed	$s = 2$ mm/μsec
	$K = 0.0535$

transform of a Gaussian function is Gaussian. At this point, therefore, $\bar{P}_{min}$ must have the smallest possible value. This is confirmed by Eq. (13b); for a rectangular i-f pass band (which is "mismatched") we obtain at the minimum a value that is 12 per cent larger than for the Gaussian case. However, from these examples it can also be seen that the differences are rather small; hence it will usually not be of practical importance to try to match the i-f pass band to the pulse shape.

---

[1] If it is remembered (Parzeval theorem) that

$$\int_{-\infty}^{+\infty} F^2(t)\, dt = \int_{-\infty}^{+\infty} G^2(f)\, df,$$

and if $e^{2\pi i f/t}$ is absorbed in $Z(f)$, since this affects only the phase spectrum, then the proof of the theorem follows from Eq. (9) by the application of the so-called "Schwartz inequality." The integrals are equal if $Z(f)$ is the Fourier transform of $F(t)$, and this is true for any $F(t)$. The *absolute* minimum of $\bar{P}_{min}$ is therefore $2\sigma^2 C/\Theta_0$.

8·7. Effects of Video Bandwidth; Sweep Speed, Focus.—As was mentioned in the last section there is a connection between the A-scope sweep speed s and the video bandwidth b. This connection is explained by the failure of the observer to see easily, on the A-scope, events that are spatially too close. This statement is equivalent to saying that he fails to see easily the *high* video frequencies, and therefore he constitutes a

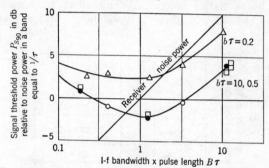

Fig. 8·14.—Signal threshold power *vs.* i-f bandwidth times pulse length for a fast sweep speed.

System parameters

Pulse repetition frequency.............................. PRF = 200 pps
Signal presentation time.............................. θ = 3 sec
Pulse length on screen............................... sτ = 1.6 mm

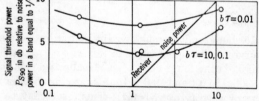

Fig. 8·15.—Signal threshold power *vs.* i-f bandwidth times pulse length for a slow sweep speed.

System parameters

Pulse repetition frequency.............................. PRF = 200 pps
Signal presentation time.............................. θ = 3 sec
Pulse length on screen............................... sτ = 0.05 mm

kind of low-pass video filter. By the same sort of argument there is a connection between focus and effective video bandwidth.

Experimental Results.—The video bandwidth b has less effect upon signal threshold power than does the i-f bandwidth. The effect can be most clearly appreciated by referring to Figs. 8·14 and 8·15. In Fig. 8·14 is shown a family of three curves, each curve representing an experimental $B\tau$ curve for different values of $b\tau$. The top curve shows the result when $b\tau$ is set equal to 0.1; the lower curve, which is actually two coincident curves, is the result when $b\tau$ is set equal to 0.5 and 10.0. For all these results the pulse length on the scope $s\tau$ is 1.6 mm, the PRF is 200 pps, and the signal presentation time θ is 3 sec. These are essentially the same conditions applying to one of the curves in Fig. 8·7. It can be seen that for values of $b\tau$ greater than 0.5, no effect can be ascribed to this parameter. The curve for $b\tau = 0.2$ is displaced to a higher absolute value and has a flatter minimum. This effect is characteristic for restriction of the video bandwidth; it will be calculated quantitatively later on.

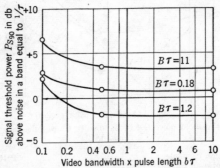

FIG. 8·16.—Signal threshold power *vs.* video bandwidth times pulse length for a fast sweep speed.

System parameters

$s\tau = 1.7$ mm	PRF = 200 pps
$\theta = 3.5$ sec	Oscilloscope screen = P7

Figure 8·15 shows similar results except that $s\tau$ has been fixed at 0.05 mm for all curves. The upper curve in this case corresponds to a value of $b\tau$ equal to 0.01; the lower curve, again really two coincident curves, applies for $b\tau$ equal to 0.1 and 10.0. In this case the effect of video bandwidth disappears when $b\tau$ exceeds 0.1. This result may be anticipated and explained qualitatively. When $s\tau$ is small, the observer, because of lack of spatial discrimination on the A-scope face, acts like a video filter whose bandwidth is small. Thus, no effect will be observed by varying the video bandwidth in the receiver as long as the latter bandwidth exceeds the "observer" bandwidth. On the other hand, if $s\tau$ is increased to larger values, the "observer" bandwidth will increase a like amount; therefore, the effect of receiver bandwidth will be noticeable for larger values of $b\tau$.

These results can be presented in a different form. Figure 8·16 shows the results of Fig. 8·14 plotted in a form in which the abscissa represents $b\tau$; each curve is taken for a fixed value of $B\tau$. Similarly, Fig. 8·17 shows the same treatment of the results of Fig. 8·15.

The appropriate parameter connected with the sweep speed s is, of course, the pulse length on the A-scope, $s\tau$. The effect of this parameter has been implied in previous discussion. From the sets of curves shown in Figs. 8·7 to 8·13, we can observe the effect of a reduction in $s\tau$ from 1.6 to 0.05 mm. This, however, does not give information concerning other values of $s\tau$. Accordingly, a threshold-signal experiment was performed in which $s\tau$ was varied from less than 0.01 to 10 mm, with the

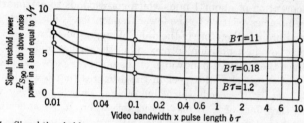

Fig. 8·17.—Signal threshold power *vs.* video bandwidth times pulse length for a slow sweep speed.

System parameters

$s\tau = 0.05$ mm   PRF = 200 pps
$\theta = 3.5$ sec   Oscilloscope screen = P7

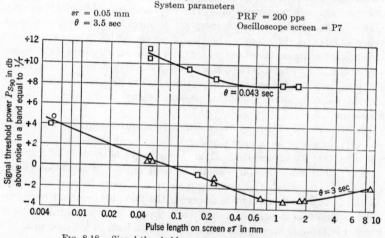

Fig. 8·18.—Signal threshold power *vs.* pulse length on screen.
A-scope system parameters
$B\tau = 1.2$
PRF = 200 pps
$b\tau = 10$

results shown in Fig. 8·18. Two curves are given, the upper one corresponding to the extremely short signal presentation time of 0.043 sec, the lower curve showing the results where the signal presentation time was equal to 3 sec. All other parameters were fixed in the two cases; their values are stated in the legend.

It can be seen that the curves exhibit flat minima in the neighborhood of $s\tau = 1$ mm. For both larger and smaller values of $s\tau$ an increase in threshold signal power is observed. For small values of $s\tau$ the threshold signal power is proportional to $(s\tau)^{-\frac{1}{2}}$. The curve shows very clearly that the observer's eye and brain mechanism responds best to the signal when the latter is made approximately 1 mm in length. At a viewing distance of 30 cm this corresponds to a subtended angle of about 0.2°. For small values of $s\tau$ the eye and brain still preferentially select events having a spatial separation of about 1 mm, which corresponds to attenuating the higher frequencies relative to the lower frequencies. The effective $b\tau$ of the eye and brain is therefore of the order of magnitude of $s\tau$.

We are now in a position to reexamine the curves of Figs. 8·16 and 8·17. Since the effective bandwidth of the observer's eye and brain is of the order of $s\tau$, we should expect in these figures that b will have little effect as long as it exceeds the value of $s\tau$. This is precisely what is observed; the effect of $b\tau$ is only noticeable where it is smaller than $s\tau$.

Both of the curves shown in Fig. 8·18 are of similar shape. This result might be expected at first sight, but closer reasoning shows that it is actually somewhat surprising. The top curve was obtained with only about eight signal pulses and therefore requires a signal power several times as large as the noise. The theory presented below concerning the dependence of signal threshold power on $s\tau$ holds strictly only if the signal power is small with respect to noise power. Nevertheless the top curve exhibits the same behavior as the bottom curve; the only difference that can be noticed, apart from the absolute value, is the slightly flatter minimum.

Now that the effects of video bandwidth and sweep speed or, more properly, $b\tau$ and $s\tau$ have been discussed, the effect of focus on the A-scope visibility may be anticipated. Poor focus is not necessarily of a simple variety; there may be, and usually is, astigmatism in the focus of the electron beam, which will produce a sharp line focus instead of a spot. As the focusing adjustment is changed, the line shortens and broadens until it becomes nearly a round disk; this procedure continues until another sharp-line segment is formed at right angles to the first one. It is thus possible to defocus in one direction without, at the same time, defocusing in an orthogonal direction. The degree of astigmatism can be made adjustable so that an experiment can be performed in which the effects of defocusing in a direction parallel to the A-scope sweep and in a direction perpendicular to the sweep can be separately studied.

We should expect these effects to be different. Since defocusing in a direction perpendicular to the sweep is equivalent to smearing out signal and noise deflections, we should expect no pronounced effect until the spot size becomes comparable to the average noise deflection. Defocusing in a direction parallel to the sweep, however, is equivalent to overlapping events that occur within the spot diameter. This is analogous to the effect of spatial discrimination by the observer, and we should expect the results to be similar in the two cases. Furthermore, because the observer does not appear to be sensitive to events that occur within a spatial distance of much less than 1 mm, we should expect the effect of defocusing to be very small as long as the spot size in a direction parallel to the sweep is smaller than 1 mm. For spot sizes larger than about 1 mm, the effect should be similar to that of a reduced value of s_T or b_T; i.e., the signal threshold power should be approximately proportional to the square root of the spot size. This conclusion assumes that the restriction of effective video bandwidth is caused primarily by the spot size and not by the receiver video bandwidth b itself.

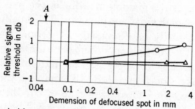

Fig. 8·19.—Signal threshold power *vs.* focusing condition. The width of the pulse on the screen $s_T = 0.05$ mm is indicated by the arrow at point A.

System parameters		Key
$B_T = 1.2$	PRF $= 200$ pps	◯ Defocusing parallel to sweep
$s_T = 0.05$ mm	$\theta = 3$ sec	△ Defocusing perpendicular to sweep

These conclusions are substantiated by experiment. In Fig. 8·19 two curves are shown, the upper one corresponding to defocusing in a direction parallel to the sweep and the lower one corresponding to a defocusing in a direction perpendicular to the sweep. The abscissa represents the extent of defocusing, i.e., the length of the small-line segment which is formed on the screen by the electron beam. The ordinate represents the signal threshold power expressed in decibels relative to the value of signal threshold power under focused conditions. Under the best condition of focus obtainable, the spot diameter was measured to be about 0.1 mm. The maximum defocusing available gave a spot length of approximately 3 mm. For this experiment the value of s_T was made very small, i.e., 0.05 mm, so that the receiver video bandwidth b would not limit the effect sought.

It is obvious from Fig. 8·19 that defocusing in a direction perpendicular to the sweep has practically no effect on threshold signals. The maximum defocusing available produces a spot length comparable to the average noise deflection; by the argument that has just been given no pronounced effect is expected. Defocusing in a direction parallel to the sweep, however, causes a rise in signal threshold power; this rise sets in where the spot length is of the order of magnitude of 1 mm and continues to rise with increasing defocusing. This situation is analogous to the effect of $s\tau$ shown in Fig. 8·18. In that case the dependence of signal threshold power on the reciprocal of the square root of $s\tau$ was reached only for values of $s\tau$ that were very much smaller than 1 mm.

Theoretical Interpretation.—If the video bandwidth is small compared with the i-f bandwidth, then instead of Eq. (6) there will be obtained for the minimum detectable signal energy an equation of the form

$$S_0^2\tau = \text{const.} \frac{N(x,y)}{H(x,y)}, \tag{15}$$

where $x = B\tau$ and $y = b\tau$. The function $N(x,y)$ is the fluctuating noise power, and $S_0^2 H(x,y)$ is the maximum value of the pulse after it has been deformed by the i-f and video amplifiers. The qualitative behavior of these functions can easily be discussed. The function N is the square root of the area of the continuous noise spectrum[1] of r^2. In Sec. 3·8 we saw that for a square-law detector, the ordinate of the continuous spectrum at the origin is proportional to B. Therefore if the video bandwidth is much smaller than the i-f bandwidth ($b \ll B$), then the area will be proportional to bB whereas, if $b \gg B$, the area will be proportional to B^2. Therefore the function $N(x,y)$ will have the asymptotic behavior

$$N(x,y) \propto \begin{cases} \sqrt{xy} & \text{for } y \ll x, \\ x & \text{for } y \gg x. \end{cases} \tag{16}$$

The function $H(x,y)$ has the same asymptotic behavior as the function $f(x)$ in Eq. (6) for any fixed value of y and reduces, of course, exactly to the function $f(x)$ if $y \gg x$. Therefore, for fixed y, $H \propto x^2$ for $x \ll 1$ and $H = $ constant (independent of x) for $x \gg 1$. On the other hand, it is easily seen that for fixed x, $H \propto y$ for $y \ll 1$. Consequently, for fixed y, $P_{\min}$ (or $S_0^2\tau$) will be proportional to $1/x$ for $x \ll 1$ and proportional to $\sqrt{x}$ for $x \gg 1$; hence a minimum value will always exist. The region where $\bar{P}_{\min} \propto \sqrt{x}$ occurs when $x \gg y$. Of course, when y itself is large, $\bar{P}_{\min}$ will be proportional to x in the region $1 \ll x \ll y$, since in this case the video bandwidth will have practically no influence and the results of the previous section will hold.

The dependence of $\bar{P}_{\min}$ on y for fixed x is more complicated. If $x \ll 1$, from the asymptotic behavior of N and H we find that $\bar{P}_{\min} \propto 1/\sqrt{y}$ for $y \ll x$ and $\bar{P}_{\min} = $ constant (independent of y) for $y \gg x$. The quantity $\bar{P}_{\min}$ will therefore be a monotonically decreasing function of y;

---

[1] By definition, $N^2 = \overline{r_N^4} - (\overline{r_N^2})^2$. According to the deflection criterion [Eq. (7·1a)] with $f = r^2$ (square-law detector). For noise alone the spectrum consists of the d-c term and the continuous part. From the general formula of Sec. 3·3 it follows that the area of the continuous spectrum is just the variance of r^2.

or in other words, if $x = B\tau \ll 1$, then the narrowing of the video will always *increase* the signal threshold. This is *no longer* the case if $x \gg 1$. Since $\bar{P}_{\min} \alpha 1/\sqrt{y}$ for $y \ll 1$ and $\bar{P}_{\min} \alpha \sqrt{y}$ for $1 \ll y \ll x$, there will be a minimum for an intermediate value of y. Therefore, if $B\tau \gg 1$, then the narrowing of the video will at first give an improvement, continuing until $\bar{P}_{\min}$ reaches a minimum value. Further narrowing of the video will then again *increase* the signal threshold. If x decreases, then the minimum of $\bar{P}_{\min}$ as a function of y becomes less pronounced, and it disappears for $x \approx 1$.

For a square-law detector it is not difficult to find an exact expression for the minimum detectable average signal power $\bar{P}_{\min}$. We find that

$$\bar{P}_{\min}$$

$$= \frac{2\sigma^2 C}{\Theta_0} \frac{\left[\int_{-\infty}^{+\infty} dt\, F^2(t) \right] \left[\int_{-\infty}^{+\infty} df\, |Z_{vid}(f)|^2 \int_{-\infty}^{+\infty} df_1\, |Z(f_1)|^2 |Z(f-f_1)|^2 \right]^{1/2}}{\int_{-\infty}^{+\infty} df\, Z_{vid}(f) e^{2\pi i f t_0} \int_{-\infty}^{+\infty} df_1\, G(f_1) G^*(f_1 - f) Z(f_1) Z^*(f_1 - f)}.$$

(17)

The notation is the same as in Sec. 8·6; $Z_{vid}(f)$ is the system function of the video amplifier; t_0 is the time at which the deformed pulse is a maximum: $Z_{vid}(f) = Z_{vid}^*(-f)$, from which it can easily be shown that the denominator of Eq. (17) is real. To put Eq. (17) in the same form as Eq. (15) we must introduce, as in Sec. 8·6, the shape functions[1]

$$F(t) = F_1\left(\frac{t}{\tau}\right); \qquad Z(f) = Z_1\left(\frac{f}{B}\right); \qquad Z_{vid}(f) = Z_{1,\,vid}\left(\frac{f}{b}\right).$$

Then we can write

$$\bar{P}_{\min} = \frac{2\sigma^2 C}{\Theta_0} \gamma \frac{N(x,y)}{H(x,y)},$$

$$N^2(x,y) = xy \int_{-\infty}^{+\infty} dv\, |Z_{-,\,vid}(v)|^2 \int_{-\infty}^{+\infty} du\, |Z_1(u)|^2 \left| Z_1\left(u - \frac{y}{x} v\right) \right|^2,$$

$$H(x,y) = xy \int_{-\infty}^{+\infty} dv\, Z_{1,\,vid}(v) e^{2\pi i y (t_0/\tau)} \int_{-\infty}^{+\infty} du\, G_1(ux) G_1^*(ux - vy)$$

$$Z_1(u) Z_1^*\left(u - \frac{y}{x} v\right),$$

$$\gamma = \int_{-\infty}^{+\infty} dz\, F_1^2(z); \qquad G_1(z) = \int_{-\infty}^{+\infty} du\, F_1(u) e^{-2\pi i u z}.$$

(18)

As the first example let us consider the case where the pulse shape and

[1] The video bandwidth b will always be defined as the width between zero frequency and the upper half-power point.

the shapes of the i-f and video pass band are all Gaussian. Then

$$F_1(z) = e^{-a^2 z^2}, \qquad Z_1(u) = e^{-a^2 u^2}, \qquad Z_{1,\,\text{vid}}(v) = e^{-\frac{a^2 v^2}{4}}, \qquad (19a)$$

with $a = 1.18$. All the integrations can be carried out, and we obtain

$$\left. \begin{aligned}
N(x,y) &= \sqrt{\frac{\pi}{2}} \frac{x}{a} \left(1 + \frac{x^2}{2y^2} \right)^{-\frac{1}{4}}, \\
H(x,y) &= \left(\frac{\pi x}{a^2} \right)^2 \left\{ \left[1 + \left(\frac{\pi x}{a^2} \right)^2 \right] \left[1 + \left(\frac{\pi x}{a^2} \right)^2 + \frac{x^2}{2y^2} \right] \right\}^{-\frac{1}{2}}, \\
\gamma &= \sqrt{\frac{\pi}{2}} \frac{1}{a}.
\end{aligned} \right\} \qquad (19b)$$

We can easily verify the qualitative behavior of $\bar{P}_{\min}$ as a function of x and y, discussed in the beginning of this section. For fixed y, $\bar{P}_{\min}$, as a function of x, always has a minimum. For $y \to \infty$ we again obtain the result of the previous section [Eq. (12a)]. Of special interest is the dependence of $\bar{P}_{\min}$ on y for fixed x. Putting $\partial \bar{P}_{\min} / \partial y = 0$, we see that at the minimum,

$$\frac{2\pi y_m}{a^2} = \left(\frac{2\pi^2 x^2}{\pi^2 x^2 - a^4} \right)^{\frac{1}{2}}. \qquad (20)$$

This shows that for $\pi x/a^2 > 1$, $\bar{P}_{\min}$, as a function of y, *has* a minimum, which, as a function of x, is given by Eq. (20). For $\pi x/a^2 < 1$, Eq. (20) requires an imaginary value for y_m, which means that the minimum has disappeared. If $\pi x/a^2 = 1$, one is just at the minimum point of the function $f(x)$ [see Eq. (12a)], and the i-f pass band is just the Fourier transform of the pulse. This is in accordance with the general theorem of Van Vleck and Middleton,[1] which states that if the i-f pass band is matched to the pulse shape, then any kind of video filter will *increase* the signal threshold.

The proof of this theorem follows from Eq. (17). At the "match point" $G(f) = Z^*(f)$. Putting

$$\left. \begin{aligned}
V^2(f) &= \int_{-\infty}^{+\infty} df_1 \, |Z(f_1)|^2 |Z(f - f_1)|^2, \\
X(f) &= Z_{\text{vid}}(f) e^{2\pi i f t_0} V(f),
\end{aligned} \right\} \qquad (21)$$

we see that

$$\bar{P}_{\min} \propto \frac{\left[\int_{-\infty}^{+\infty} df \, |X|^2 \right]^{\frac{1}{2}}}{\int_{-\infty}^{+\infty} df \, X(f) V(f)}. \qquad (22)$$

To find what video system function $Z_{\text{vid}}(f)$ will give the lowest signal

[1] J. H. Van Vleck and D. Middleton, *J. Applied Phys.*, **11**, 940 (1946).

threshold, we may multiply Eq. (22) by

$$\left[\int_{-\infty}^{+\infty} df\, V^2(f) \right]^{1/2},$$

and, from the Schwartz inequality, we then find that the best choice for $X(f)$ is $X(f) = V(f)$, which means, according to Eq. (21), that except for a nonessential phase factor the optimum solution is $Z_{\text{vid}} = 1$, or *no video filter at all*.

For the comparison of theory with experiment there will be discussed as a second example the case of a square pulse and Gaussian i-f and video pass bands. Then

$$F_1(z) \begin{cases} =1, |z| < \tfrac{1}{2}; \\ =0, |z| > \tfrac{1}{2}; \end{cases} \qquad Z_1(u) = e^{-a^2u^2}; \qquad Z_{1,\text{vid}}(v) = e^{-\frac{1}{4}a^2v^2}; \quad (23a)$$

and again $a = 1.18$. We obtain

$$\bar{P}_{\min} = \frac{2\sigma^2 C}{\Theta_0} \frac{(x^2 + 4y^2)^{1/2}}{(2x^2y^2 + 4y^4)^{1/4}} \frac{1}{F(x,y)}, \quad (23b)$$

where

$$F(x,y) = \int_0^1 dz\, e^{-\frac{z^2}{4\alpha}} \left\{ \text{Erf}\left[\frac{\alpha + \beta z}{2\sqrt{\alpha(\alpha^2 - \beta^2)}} \right] + \text{Erf}\left[\frac{\alpha - \beta z}{2\sqrt{\alpha(\alpha^2 - \beta^2)}} \right] \right\},$$

$$\alpha = \frac{a^2}{\pi^2}\left(\frac{1}{x^2} + \frac{1}{4y^2} \right), \qquad \beta = \frac{a^2}{4\pi^2 y^2}, \quad (23c)$$

TABLE 8·4.—VALUES OF $(\Theta/\sigma^2 C)P_{\min}$ FOR DIFFERENT VALUES OF x AND y [CF. EQS (23b) AND (23c)]

The numbers in parentheses are $10 \times$ the logarithms to the base 10 of the numbers immediately above, i.e., a "decibel" value.

x \ y	0.1	0.5	1.0	5.0	10	∞
0.2	6.38	5.01	4.95	4.95	4.95	4.95
	(8.04)	(7.00)	(6.94)	(6.94)	(6.94)	(6.94)
1	3.88	2.34	2.33	2.39	2.39	2.39
	(5.89)	(3.69)	(3.68)	(3.79)	(3.79)	(3.79)
2	4.52	2.84	3.27	4.15	4.22	4.23
	(6.55)	(4.53)	(5.14)	(6.18)	(6.26)	(6.27)
5	6.45	4.32	5.53	9.60	10.3	10.5
	(8.10)	(6.36)	(7.43)	(9.82)	(10.13)	(10.2)
11	9.34	6.40	8.39	17.2	20.9	23.3
	(9.70)	(8.06)	(9.24)	(12.36)	(13.20)	(13.67)
15	10.7	7.39	9.55	22.8	26.3	31.8
	(10.3)	(8.69)	(9.80)	(13.58)	(14.2)	(15.02)

and Erf(z) is the error function.   In Table 8·4 is tabulated $(\Theta/\sigma^2 C)P_{\min}$ for different values of x and y, and in Fig. 8·20 the same quantity is shown as a function of y for different values of x.   We see that the qualitative behavior is again as expected.

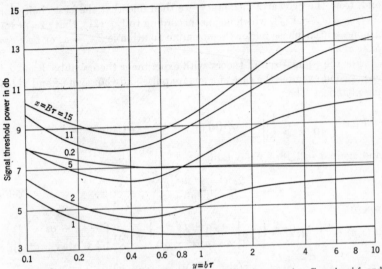

Fig. 8·20.—Signal threshold power $\Theta P_{\min}/\sigma^2 C$ vs. $b\tau$ for square pulse, Gaussian i-f, and Gaussian video pass band; the different curves are for different values of $B\tau$.

These results have been compared with experiment in different ways. In the first place they have been used to explain the dependence of the signal threshold on the sweep speed s.   As mentioned before, the assumption that the human eye averages over a certain length l on the A-scope is equivalent to ascribing to the eye the characteristics of a low-pass video filter of width $b \approx (s/l)$.   The experimental result that for small values of s the signal threshold increases approximately as $s^{-\frac{1}{2}}$ is then an immediate consequence[1] of the very general Eq. (15).   Assuming that this "video filter of the eye" has a Gaussian shape,[2] we can use Eq. (23a) for a quantitative comparison with experiment, since the i-f pass band is also nearly Gaussian in shape.   First we must determine the constant C. This value has been determined from the experimental results giving the signal threshold as a function of $x = B\tau$ for *small* values of x (see Fig. 8·8).   Since in these experiments b was much larger than B, and also

---

[1] For $y \ll x$, $N \propto \sqrt{xy}$, $H \propto y$; thus $\bar{P}_{\min} \propto y^{-\frac{1}{2}} \propto s^{-\frac{1}{2}}$.

[2] This means that the "attention function" of the eye is also Gaussian, and we may define its width l as the s/l.   Usually s is expressed in millimeters per microsecond, so that if we express b in megacycles per second, l comes out in millimeters.

since the video bandwidth of the eye can be expected to be larger than B, we can put $y = \infty$ in Eq. (23a) and, of course, obtain Eq. (13a). The experimental data are always expressed as the minimum detectable signal pulse power in decibels above the noise power for an i-f bandwidth, $B_0 = 1.0$ Mc/sec. Since for a Gaussian i-f pass band the noise power is

$$\frac{1}{a} \sqrt{\frac{\pi}{2}}\, \sigma^2 B,$$

and since the pulse power is $\frac{1}{2}S_0^2$, it is clear that the experimental quantity plotted is

$$10 \log_{10}\left(\frac{\bar{P}\Theta_0}{2\tau} \frac{a}{B_0} \sqrt{\frac{2}{\pi}} \frac{1}{\sigma^2}\right). \tag{24}$$

From Eq. (13a) and Fig. 8·8, we find that for a 1-μsec pulse, an observation time of 3 sec, and a PRF of 200 pps and for $B < 1$ Mc/sec, the best

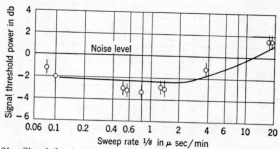

FIG. 8·21.—Signal threshold power *vs.* sweep rate; comparison with experiment.

fit is obtained if $C = 0.535$. Using this value we can try to fit the experimental results of the signal threshold as a function of the sweep speed s by choosing a suitable value of l and putting $y = s\tau/l$ in Eq. (9a). The result is shown in Fig. 8·21; l is found in this way to be 0.9 mm.

Referring to Fig. 8·13, we can now correct the experimental results for *large* values of x. Since the sweep speed used was 2 mm/μsec, the video bandwidth of the eye was 2.2 Mc/sec, and y is therefore comparable with, or smaller than, x and should have an appreciable effect on the signal threshold. For the theoretical curve, Eq. (23a) was again used (with $C = 0.535$, $y = 2.2$), and we see that there is satisfactory agreement between theory and experiment. In the same figure an experimental point determined for an actual[1] video bandwidth of 0.5 Mc/sec is recorded. To compare this result with theory we must take into account the com-

[1] In the actual experiment the PRF was 3200 pps. According to the square-root law (see Sec. 8·8), 6.02 db $[= 10 \log_{10} (\frac{3200}{200})^{\frac{1}{2}}]$ was added to the experimental result, and this value is shown in Fig. 8·13.

bined effect of the real video bandwidth b_v and the video bandwidth of the eye b_s. It can easily be shown that, if all shapes are Gaussian, the combined video bandwidth b is given by

$$\frac{1}{b^2} = \frac{1}{b_v^2} + \frac{1}{b_s^2}. \tag{25}$$

We must therefore put $y = 0.487$ in Eq. (23a), and there is then again agreement with experiment.

Finally, in Fig. 8·22 a comparison with theory of the experimental results of the signal threshold as a function of the video bandwidth for different values of the i-f bandwidth B is made. The correction for the video bandwidth of the eye has been made according to Eq. (25), with

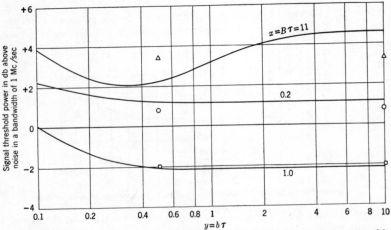

FIG. 8·22.—Signal threshold power *vs.* $b\tau$ with sweep-rate correction; comparison with experiment.

$l = 0.9$ mm. The constant C was chosen somewhat larger (0.556). The agreement with experiment is not very good and, especially for $B = 11$ Mc/sec, $b_v = 0.1$ Mc/sec, there is the rather large discrepancy of about 3 db. However more observations are clearly needed before we can be entirely sure that the discrepancy is real.

8·8. The Dependence upon Repetition Frequency. *Experimental Dependence on PRF.*—Experimental results have already been presented in the previous section that demonstrate the effect of the PRF on the threshold signal. These results are shown in Fig. 8·7; however, it is convenient to plot the data in a somewhat different form. In Fig. 8·23 is shown the threshold signal power as a function of PRF; the power is measured in decibels relative to noise power contained within an i-f band equal in width to $1/\tau$. The three curves represent different conditions of i-f bandwidth; other fixed parameters are stated in the legend. It can be seen that the threshold power is very nearly inversely proportional to the square root of the PRF. However, it will be noticed that a slight flattening of the lowest curve begins to take place at very large values of PRF. This is the first intimation we have had of the limitation of threshold signal by a phenomenon different from noise fluctuation, namely, *contrast*. When signals are much smaller than noise, the contrast between the

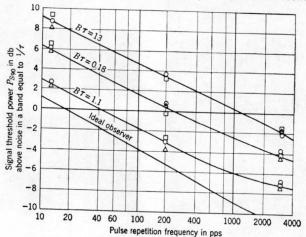

FIG. 8·23.—Signal threshold power *vs.* PRF.

System parameters

Pulse length on screen... $s\tau = 1.7$ mm
Video bandwidth.. $b = 10$ Mc/sec
Signal presentation time.. $\theta = 3$ sec
Screen material.. P1

average signal plus noise deflection and the average noise deflection begins to approach the value of contrast in light intensity that can just be discerned by the human eye. This figure has often been quoted as 4 per cent, but recent measurements show the 4 per cent figure applies for nearly ideal conditions only. At any rate, when the average noise fluctuation is reduced below this critical value, the signal must be recognized by contrast changes rather than by deflections exceeding noise fluctuations; hence the threshold signal is expected to be independent of PRF. This statement is not strictly true, however, for it assumes that the observer makes use of light intensity which is proportional to the average video deflection. This is clearly not the case; the entire video amplitude distribution is visible to the observer, and he makes use of that part of it best suited to his needs. For a given small average signal deflection the contrast produced on the A-scope is a function of the part of the noise distribution under scrutiny. A contrast as large as desired

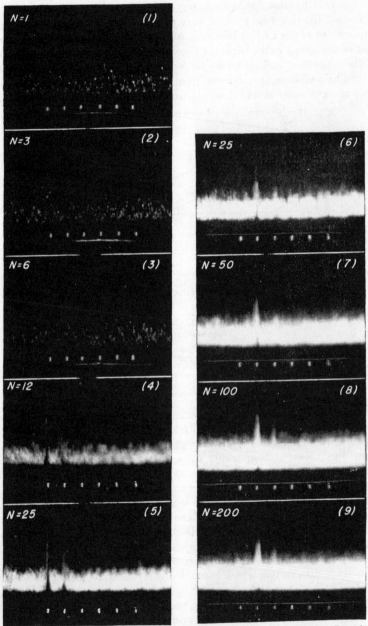

FIG. 8·24.—A-scope photographs illustrating the effect of the
Position 1: Signal = noise + 10 db
Position 2: Signal = noise + 5 db
Position 3: Signal = noise

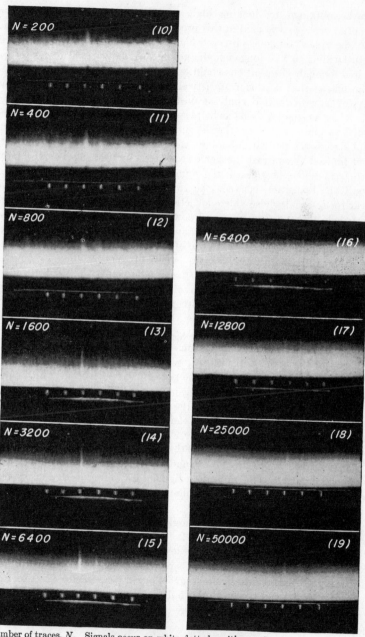

number of traces, N. Signals occur on white dotted positions only.

Position 4: Signal = noise − 5 db
Position 5: Signal = noise − 10 db
Position 6: Signal = noise − 15 db

can be obtained by looking high enough in the distribution. The essential price that is paid in this procedure is the small fraction of time that the video voltage is observed high in the distribution. However, if we are willing to wait long enough and have as many signal sweeps as are desired, enough observations could be made in the high part of the distribution so that a proper statistical reading could be made. In this way, even with limited contrast discernibility, the observer should be able to see as small a signal as he pleases if enough signal sweeps are presented to him. However, the dependence of signal threshold power on total signal sweeps will not follow the same law; it can be shown that when limited by contrast the signal threshold power changes only slightly with tremendous changes in the number of signal sweeps. We should expect the transition between the two regions of different behavior to occur for a signal whose video deflection is a few per cent of the average noise deflection, i.e., one whose i-f power is a few per cent of the i-f noise power. This expectation is substantiated by experiment; when the relative signal-to-noise power in the i-f amplifier approaches -10 or -15 db, the contrast limitation becomes easily apparent.

In order to demonstrate this effect and to give the reader a clear picture of the various processes involved, a series of photographs were taken of the A-scope. These photographs (Fig. 8·24) differ from each other only in the number of sweeps that are recorded. In each photograph six signal positions are indicated along the base line by small white dots, but for this series of photographs the signal does not occur randomly on one of the six signal positions. Signals on the first position always have a power 10 db relative to noise power in an i-f band of width equal to $1/\tau$. Similarly signals appearing on positions 2 to 6 have powers of $+5, 0, -5, -10,$ and -15 db relative to the same noise power. In each photograph two signals occur on adjacent positions, so chosen that generally one signal is easily visible while the other one is not. As the weaker signal becomes more visible, through a change in the total number of sweeps, the stronger signal is reduced in intensity to the appropriate value and moved to the appropriate signal position. The various system parameters that apply to these photographs are stated in the figure legend.

The first photograph shows a single A-scope trace, i.e., $N_s = 1$ with signals occurring in positions 1 and 2. The stronger first signal is visible with some difficulty, while the second signal is probably below the threshold value. As the number of sweeps is increased in the succeeding photographs, smaller and smaller signals become discernible; a reduction of threshold signal power of about 5 db is possible for every increase in N_s by a factor of 10. This procedure continues until the signal reaches a power of -10 db relative to noise.

The signal is visible in the first photograph ($N_s = 1$) because of its large deflection compared with chance noise fluctuations. In succeeding photographs the average deflection of all of the sweeps is used to indicate the signal. It is easy to see the smoothing effect of a large number of observations; indeed the pictures for $N_s > 10^4$ show almost no "grain," or roughness, caused by noise. It is also easy to see by the density of traces the probability distributions of video amplitudes due to noise.

The reader has no doubt wondered why the abscissa in Fig. 8·23 represented the PRF itself rather than the total number of signal sweeps

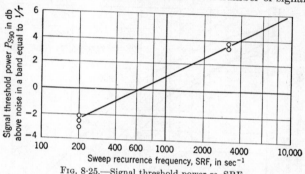

Fig. 8·25.—Signal threshold power *vs.* SRF.

System parameters

Pulse length × i-f bandwidth...............................	$B\tau = 1.2$
Pulse length on screen....................................	$= 1.7$ mm
Signal presentation time..................................	$\theta = 4$ sec
Recurrence rate for sweeps containing signal.............	$= 200$ pps

N_s given by the product PRF and signal presentation time θ. Since we should expect the signal threshold power to be dependent only on N_s (which in this experiment is equal to N_N the total number of sweeps), it would seem better to use N_s directly as the abscissa. Unfortunately, it is not so simple as this; for in the experiment whose results are shown in Fig. 8·23, we cannot yet be assured that the human observer can properly remember and integrate the sweeps over the complete signal presentation time θ of 3 sec. This problem has been studied, and the results are presented in the next section.

Experimental Dependence on SRF.—In the experimental results just presented it has been assumed that each A-scope trace contains noise and the desired signal pulse. It is useful to remove this restriction and to examine the separate effects of the A-scope sweeps containing noise and the sweeps containing the signal. In what is to follow we shall assume all sweeps to contain noise; the number of such sweeps will be denoted by N_N; and the sweep repetition frequency by SRF. Likewise the number of sweeps containing the pulsed signal will be denoted by N_s and the pulse repetition frequency by PRF, as before.

In Fig. 8·25 is shown the experimental signal threshold power as a function of SRF keeping the PRF constant at 200 per second. It can be seen that the signal threshold power is *directly* proportional to the *square root* of SRF and, of course, also to the square root of N_N. In a similar type of experiment in which the SRF is held constant (at 3200 per second), the signal threshold power is found to be *inversely* proportional to the *first power* of the PRF. This result is shown graphically in Fig. 8·26; the inverse linear relationship holds for several conditions as long

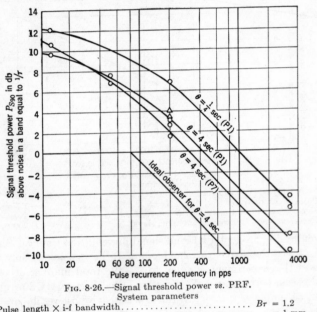

FIG. 8·26.—Signal threshold power *vs.* PRF.
System parameters

Pulse length × i-f bandwidth............................	$B\tau = 1.2$
Pulse length on screen...................................	= 1 mm
SRF..	= 3200 pps

as the signal threshold power is not much larger than noise power. Three experimental curves are shown differing essentially in the presentation time and screen material used. The significance of these parameters will be brought out in the next section. In addition to the experimental curves there is shown a theoretical curve for the ideal observer derived by the methods described in Sec. 7·5. It can be seen that the functional dependence of the experimental curves is the same as that of the ideal observer, but the absolute signal threshold power is higher. This is not surprising; the human observer is not expected to be so efficient as the ideal observer.

Theoretical Interpretation.—Since the dependence of the signal threshold on the total number of observations has already been discussed in Chap. 7, and since we shall not attempt to describe quantitatively the effect of contrast, we shall try only to interpret the regularities found with regard to the dependence of the signal threshold on the SRF.

Let N_N be the total number of sweeps, and let N_S of these contain the signal while the others contain only noise. As in Sec. 7·3, we assume that the observer determines the average value of some function $f(r)$ of the deflection on the scope at the signal spot and at a spot where there is only noise. Or in other words the observer makes N_N observations of the deflection at the signal spot and compares the average value

$$y_{s+N} = \frac{1}{N_N} \left[\sum_{k=1}^{N_S} f_{s+N}(r_k) + \sum_{k=1}^{N_N - N_S} f_N(r_k) \right] \qquad (26a)$$

with the average value

$$y_N = \frac{1}{N_N} \sum_{k=1}^{N_N} f_N(r_k) \qquad (26b)$$

obtained from N_N observations of the deflection at a spot where there is only noise. As in Sec. 7·3 we assume further that the signal is just detectable if the shift of the average value of y due to the signal is of the same order of magnitude as the standard deviation of y when only noise is present. Since the successive observations of r are independent, it follows from (26a) and (26b)

$$\bar{y}_{s+N} = \frac{1}{N_N} [N_S \bar{f}_{s+N} + (N_N - N_S) \bar{f}_N],$$

$$\bar{y}_N = \bar{f}_N,$$

$$\overline{y_N^2} = \frac{1}{N_N^2} [N_N \overline{f_N^2} + N_N(N_N - 1)(\bar{f}_N)^2].$$

Hence

$$\frac{\bar{y}_{s+N} - \bar{y}_N}{[\overline{y_N^2} - (\bar{y}_N)^2]^{1/2}} = \frac{N_S}{\sqrt{N_N}} \frac{\bar{f}_{s+N} - \bar{f}_N}{[\overline{f_N^2} - (\bar{f}_N)^2]^{1/2}}. \qquad (27)$$

Since for small signal power the shift of the average value of f is proportional to the signal power, the detectability criterion

$$\frac{\bar{y}_{s+N} - \bar{y}_N}{[\overline{y_N^2} - (\bar{y}_N)^2]^{1/2}} = \text{const.}$$

clearly leads to a minimum detectable average signal power

$$\bar{P}_{\min} \sim \frac{\sqrt{N_N}}{N_S}. \qquad (28)$$

Or in words: The signal threshold for constant observation time is proportional to the square root of the SRF and inversely proportional to the first power of the PRF, in accordance with the experimental facts mentioned earlier in this section.   It hardly needs to be said that if all sweeps contain the signal and noise so that $N_N = N_S$, Eq. (28) reduces to the familiar inverse-square-root dependence of the signal threshold on the total number of observations.

8·9. The Influence of the Signal Presentation Time and of the Screen Material.   *The Effect of the Signal Presentation Time.*—From the discussion in the preceding section one would expect the signal threshold power

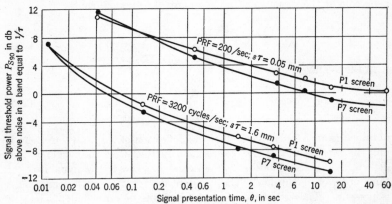

Fig. 8·27.—Signal threshold power *vs.* signal presentation time.

to be inversely proportional to the square root of the signal presentation time θ when the PRF is held constant.   An experiment to test this dependence was performed by Sydoriak, Ashby, and one of the authors, and the results are shown in Fig. 8·27.   Four curves are given; the top two curves were taken for a PRF of 200 cps and a value for $s\tau$ of 0.05 mm. The open circles show the experimental points for a P1 (short persistence) screen, and the solid circles the points for a P7 (long persistence) screen. The lower two curves were also taken for a P1 and P7 screen (using the same coding), but the PRF was set at 3200 cps, and $s\tau$ was fixed at 1.6 mm.   The expected dependence is obtained roughly for all curves, but there are departures from a square-root relationship for both small and large values of θ.   For values of θ smaller than 0.1 sec, the signal threshold power appears to be inversely proportional to the first power of θ; for values of θ greater than about 10 sec, the threshold power is nearly independent of θ.   Both of these facts can be easily understood.   It is well known that there is a maximum frequency with which the eye can perceive successive events; this so-called "flicker frequency" is dependent on many factors but usually lies between 10 and 60 cps. It therefore follows that if the sweeps are being continuously presented on the A-scope, the total number of effective noise sweeps will never be smaller than that given by the product of the PRF and the minimum resolution time of the eye. Under conditions where θ is very short, therefore, we should expect N_N to be constant and from Eq. (28) the signal threshold power to be inversely proportional to the first power of N_S. The transition between the regions of different dependence is expected to occur where θ is of the order of the reciprocal of the flicker frequency, i.e., somewhat less than 0.1 sec. This result is precisely what is observed in Fig. 8·27.

It is clear that the human observer will not be able to integrate properly what he sees over a very long time. If we assume him to have a finite "memory" time, we should expect the threshold signal to be nearly independent of θ when θ exceeds the memory time. This follows because the total number of effective signal and noise sweeps, i.e., those occurring within the memory interval, is independent of θ. From an inspection of Fig. 8·27 it can be seen that the effective memory time appears to be perhaps 10 sec. It is not surprising that there is not a sudden transition region for the effect; one would indeed be astonished if the human memory time were characterized by sharply defined limits.

Nevertheless, the human memory time appears to be long enough so that only slight help is noticeable in using the P7 screen, whose long persistence acts to integrate noise and signal over a relatively long period. It has been found by Sydoriak, Ashby, and one of the authors that training an observer appears primarily to lengthen his memory time. Untrained observers may find the P7 screen much more sensitive than the P1, although, as training proceeds, the scoring on the P1 screen improves to nearly that measured on the P7 screen.

It may seem surprising that in the curves for the P7 screen at small values of θ, a rapid departure from the P1 results does not occur. If the P7 screen integrates all sweeps over an interval of a few seconds, it would be expected to yield a signal threshold power inversely proportional to the first power of θ for values of θ less than this integration interval. This was not observed; it is believed to be caused by the existence of the short-persistence initial "flash" on the P7 screen. For small values of θ this flash causes the P7 to act very much like the P1 screen.

It is possible to check the assumption that was made concerning the minimum resolution time of the eye and brain. It was stated that for very small values of θ, the total number of effective noise sweeps was independent of θ because of this minimum resolution time. However, it is possible to conduct the experiment so that only the sweeps containing the signal (and noise) are presented on the A-scope. This can be done by the commutator shown near the upper left-hand corner of Fig. 8·1.

For this type of experiment the signal threshold power would be expected to be inversely proportional to the square root of θ, even for the smallest values of θ. This is just what is experimentally observed.

The Effect of the Screen Material.—Evidence has just been presented that shows the effect on threshold signal of the use of different A-scope screen materials. The chief characteristic of the screen with which we are concerned is the time required for the light to decay after excitation. Screen materials are now available that show widely different life times; the P1 screen is the most commonly used short-lived material, and the P7 the most widely used long-lived material. The decay of light from these screens is not exponential; it follows more closely a law given by the reciprocal of the time. In the P7 screen an appreciable amount of light can be observed several seconds after excitation, while in the P1 screen no appreciable light remains after perhaps 0.1 sec.

In any case the persistence of the screen may be thought of as an aid in the integration of multiple sweeps, a process that has just been discussed. The degree to which this integration aids in detecting a signal depends upon how effective the observer memory time is. It has been shown in Fig. 8·27 that for a trained observer the signal threshold power is only slightly influenced by the added effect of screen integration. The greatest influence, of course, is felt where the signal presentation time is long; where the latter parameter is a few seconds, the P7 screen shows perhaps a 2-db lower signal threshold power than does the P1 screen.

It is the importance of the observer memory time that led to the early disappointment in the use of long-persistence screens. It was at first believed that a substantial reduction in threshold signal would be observed because of the screen integration. We now know that such integration will not be effective in reducing the threshold signal power unless the screen life time exceeds by a substantial factor the observer memory time. Even so, a better method is a photographic process. Information can be stored on a photographic film over as long a period of time as is necessary. This procedure is easily demonstrated by observation of the photographs of Fig. 8·24. However, the usefulness of such photographic storage is greatly limited by the contrast requirements of the observer, already discussed, and the extremely long time inevitably required for signal detection. Furthermore scanning requirements and target motion reduce its utility.

8·10. The Dependence upon the Number and Spacing of Possible Signal Positions and upon the Attention Interval. *The Dependence upon the Number and Spacing of Possible Signal Positions.*—It was categorically stated in Sec. 8·3 that the signal threshold power increases with the number of possible signal positions. The phenomenon is shown graphically in Fig. 8·28 where the ordinate represents the signal threshold power in decibels relative to its value for 50 possible signal positions. The abscissa shows the number of possible signal positions. Two curves are shown, the lower one representing results when the positions had a uniform spacing of 1 mm and the upper one representing results when the first and last positions were separated by 50 mm. The difference between the two curves is not surprising; it has already been noted that the human observer sees events on the A-scope face most easily when their separation is about 1 mm. If we were to draw a curve representing results where the total distance of search remains approximately constant, we should probably obtain a curve similar to the dotted line shown. This line,

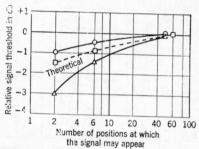

Fig. 8·28.—Signal threshold power *vs.* number of possible signal positions.

System parameters

Pulse length × i-f bandwidth.............................. $B\tau = 1.2$
Pulse length on screen.................................... = 0.05 mm

Key

○ First and last positions 50 mm apart
△ Positions 1 mm apart

however, is actually a theoretical curve showing the expected dependence on number of positions. It has been derived by arguments that are given in Sec. 7·5.

The agreement in shape between the theoretical curve and the average experimental result lends support to the view that the fundamental limitation in signal threshold power is due to the chance of a noise fluctuation exceeding the average signal deflection.

The Dependence on the Attention Interval.—It is necessary to introduce a new parameter called the attention interval θ_A. We have assumed in all the discussion so far that the observer searches for the signal only during the signal presentation time θ. Actually we have seen that the information which the observer assimilates may extend over a time longer than θ; the reason for this phenomenon has been stated to be the minimum resolution time of the eye and brain. There is still another mechanism, however, by which the total information may extend over a time interval longer than θ. Let us suppose that the observer is told that the signal is to appear at an unspecified time within an interval θ_A.

To pick out the signal he will have to fix his attention on the A-scope during the entire attention interval θ_A even though he knows the signal presentation time itself to be θ. As θ_A becomes much larger than θ, the signal threshold power must rise to offset the increased chance of finding a large noise peak that would be confused with the signal. This increase is just analogous to the increase in signal threshold required for an increase in the number of possible signal positions. In other words, the total number of possible signal positions is really the number of spatial signal positions on the A-scope multiplied by the ratio θ_A/θ, since for any spatial interval there are θ_A/θ possible time intervals.

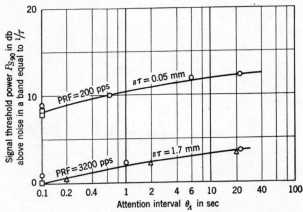

Fig. 8·29.—Signal threshold power *vs.* attention interval.

System parameters

Pulse length × i-f bandwidth.............................. $B\tau = 1.2$
Signal presentation time.................................. $\theta = 0.1$ sec

Key

○□ Experimental points
△ Theoretical values

Experimental data by S. Sydoriak showing the effect of attention interval are presented in Fig. 8·29. In this figure two experimental curves are shown in which the signal threshold power as ordinate is plotted against the attention interval θ_A as abscissa. The upper curve was taken for conditions in which the PRF was 200 cps, and the signal length on the A-scope $s\tau$ was set at 0.05 mm. The lower curve was taken for a PRF of 3200 cps and $s\tau$ of 1.7 mm. In both cases the signal presentation time θ was fixed at 0.1 sec while the attention interval θ_A was varied from 0.1 sec to more than 20 sec. The results shown indicate the signal threshold power $P_{S_{90}}$ for six spatial signal positions on the A-scope. The A-scope screen used for all experimental points was of the P7 long-persistence type.

Three types of coded points are indicated on the diagram; two of these are experimental points, and the third represents theoretical results to be discussed below. The open circles show the experimental points obtained when the attention interval was defined to the observer by ringing a bell at its beginning and end. It was soon appreciated that for small values of attention interval the reaction time of the observer would cause his attention to be spread over a time interval not necessarily identical with the interval selected for the appearance of the signal. This defect was remedied by triggering the A-scope trace only during the desired attention interval, thereby giving the observer information during the specified time only. This procedure yielded the experimental points indicated by squares. To show how the experimental curves agree with simple theoretical considerations, three theoretical points, shown by triangles, are indicated on the lower curve. These have been derived from calculations made by M. C. Wang following a suggestion of E. M. Purcell. Using the probability distributions derived in Sec. 7·5, she has calculated the probability w that a given possible signal position will display a larger deflection due to noise than

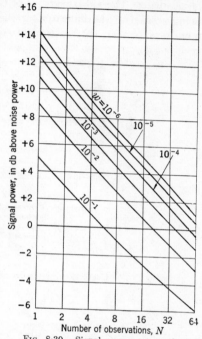

Fig. 8·30.—Signal power *vs.* number of observations N for various values of w. The symbol w represents the probability that a noise deflection exceeds the deflection of signal plus noise.

the position actually occupied by the signal itself. The probability w depends on the number of pulses N and on the signal strength. The results of these calculations are shown in Table 2·1 of Vol. 1 of this series[1] and are reproduced in Fig. 8·30, where for various values of w the signal strength is plotted against the number of observations, N.

For a given criterion of threshold signal one must require the probability w to be inversely proportional to the total effective number of signal positions. For the system parameters of Fig. 8·29 and with the threshold power adjusted at one point in order to take into account the

[1] Ridenour, *Radar System Engineering*, Vol. 1, Radiation Laboratory Series, p. 39.

difference between the ideal observer and the actual observer, one obtains the theoretical points shown in Fig. 8·29.

8·11. The Influence of Video Mixing.—It is often desirable to mix the output indications of two or more separate receiving systems in such a way that signals from either system can be seen. This can be done in one of two ways: The video voltages of both systems may be added before being applied to the indicator, or the A-scope sweep may be triggered more rapidly than the repetition frequency of the various pulses, thus

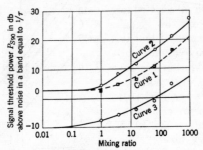

Fig. 8·31.—Signal threshold power *vs.* mixing ratio.
System parameters
Curve 1 (upper half of trace masked)
$s_T = 1.7$ mm
$B_T = 1.5$
PRF $= 400$ pps
$\theta = \frac{1}{16}$ sec
Curve 2, curve theoretical, points experimental
$s_T = 0.083$ mm
$B_T = 1.5$
PRF $= 400$ pps
$\theta = \frac{1}{16}$ sec
Curve 3, curve theoretical, points experimental
$s_T = 5.8$ mm
$B_T = 5.1$
PRF $= 720$ pps
$\theta = 2$ sec

allowing the video signals from the several systems to be interlaced in time. In the latter method, if we assume the average noise voltages in the several systems to be identical, we may consider the signal from a given system to occur at a given PRF, while the noise occurs at a higher SRF. This is just the problem discussed in Sec. 8·8 in which the signal threshold power was found experimentally and theoretically to depend upon the quantity $N_N^{1/2}/N_S$. The quantities N_N and N_S refer to the numbers of sweeps containing noise and signal, respectively. In principle, it does not matter whether the video voltages are added before the application to the A-scope or appear alternately on successive A-scope sweeps. We have assumed in either case that the observer makes use only of the average video deflections; therefore the two procedures should yield similar results.

Let us now consider the more general case of the mixture of two video systems (which we shall label Channel A and Channel B) in which the average noise power in the two channels may be unequal. If the noise in Channel B is much larger than that in Channel A, the threshold signal measured in Channel A will have to be greatly increased to overcome the greatly increased noise background. On the other hand, the threshold signal measured in Channel B will be hardly affected by the slight increase in its noise due to Channel A. It is convenient to introduce a new parameter, which we may call the *mixing ratio*. The mixing ratio is assumed to be unity when the video noise levels in the two channels are equal. Let us assume for the sake of simplicity that in this condition the i-f power gains G_A and G_B for Channels A and B, respectively, are also equal. Under general conditions the mixing ratio M_A for Channel A will then be given by the ratio G_B/G_A, while the mixing ratio M_B for Channel B is the inverse, G_A/G_B. We may ask how the signal threshold power depends upon these mixing ratios.

In Fig. 8·31 is plotted the experimental results for a two-channel mixing experiment. The system parameters are indicated in the legend. The signal threshold power is shown on the ordinate scale, while the mixing ratio is indicated (logarithmically) on the abscissa. Three curves are shown for different system parameters. Curves 2 and 3 have been computed using the deflection criterion of Sec. 7·3 in which the constant k has been adjusted to fit the experiments for very small mixing ratios. The open circles are experimental points taken by S. G. Sydoriak and seem to agree satisfactorily with the curves. However, the experimental square points that were made with the upper half of the A-scope trace masked lie about 5 db below the theoretical curve. This has been traced to a peculiar method by which the observer recognizes the signal. For large mixing ratios the signal in Channel A has practically no noise associated with it, therefore displaces the entire noise distribution of Channel B by a fixed amount. Hence, just at the baseline the signal creates a small open "hole" within which no noise fluctuations can be observed. This small hole is clearly discernible if $s\tau$ is large enough and the observer is no longer forced to average the entire noise deflection. The "mouse under the rug," however, will not be apparent if $s\tau$ becomes smaller than the spot size on the A-scope as is the case in Curve 2 of Fig. 8·31. The "mouse under the rug" effect is not apparent in Curve 3 perhaps because of the excessive value of $s\tau$.

CHAPTER 9

PULSE TRAINS IN INTERNAL NOISE; OTHER METHODS OF PRESENTATION

In Chap. 8 an account was given of the factors that influence threshold signals which are displayed on an A-scope. It has been mentioned in Chap. 2 that other forms of presentation are in wide use; indeed, for radar the intensity-modulated display, such as the PPI or B-scope, is at present more widely used than any other display. For some applications the detection of pulse trains by aural means is highly desirable, since by this means the observer's eyes are free for other essential tasks. In this chapter an attempt is made to treat very briefly some of these display systems. They have not, however, been so intensively investigated as the A-scope from the point of view of signal visibility, and in some cases even the experimental observations are not completely understood.

INTENSITY-MODULATED DISPLAY (PPI)

9·1. Similarities to the A-scope.—In Sec. 2·6 a brief description was given of the various commonly used intensity-modulated displays. In all cases the signal causes the trace on a cathode-ray tube to brighten; the position and direction of the trace is made to display appropriate coordinates of the antenna. In the ordinary PPI (plan-position indicator), the cathode-ray trace is caused to sweep radially outward from the center of the tube; range is indicated by the distance along a radius from the tube center. The sweep is oriented at an angle corresponding to the azimuthal angle of the antenna. In this fashion the face of the tube displays echo signals from reflecting objects as bright spots; the positions of these spots on the tube face correspond to the actual positions of those objects with respect to the antenna. It is this mapping feature of the PPI which has made it one of the most widely used display systems. The PPI will therefore be treated in all the following discussions on intensity-modulated displays; the results are, with minor changes, expected to hold for other intensity-modulated presentations, such as the B-scope (which displays the range-azimuth data in Cartesian coordinates).

The PPI differs from the A-scope in at least two ways. (1) To prevent defocusing of the cathode-ray spot by large signals, the strength of the video signal must be *limited* before application to the oscilloscope terminals. In practice one finds that this limiting action must occur even for some of the normal noise distribution and, if carried too far, can profoundly affect threshold signals. This fact will be brought out in Sec. 9·3. (2) The manner in which the PPI is used nearly always brings in a more or less complicated *scanning factor*. In the use of the A-scope, discussed in Chap. 8, it was assumed that the signal pulse train was of uniform amplitude for a time θ called the signal presentation time; however, as pointed out in Sec. 2·6, in the PPI the signal consists of a finite pulse train (because of the narrow antenna beam scanning over the target), which is repeated from scan to scan. We may already anticipate from the A-scope results that this repetition feature may influence threshold signals through some form of integration; the extent of this influence clearly must depend upon the memory time of the integrating device. These effects will be discussed in Sec. 9·2.

In addition to these new features of the PPI, there is an important feature that applies to both the PPI and the A-scope. In radar search problems one is seldom interested in the detection of stationary objects producing steady echoes. An echo from an airplane, for example, continually fluctuates at rates that are generally functions of the nature of the aircraft, flying conditions, and the wavelength of the radar system. It is clear that the specification of threshold power for a fluctuating signal is more difficult than for a steady one. Some remarks and observations on this subject are given in Sec. 9·5.

In spite of the new features introduced by the PPI, much that has been learned about the A-scope still applies. Most important, the basic ideas that were developed for an understanding of the A-scope can be carried over to the PPI. This feature has eliminated a great deal of experimental labor.

The Influence of I-f Bandwidth.—As in the case of the A-scope (see Sec. 8·6), an important parameter is the product of i-f bandwidth B and the signal pulse duration τ. A detailed experimental study of the effect of $B\tau$ has not yet been made; preliminary work by R. R. Meijer and S. G. Sydoriak,[1] however, has shown the same general behavior with the PPI as with the A-scope (see Fig. 8·7). There appears to be an optimum value of $B\tau$, above which the threshold signal power rises approximately proportional to the bandwidth and below which it rises approximately inversely proportional to the bandwidth. The reasons for this behavior are the same as in the A-scope case. The essential difference between the PPI and the A-scope curves, as indicated by the preliminary data, is that the PPI curve is somewhat flatter and the minimum is shifted to somewhat higher values of $B\tau$. Neither of these characteristics is certain; they should be verified by further experiments made under a wide variety of conditions.

[1] Unpublished.

The Influence of Video Bandwidth and Sweep Speed.—It has been found that the effects of the video bandwidth and of the sweep speed are interdependent, just as they were in the A-scope case (see Sec. 8·7). The effect of sweep speed is, in fact, equivalent to a kind of video-bandwidth limitation; the connection between the two is made through the characteristics of the eye (and brain). In the A-scope case, experiment showed that the eye was able to see signals most easily when the pulse length on the oscilloscope face $s\tau$ was approximately 1 mm. Experiments on the PPI have shown exactly the same behavior; an experimental curve taken by C. M. Allred and A. Gardner is shown in Fig. 9·1. Signal

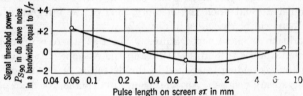

FIG. 9·1.—Signal threshold as a function of pulse length on the screen.

System parameters

$B\tau = 1.2$	Beam width $= 6.0°$
PRF $= 320$ pps	Scanning time $= 10$ sec/rev

threshold power in terms of receiver noise power is plotted (logarithmically) as ordinate, and the pulse length on the tube face $s\tau$ is shown as abscissa. The behavior of the threshold power is just the same as for the A-scope (e.g., *cf.* Fig. 8·18). The conditions under which Allred ·and Gardner took the data were approximately as follows. The signal was made to appear at one of six random range positions at a defined azimuth (known to the observer). The antenna beam width ϕ was constant at 6°, and the scanning frequency was constant at 6 rpm. The ordinates shown in Fig. 9·1 are $P_{S_{90}}$, i.e., the signal power at 90 per cent correlation on the "betting" curve (see Chap. 8). During these experiments virtually no limiting of video voltages was present.

While no detailed data on the influence of video bandwidth b (or more properly the quantity $b\tau$) are yet available to the author's knowledge, there is no information that indicates a markedly different dependence on this parameter for the PPI and A-scope. It is entirely possible, however, that in the presence of severe limiting, different results will be obtained; the limiter serves as a highly nonlinear element that distorts both amplitude distributions and power spectra. Nevertheless, in the usual case it is believed that the A-scope results will apply fairly well to the PPI.

There is, in addition to the connection between video bandwidth and sweep speed, a connection between video bandwidth and focus. This fact was recognized in the A-scope case by the observation that defocusing in a direction parallel to the sweep was not serious so long as the spot size did not exceed 1 mm (see Sec. 8·7); this fact was in accord with the sweep-speed effect; for as long as the eye (and brain) partially neglects events with a spatial separation of less than 1 mm, defocusing of this order of magnitude was expected to have small effect. This same phenomenon has been observed by R. Rollefson and J. L. Lawson[1] on the PPI. Defocusing parallel to the sweep was not detrimental unless the spot exceeded 1 mm; defocusing in a direction perpendicular to the sweep had no effect until the spot size exceeded the spatial size of the signal caused by the antenna beam angle ϕ.

9·2. The Influence of Scanning.—It is through the process of scanning that various time factors are introduced which correspond to the (A-scope) signal presentation time θ. It is clear that because of the scanning frequency and the antenna beam width ϕ an effective signal presentation time θ exists for each scan. The pulse train may or may not be repeated on subsequent scans, depending upon the conditions of operation. Scanning, therefore, involves time factors that are expected to influence threshold signal power because of memory, or integration, effects. The main parameters with which we are concerned are (1) scanning frequency, (2) antenna beam angle ϕ, (3) PRF. The signal presentation time θ can be obtained from (1) and (2). A complete treatment of integration effects, which will not be possible here, would also include extra noise sweeps (see Sec. 8·8), screen material (see Sec. 8·9), the number of possible signal positions (see Sec. 8·10), and the total length of time the signal has existed. No experimental information exists on extra noise sweeps, however. The screen material in a PPI is so universally P7 (long persistence) that data on other screen materials are scarce. The signal will also be assumed to exist either for *one* scan or for an *infinite* number of scans. Finally, in most of the experiments that will be mentioned, only six signal positions (in range) were available and those at a defined azimuth (known to the observer). This corresponds to the conditions most used in the A-scope experiments (see Chap. 8) but does not necessarily represent the condition most often encountered with a PPI in actual radar use. Preliminary experiments have shown that in accordance with the theoretical arguments of Sec. 8·10, an increase in the number of possible signal positions brings about a rise in threshold signal power. This is a relatively important consideration in a high-resolution PPI used for search purposes, where the number of possible signal positions (all ranges and all azimuths) can easily exceed 10^6.

The Effect of Beam Angle ϕ.—We may anticipate the effect expected by a change in the value of the antenna beam angle from the results of Sec. 8·9. If the scanning frequency is constant, a change in ϕ is tanta-

---

[1] Unpublished data.

mount to a change in signal presentation time θ as long as the signal appears on only one scan, i.e., single-scan operation. For a constant PRF, one would therefore expect the threshold signal power to vary as $\theta^{-\frac{1}{2}}$, and hence as $\phi^{-\frac{1}{2}}$; this result is expected only if integration or memory exists over the entire interval θ and if there is no inherent difference in threshold power caused by the difference in geometrical shape of signal on the oscilloscope face.

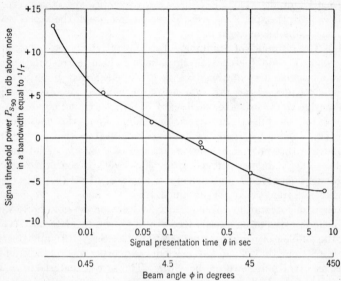

Fig. 9·2.—Signal threshold as a function of the presentation time for constant rpm.

System parameters

Pulse length $\tau = 1$ μsec	$s\tau = 0.75$ mm
$B\tau = 1.1$	Scanning time = 8 sec/rev
PRF = 800 pps	

An experimental curve showing the effect of ϕ is reproduced in Fig. 9·2. The ordinate represents the signal threshold power (at 90 per cent correlation) $P_{S_{90}}$; the abscissa represents the antenna beam angle ϕ plotted logarithmically. Also shown on the abscissa scale is the signal presentation time θ, which in this experiment is simply proportional to ϕ. The data were taken for beam angles from 0.18° to 360°, corresponding to θ's of 0.004 and 8 sec, respectively; the PRF was held constant at 800 pps and the scanning frequency was constant at 7.5 rpm. As can be seen, over most of the range the threshold power is proportional to $\phi^{-\frac{1}{2}}$ in accord with expectation; however, deviations exist at both ends of the range. For very large beam angles ($> 45°$) it is understandable that signals are less efficiently seen, since one cannot simultaneously view the entire arc. Likewise for very small beam widths ($<1°$) the geometrical size of the signal spot becomes smaller than 1 mm; one would expect under this condition an increase in signal threshold power analogous to the effect of sweep speed (see Fig. 9·1). In other words the eye (and brain) discriminates against the (geometrically) small signal in favor of wider noise fluctuations.

The results shown in Fig. 9·2 are important in that they show no essential change in signal threshold caused by the *geometrical arc length;* the entire effect can be thought of as a change in threshold signal caused by a change in the number of (integrated) individual signal pulses. This conclusion is interesting in that it contradicts the widespread opinion that the wider signal arcs from broad antenna beam angles are easier to see "because they become more and more different from noise, which

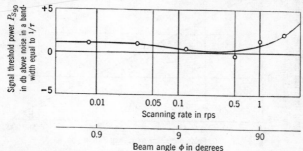

FIG. 9·3.—Signal threshold as a function of scanning angle at constant signal presentation time.

System parameters

Pulse length $\tau = 1$ μsec $s\tau = 0.6$ mm
$B\tau = 1.2$ Signal presentation time $\theta = \frac{1}{4}$ sec
PRF $= 800$ pps

appears as a uniform, grainy background." The fact is that the grainy "uniform" noise can simulate false signals of any prescribed geometrical shape; the particular shape is relatively unimportant as long as the total number of signal (and noise) pulses is constant. To show this effect in a somewhat different way, an experiment was performed in which the signal presentation time θ and the PRF were held constant. The beam angle ϕ was varied by changing the scanning frequency. Thus, throughout the experiment the signal arc length was changed over a wide range but the total number of signal pulses was held constant. The result is shown in Fig. 9·3; it is evident that over nearly all the range the threshold signal power is virtually independent of ϕ.

The results of Figs. 9·2 and 9·3 demonstrate that, at least in the range from 1° to 45°, the antenna-beam angle ϕ *per se* has little to do with signal threshold power. It is important, however, in that usually the PRF and scanning frequency are fixed; therefore the total number of signal pulses is proportional to ϕ. It is only through this connection that the threshold signal power does depend upon ϕ.

The Effect of Pulse Repetition Frequency.—Figure 9·4 shows a single-scan experimental curve of threshold signal power as a function of the PRF. For this experiment the scanning frequency was constant at 2 rpm, the beam angle constant at 2°, and θ consequently constant at $\frac{1}{15}$ sec. The PRF, however, was varied from 25 to 6000 pps; this variation produced the result shown. As can be seen, over most of the range the signal threshold power is inversely proportional to the square root of the PRF; this is exactly the result expected for signal integration over the interval θ (see Sec. 8·8).

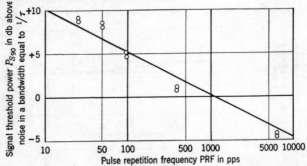

FIG. 9·4.—Signal threshold as a function of PRF.

System parameters

Pulse length $\tau = 1$ μsec
$B\tau = 1.1$
Beam width = 2°

$s\tau = 0.8$ mm
Signal presentation time $\theta = \frac{1}{15}$ sec

The Effect of Scanning Frequency.—It can be anticipated that if ϕ is held constant, the scanning frequency would affect the signal presentation time θ and hence the signal threshold power; in fact the signal power should be directly proportional to the square root of scanning frequency. This relationship, however, is not generally true at all for multiple-scan data and only partially true for single-scan data. It is approximately true for single-scan operation provided the scanning frequency is between certain limits. The lower limit is fixed by the maximum signal presentation time θ over which effective integration can take place; this maximum time has been found to be several seconds, in agreement with the corresponding A-scope value (see Sec. 9·9). In other words, the signal threshold power does not decrease with scanning frequency beyond the point where the signal is within the antenna beam for several (perhaps 10) seconds. The upper limit of scanning frequency is fixed by the condition that at least one and preferably a few signal pulses must be present during the antenna transit. If this condition is not met, a high correlation on the "betting" curve may not be experienced even for very large signals.

As soon as the signal is allowed to be present on several scans, a new factor is introduced, namely, scan-to-scan integration. Since there is no reason to expect the system's memory for scan-to-scan integration to be longer than the largest useful value of θ (about 10 sec), one might anticipate that scan-to-scan integration would be appreciable only if the scanning frequency were higher than perhaps 6 rpm. This argument indeed proves to hold; in fact, above 6 to 10 rpm the signal threshold power is found to be relatively independent of scanning frequency. This result is shown clearly in Fig. 9·9.[1] It is sufficient for the present to note that for high scanning rates, the scanning loss, i.e., loss in decibels because of scanning, is relatively independent of scanning frequency. (The scanning loss is, of course, proportional to the increase in threshold signal power.) To understand this independence of scanning frequency it should be noted that over a given integration interval, let us say 10 sec, the total number of signal pulses is independent of scanning frequency. As the scanning frequency is doubled, the number of scans to be integrated doubles but the number of pulses per scan is halved; hence the total number of signal pulses is constant. Using this argument, we can go one step further toward understanding Fig. 9·9. The total number of signal pulses in the integration interval may be compared for the two conditions (1) in which no scanning occurs ("searchlighting" on the target) and (2) in which rapid scanning occurs. One would expect the scanning loss to be simply proportional to the square root of the ratio of the number of searchlighting pulses to the number of scanning·pulses; this ratio is clearly $360°/\phi$. This result is approximately verified in Fig. 9·9; for the 2° beam width applying to the aircraft data the expected scanning loss is 11 db, whereas for the signal-generator (2.8° beam width) data the expected loss is 10.5 db. It should be emphasized that this simplified method of computing scanning loss applies only for scanning systems in which the frame-to-frame or scan-to-scan signal repetition frequencies are relatively high.

Although the qualitative effects of scanning are understood, the extension of simple formulas to the very high discrimination radar sets (short pulse and narrow beam angle ϕ) must be made with great care. If searching is done with extreme definition, it may happen that the total number of signal pulses per integration interval is only two or three. This condition usually invalidates the simple formulas; recourse must be had

---

[1] The lower curve was taken with a (steady) signal from a signal generator; the upper curve shows the results obtained with an actual (fluctuating) airplane echo. The significance of the difference between the two curves will be brought out in Sec. 9·5.

to the exact statistical calculations, such as those indicated in Sec. 8.10. Such calculations usually indicate that the sensitivity of the high-discrimination system is somewhat reduced over that given by the simple formulas.

9.3. The Influence of Limiting.—In the use of the PPI a certain amount of video limiting occurs. This limiting is necessary in order to prevent the oscilloscope from being defocused by large signals. In addition, limiting has been found helpful in reducing the effect of certain types of interference such as "railing" interference (see Sec. 12.6). The degree of limiting required depends upon the indicator, sweep speed, amount of interference, etc.; the proper amount is usually estimated and set by the observer. It has been found that, if limiting is not severe, the

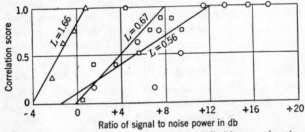

FIG. 9.5.—Betting curves for the one-channel limiting experiment.

signal threshold power is not greatly affected by it. The unfortunate characteristic of limiting, however, is that under certain conditions the observer cannot tell by an examination of the noise background pattern on the PPI whether the limiting is or is not severe. In other words, it is very easy to set the limit level in terms of rms or average noise voltage at a point such that the signal threshold power is very large, without being aware of such a condition. For this reason it has been urged that the limit level be set by a suitable instrument rather than on the basis of the operator's estimate; when this practice has been followed, it has prevented large "unknown" decreases in system sensitivity.

The important characteristic in limiting is clearly the ratio L of the limit-level voltage to the average video noise voltage. Some other feature of the video noise amplitude distribution could, of course, be chosen as a reference; however, the average noise voltage is convenient as it can usually be measured directly with a d-c meter. Large values of L indicate only mild limiting; small values of L (perhaps less than 2) show relatively strong limiting.

The effect of the limit level L is made evident in at least two important ways: (1) The signal threshold power at any point on the "betting" curve rises as L is reduced: and (2) the slope of the betting curve decreases with decreasing L. These two characteristics are brought out clearly in Fig. 9·5, where three sample betting curves are shown for different values of L. The data were taken by Sydoriak.[1] In this series it can be seen that as L is reduced, the signal threshold power increases and the slope of the betting curve decreases. In fact, for a value of 0.56 for L, it is not certain that the betting curve ever actually reaches 100 per cent correla-

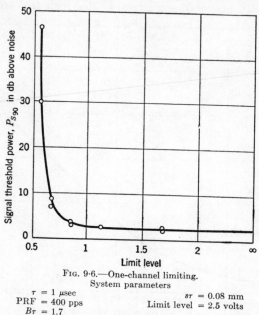

FIG. 9·6.—One-channel limiting.
System parameters

$\tau = 1$ μsec $s\tau = 0.08$ mm
PRF $= 400$ pps   Limit level $= 2.5$ volts
$B\tau = 1.7$

tion. The reason for this effect appears to be that a highly limited signal cannot necessarily override chance noise fluctuations if the tube spot size is large compared with the signal pulse. On short sweeps the effect is much less noticeable; this observation is in accord with simple reasoning.

The relationship of signal threshold power to limit level L is shown in Fig. 9·6 for a typical case. It can be seen that for values of L less than unity a substantial increase in signal threshold power occurs. Therefore in the operation of a PPI care should be taken to ensure that L is larger than unity.

It has been found that when video mixing occurs (see next section), one has to be especially careful about limiting. Consider the case in which one channel is severely limited while the other is not; the mixed

[1] S. G. Sydoriak, "The Effects of Video Mixing Ratio and Limiting on Signal Threshold Power," unpublished.

video output will show no well defined "ceiling" because of the unlimited part of the noise. Consequently, the appearance on the PPI will be nearly normal regardless of the limiting in the first channel; the operator is, therefore, completely unable to judge the system sensitivity by an examination of the noise pattern.

9·4. Video Mixing.—The influence of video mixing on signal threshold power with PPI presentation is similar to that with an A-scope display

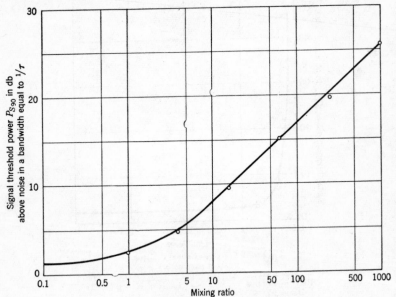

FIG. 9·7.—Signal threshold as a function of the mixing ratio.
System parameters

$B\tau = 1.5$	$\theta = \frac{1}{16}$ sec
PRF = 400 pps	$\phi = 1°$
$s\tau = 0.08$ mm	RPM = 6

(see Sec. 8·11). In the A-scope case, however, it was possible to utilize the "mouse under the rug," i.e., "holes" near the baseline of the amplitude distribution, to obtain greatest sensitivity. In the PPI, the most sensitive part of the amplitude distribution cannot be selected; the entire distribution is averaged in some manner to create the total light output from the screen. One might expect intuitively, therefore, that the PPI would give mixing results more in accord with simple theoretical considerations.

Experiments by R. R. Meijer, S. G. Sydoriak, and D. Gillette[1] on two-channel single-scan PPI mixing have yielded results similar to those shown in Fig. 9·7. In this figure the system conditions were as follows:

[1] Unpublished.

scanning frequency 6 rpm, beam width ϕ 1°, PRF 400 pps, $B_\tau = 1.5$, $s_\tau = 0.8$ mm. The curve agrees qualitatively with a mixing theory similar to that for the A-scope (see Sec. 8·11). However, unlike A-scope presentation, the PPI does not permit one to see any "mouse under the

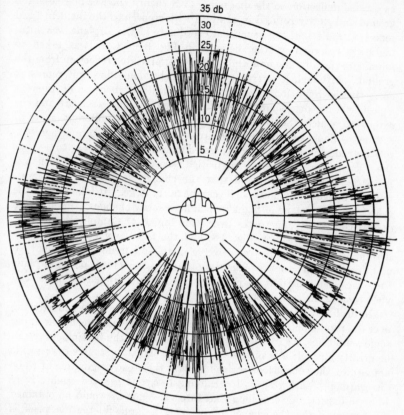

FIG. 9·8.—Scattering cross section of a B-26 airplane at a wavelength of approximately 10 cm.

rug"; the brightness of a spot is proportional to an average of a function of the *entire* amplitude distribution. This function of the amplitude distribution is uncertain; it is determined by the linearity of the video amplifier, the limiting, and the dependence of the screen brightness on the exciting current.

9·5. Signal Fluctuations and Target Movement.—In many instances, for example, in radar search, one is interested in the detection of a feeble signal that is not necessarily steady but may fluctuate in time. A reflection pattern[1] from a B-26 airplane is shown in Fig. 9·8 to help the reader appreciate the magnitude of such fluctuations. This pattern was obtained on a special automatic recording device that plotted the relative back-reflected signal strength (at a wavelength of approximately 10 cm) as a radial deflection on the diagram. A B-26 airplane was placed on the ground and slowly rotated in azimuth with respect to the incident (and reflected) radiation; the azimuthal coordinate of the airplane was automatically recorded on the diagram in Fig. 9·8. Care was taken to illuminate the airplane uniformly without appreciable reflection from the ground. Although it is true that the finished plot does not represent correctly the reflection pattern of a B-26 in flight (because of different aspect, etc.), it does show clearly the type of detailed structure and the extent to which the reflection intensity varies at different azimuth settings. The concentric marker circles shown on the diagram represent relative reflected signal power expressed in decibels. It is easy to see that the total range in reflected intensities exceeds 35 db, or more than a factor of 3000 in power, and that the change in intensity with even minute changes in azimuth angle can be fairly large. It follows that the echo from an airplane in flight (which necessarily changes azimuth more or less constantly) fluctuates over wide limits; the amplitude of these fluctuations is shown by Fig. 9·8, and the frequency of fluctuation is determined primarily by radar wavelength and flying conditions. In addition to the fluctuation caused by the gross movement of the airplane there are rapid contributions caused by the rotating propellers,[2] which can yield frequencies up to 1000 or 2000 cps.

In dealing with fluctuating signals care must be exercised in carrying over the results obtained with a steady signal. We have seen that under some conditions, e.g., severe limiting, the slope of the betting curve can be greatly altered; it is obvious that, if the signal fluctuates over a wide amplitude, the conclusions arrived at with the steady signal ought to be disregarded. With respect to scanning loss, one can see qualitatively what to expect. Over a long time interval (such as would be obtained "searchlighting") the chance of utilizing a large fluctuation peak is relatively great, whereas for a single-scan measurement with a narrow beam and hence a small signal presentation time θ, the chance of finding a high signal fluctuation is relatively smaller. Therefore one would expect a greater scanning loss with fluctuating signals, e.g., airplane echoes, than with a steady signal. An experimental confirmation of this reasoning is shown in Fig. 9·9, where the scanning loss in decibels is shown

[1] This pattern was taken by R. M. Ashby, F. W. Martin, and J. L. Lawson. See their "Modulation of Radar Signals from Airplanes," RL Report No. 914, Mar. 28, 1946.

[2] *Ibid.*

as a function of scanning frequency in revolutions per minute. Two experimental curves are shown; the lower curve is the result obtained with a signal generator; the upper curve shows the result using actual echoes from an airplane in flight at a wavelength of 10 cm. All system parameters for the two curves were the same, with the exception of the effective antenna beam width; i.e., PRF = 400 pps, $B\tau = 1.5$, $s\tau = 0.5$ mm. The beam width for the upper curve was 2° and for the lower curve 2.8°. It will be noticed that the airplane-echo scanning loss was 4 db

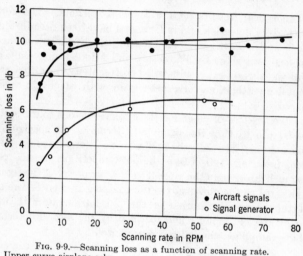

Fig. 9·9.—Scanning loss as a function of scanning rate.

Upper curve airplane echo	Lower curve signal generator
PRF = 400 pps	PRF = 400 pps
$B\tau = 1.5$	$B\tau = 1.5$
$s\tau = 0.5$ mm	$s\tau = 0.5$ mm
$\phi = 2°$	$\phi = 2.8°$

higher than that for the signal generator, of which 0.5 db can be accounted for in the difference of beam angles (see Sec. 9·2). It appears that the remaining 3.5-db loss is due to the fluctuating character of the signal, in line with qualitative expectations.

In addition to the lack of complete treatment of fluctuating signals, answers do not exist at present to a number of interesting and fundamental questions. One of these questions is the effect of target movement on signal threshold power. It is clear that the scan-to-scan integration which leads to a scanning loss independent of (high) scanning frequency might be upset if the signal is displaced appreciably on the PPI from scan to scan. Certainly no screen integration takes place under these conditions; yet it is possible that the eye and brain can recognize uniform movement and still perform the equivalent of integration. Some preliminary experiments on this point by V. Josephson have shown a dependence of signal threshold power on target velocity, but these experiments are not sufficiently complete to show the precise mechanism involved. On the other hand it is a common experience with radar observers that a moving signal-generator pulse is apparently as easy to recognize as a fixed signal. More experimental information is required to understand this problem.

AURAL AND METER METHODS OF DETECTION

9·6. Theoretical Results for the Signal Threshold.—The aural and meter methods of detection of a radar signal have been described already in Sec. 2·6, and a rather complete theoretical discussion of the signal threshold has been given by Van Vleck and Middleton.[1] Only a short account of the theoretical results will be presented, since no systematic experimental investigations have been made with which the theory can be compared.

In the *aural method* of detection the observer listens to the audio tone produced by the PRF of the signal. In terms of the spectrum of the signal and noise (*cf.* Sec. 7·2) the audio tone is represented by the signal peak at the frequency $1/\Theta_0$ if Θ_0 is the pulse repetition period. Since Θ_0 is always much larger than the pulse length τ, the power of the signal peak will be the same as the power of the d-c component, that is, the average value of the power distribution in the pulse train after it has been deformed by the i-f amplifier and rectified by the second detector. If, before the i-f amplifier, the pulse is represented by

$$S(t) = S_0 F \left(\frac{t}{\tau} \right) \cos 2\pi f_c t,$$

then it can be easily shown (*cf.* Sec. 7·2) that the average value of the deformed and rectified pulse train is given by

$$\frac{S_0^2 \tau}{\Theta_0} \int_{-\infty}^{+\infty} dx \left| G(x) Z_1 \left(\frac{x}{B\tau} \right) \right|^2, \tag{1}$$

where

$$G(x) = \int_{-\infty}^{+\infty} dy \, F(y) e^{-2\pi i y x}$$

and $Z_1(f/B)$ is the system function of the i-f amplifier, which has the bandwidth B. A *quadratic* second detector has been assumed.

The qualitative behavior of the function

$$h(B\tau) = \int_{-\infty}^{+\infty} dx \left| G(x) Z_1 \left(\frac{x}{B\tau} \right) \right|^2 \tag{2}$$

[1] J. H. Van Vleck and D. Middleton, "Theoretical Comparison of the Visual, Aural and Meter Reception of Pulsed Signals in the Presence of Noise," *J. Applied Phys.*, **11**, 940 (1946).

can be seen as follows.   For small values of $B\tau$ the i-f amplifier lengthens the pulse from τ to $1/B$ and diminishes the signal amplitude from S_0 to $S_0 B\tau$.   The average pulse power is therefore in this case of the order

$$S_0^2 B^2 \tau^2 \frac{1}{B\Theta_0} = S_0^2 \frac{\tau}{\Theta_0} B\tau.$$

On the other hand for $B\tau \gg 1$ the pulse will not be deformed by the i-f amplifier, so that the average power will be $S_0^2 \tau / \Theta_0$.   Therefore the function $h(B\tau)$ approaches unity for $B\tau \gg 1$ and is proportional to $B\tau$ for small values of $B\tau$.

The power of the signal peak has to compete with the noise power in a narrow range of frequency Δ around the audio tone $1/\Theta_0$.   Since $1/\Theta_0$ is so small, one may take the initial value of the continuous noise spectrum, which for a square-law detector is proportional to the bandwidth B. Hence in the notation of Sec. 7·2, the square of the noise power in the frequency range Δ is [*cf.* Eq. (7·28)][1]

$$8\sigma^4 B\Delta. \tag{3}$$

According to the power criterion (*cf.* Sec. 7·3) the minimum detectable signal power is determined by putting the ratio of the signal power to the noise power equal to a constant.   Thus one obtains

$$\bar{P}_{\min} = \left(\frac{S_0^2 \tau}{\Theta_0}\right)_{\min} = k_a \sigma^2 \sqrt{\frac{\Delta}{\tau}} \frac{\sqrt{B\tau}}{h(B\tau)}. \tag{4}$$

At this point it is good to remember that in the aural method of detection one usually gates or strobes the incoming signals.   In this way a considerable improvement of the signal threshold can be achieved, since it is clear that the gating will *not* change the power of the audio tone whereas the noise power will be reduced.   In fact it can be seen that if l is the length of time that the gate stays open, the signal threshold is reduced by the *gating factor* $(l/\Theta_0)^{1/2}$.   A simple formal proof of this statement runs as follows.   With gating, the noise amplitude after the i-f amplifier can be represented by

$$N(t) = f(t)[X(t) \cos 2\pi f_c t + Y(t) \sin 2\pi f_c t],$$

where $f(t)$ is a function that is unity when the gate is open and zero otherwise.   Assuming a square-law detector, the video output will be

$$r^2(t) = f^2(t)(X^2 + Y^2) \equiv f^2(t) r_N^2(t).$$

To find the spectrum we calculate first the correlation function

$$R(\tau) = \widetilde{\widetilde{r^2(t)r^2(t+\tau)}} = 4W^2\rho^2(\tau) \frac{1}{\Theta_0} \int_0^{\Theta_0} dt\, f^2(t)f^2(t+\tau), \tag{5}$$

[1] This is for a rectangular i-f pass band of width B.

where we have made use of the fact that for a square-law detector and without gate the correlation function of noise alone is equal to $4W^2\rho^2(\tau)$ (*cf.* Sec. 7·3). Now if $l \gg 1/B$, then for all values of τ for which $\rho(\tau)$ is different from zero, the integral in (5) is very nearly equal to l. The gating therefore reduces the correlation function by the factor l/Θ_0. Consequently, the square of the noise power in the frequency range Δ will be reduced by the same factor; and since the power of the signal peak has not changed, the signal threshold will be lowered by the factor $(l/\Theta_0)^{1/2}$.

In the *meter method* of detection the aural signal is rectified and impressed on an ordinary d-c meter. The deflection of the meter determines the presence of a signal. In terms of the spectrum the situation is clearly similar to the case of the visual detection of a c-w signal. The audio filter takes the place of the i-f pass band and the meter is analogous to a low-pass video filter. Further investigation is necessary, however, to show that for the rectification of the audio signal and noise the formula of Sec. 7·2 can be used again. The difficulty lies in the fact that the audio noise is *not* Gaussian, since it originates from the rectification of the original Gaussian noise passed by the i-f amplifier. In general, therefore, the different frequency components of the audio noise are not independent of each other, nor are their amplitudes distributed according to a Gaussian distribution. However, it can be shown that, if the width Δ of the audio filter is small compared with B, then the noise passed by the audio filter is again approximately Gaussian.[1] In this case, therefore, the equations of Sec. 7·2 can be used again. Using again the power criterion it is then easily shown that for the meter method of detection

$$\bar{P}_{\min} = \left(\frac{S_0^2\tau}{\Theta_0}\right)_{\min} = k_m\sigma^2 \sqrt[4]{\frac{\Delta\Delta_m}{\tau^2}} \frac{\sqrt{B\tau}}{h(B\tau)}, \tag{6}$$

where Δ_m is the width of the low-pass filter, which is characteristic for the d-c meter, and k_m is a constant of the order of magnitude unity.

9·7. The Equivalence with the Visual Method of Detection.—In Sec. 8·7 it has been shown that for the visual method of detection the minimum detectable signal energy is given by an expression of the form

$$(S_0\tau)_{\min} = \sigma^2 C \frac{N(x,y)}{H(x,y)}, \tag{7}$$

where $x = B\tau$, $y = b\tau$, and C is a constant, which still depends on the time of observation. The function $N(x,y)$ is the fluctuating noise power, and $S_0^2 H(x,y)$ is the maximum value of the pulse after it has been deformed

[1] *Cf.* M. Kac and A. J. F. Siegert, "On the Theory of Noise in Radio Receivers with Square Law Detectors," *J. Applied Phys.*, **18**, 383 (1947). In this paper a detailed study is made of the probability distribution of the output of the audio filter for different values of the ratio Δ/B.

by the i-f and video amplifiers. For an explicit expression of the functions H and N see Eq. (8·18); here we will need only the qualitative dependence of $S_0^2\tau$ on the i-f and video bandwidths. As has been shown in the beginning of the theoretical part of Sec. 8·7, $S_0^2\tau$ will be an absolute minimum if $x = B\tau$ is of order unity and if $y \gg x$. The ratio N/H is then of order unity. Suppose, furthermore, that the train of pulses has the length θ, so that it contains θ/Θ_0 pulses. Every time a pulse is presented, a visual observation can be made; and if the observer can integrate all the observations, then, as has been shown in Secs. 7·3 and 7·5, the constant C will be inversely proportional to the square root of the total number of observations, so that

$$C = k_v \sqrt{\frac{\Theta_0}{\theta}}, \tag{3}$$

where k_v is a constant of the order of magnitude unity. In the case $B\tau \approx 1$ the visual method can therefore detect, at best, the average signal power $\bar{P}_{\min}$ given by

$$\bar{P}_{\min} = k_v \sigma^2 \frac{1}{\sqrt{\theta \Theta_0}}. \tag{9a}$$

Let us compare this result with Eq. (4), which gives the minimum detectable average signal power for the audio method of detection. Since for $B\tau \approx 1$, $h(B\tau)$ is of order unity, one would get from Eq. (4)

$$\bar{P}_{\min} = k_a \sigma^2 \sqrt{\frac{\Delta}{\tau}}, \tag{9b}$$

which is usually much larger than the value given by Eq. (9a). However, as already mentioned in Sec. 9·6 a considerable improvement can be achieved by gating or strobing the incoming signal. The improvement factor is $(l/\Theta_0)^{1/2}$ if l is the length of time that the gate stays open. Clearly it is best to take $l \approx \tau$ in order to admit the maximum amount of signal power and the minimum amount of noise. For a pulse train of length θ the signal peak will have a width of the order $1/\theta$. The best value for the width Δ of the audio filter will therefore also be of the order $1/\theta$. Taking in Eq. (9b) $\Delta = 1/\theta$ and multiplying Eq. (9b) by the best gating factor $(\tau/\Theta_0)^{1/2}$ lead to an equation of exactly the same form as Eq. (9a), which shows that in the case $B\tau \approx 1$ the visual and aural method of detection are equivalent.

The same conclusion is reached for the case $B\tau \ll 1$. With the visual method of detection it is best to take the video bandwidth b much larger than B. Since for $y \gg x$ and $x \ll 1$, $N \approx x$ and $H \approx x^2$ (see Sec. 8·7), one obtains from Eqs. (7) and (8)

$$\bar{P}_{\min} = k_v \sigma^2 \frac{1}{\sqrt{\theta \Theta_0}} \frac{1}{B\tau}.$$ (10a)

An equation of the same form is obtained for the aural method from Eq. (4). Since for $B\tau \ll 1$, $h(B\tau) \approx B\tau$, Eq. (4) becomes (with $\Delta = 1/\theta$)

$$\bar{P}_{\min} = k_c \sigma^2 \frac{1}{\sqrt{\theta \tau}} \frac{1}{\sqrt{B\tau}}.$$ (10b)

Since the pulse is now strongly deformed, so that the pulse length has become of the order $1/B$, the gate length l should now be taken equal to $1/B$. Multiplying Eq. (10b) with the best gating factor $(1/B\Theta_0)^{1/2}$ one obtains an equation of the same form as Eq. (10a).

Finally consider the case $B\tau \gg 1$. With the visual method of observation an improvement can now be obtained by narrowing the video bandwidth b to a value of the order $1/\tau$. Since for $x \gg 1$ and $y \approx 1$, N/H is of order $x^{1/2}$, one obtains from Eqs. (7) and (8)

$$\bar{P}_{\min} = k_v \sigma^2 \frac{1}{\sqrt{\theta \Theta_0}} \sqrt{B\tau}.$$ (11)

An equation of the same form is obtained for the aural method from Eq. (4), since for $B\tau \gg 1$, $h(B\tau) \approx 1$, $\Delta = 1/\theta$ and the best gating factor is $(\tau/\Theta_0)^{1/2}$.

Also for the *meter* method one reaches the same conclusions, since obviously the best choice for the meter bandwidth Δ_m is also $1/\theta$, just as the bandwidth Δ of the audio filter. This choice makes Eqs. (4) and (6) of exactly the same form, so that the arguments given for the aural method are also applicable to the meter method of detection.

CHAPTER 10

MODULATED PULSE TRAINS

This chapter treats the problem of the modulated pulse train. As is pointed out in Secs. 2·7 and 2·8, many types of modulation are possible, namely, a-m pulses, f-m pulses, width-modulated pulses, etc. These methods differ somewhat in detail, but the general solutions are similar. A detailed discussion of the a-m pulse train will therefore serve as a suitable example for other types of modulated pulse trains. To be specific, let us consider the case where the amplitude modulation consists of propeller modulation on the radar echo pulses returned from an aircraft. Before examining the effect of the propeller modulation itself (see Sec. 10·4), however, the behavior of the receiving system in response to a single modulating tone or frequency must first be discussed in detail (see Secs. 10·1 and 10·2).

10·1. The Receiving System. *The Receiver.*—As is pointed out in Sec. 2·7, the receiver is usually of a superheterodyne type with a linear second detector, with a linear third detector (or "boxcar" generator), and with some form of AGC. A block diagram of such a receiver is shown in Fig. 2·12. To be definite, let us assume the demodulated audio signal to be the voltage output of the third detector, or boxcar generator, and the AGC feedback to be derived from the average value of the audio signal. This average value is, of course, obtained from several cycles of the modulation, and it can be assured if the low-pass filter in the line between the third detector and the gain-control connection has an h-f cutoff much lower than the lowest desired audio frequency.

The third detector will be assumed to be a boxcar generator of the type described in Sec. 2·7. In the formation of boxcars the potential of some storage element, such as a capacitor, is made to assume the voltage of video signal at the instant of the latter's occurrence. The storage element is then disconnected from the video system and remains so until the arrival of the next video signal. In this fashion, flat steplike segments occur in the boxcar output voltage waveform, whose amplitudes are governed by the desired signal. As is pointed out in Sec. 2·7, the advantage of the boxcar output over other forms of audio demodulation is that it furnishes a large audio amplification plus a type of filter action that completely suppresses the PRF and all its harmonics.

There are several methods that make the storage element assume the potential of the signal.　In order that only the desired signal be made to actuate the storage element, a selection circuit is needed to sensitize the boxcar generator at the desired instant.　This selection circuit may consist of an accurately timed impulse that is made to coincide in time with the desired radar echo and allows the boxcar circuit to be activated by the desired video signal.　Thus the errors in timing that can be tolerated in this form of selection circuit are obviously less than the radar pulse duration, i.e., usually less than 1 μsec.　Since this precision is difficult to obtain, it is customary to provide a time *gate*, or *strobe* (see Sec. 2·6), which sensitizes the video section only during a defined range interval. This range interval may be several times the pulse length; hence it is much easier to set the gate on the desired echo than in the case of the accurately timed impulse already described.　The gate length G has a direct bearing on signal detectability, as will be shown in the next section.

Within the time interval allowed by the gate, it is possible that besides the desired echo, both receiver noise and perhaps other undesired signals or interference will appear.　The signal-modulation perceptibility in the boxcar output depends upon how the boxcars are formed from the gated video signals.　Two methods of formation are customarily considered. In the first method the boxcar height is proportional to the *average* video signal within the gate, and in the second method the height is proportional to the *peak* video signal in the gate.　Since the signal-modulation detectability depends upon the method of boxcar formation, it will be convenient to distinguish them.　If the boxcars are formed from the average video signal, they will be referred to as "average value" boxcars; and if they are formed from the peak-video-signal model, they will be denoted by "peak value" boxcars.　It is clear that peak-value boxcars tend to accentuate the effects of the larger video signals within the gate; and since the largest signal is usually the desired echo, the peak-value boxcar circuits are usually desirable.

The AGC is indispensable to keep the average value of the third-detector output signal constant.　This is done to reduce the effects of signal fading.　In the absence of input-signal fading the AGC is essentially inoperative and can therefore be neglected in the following discussion.　As will be shown in the next section, the properties of the system depend, however, upon the ratio of carrier signal power to noise power; therefore, as a function of this parameter, the magnitude of the output voltage of the audio system will depend upon whether the AGC is used or not.　If the AGC is used, the average value of the third-detector voltage output is constant; if not, the over-all gain of the receiver is constant.　With this in mind, a little thought will show that in both cases the average value of the boxcar-generator output is independent of the PRF.　This characteristic makes such a type of audio demodulator ideal for deriving AGC voltages in a system with a variable PRF.   It is probably the only type of demodulator that has this desirable feature.

There are certain practical difficulties in the construction of a high-quality boxcar generator, chiefly the provision of a storage element that has a small leakage of charge between pulses and can be rapidly charged or discharged during the desired video pulse.   The circuit developed by H. L. Johnson and J. L. Lawson[1] produces exceptionally high-quality boxcars.   They are flat to within a few per cent for time intervals as long as 1 sec, yet they can be actuated by a video signal as short as 0.03 μsec. This is accomplished in two steps: (1) The video signals are "stretched" into pulses perhaps 20 μsec long by a special diode circuit; (2) then the "stretched" pulses actuate the condenser storage element.   In this way the storage-element leakage can be minimized because the maximum charging current is kept low.   The entire circuit is shown in Fig. 10·1. It is designed to accept positive video input signals not greater than 5 volts in amplitude and will deliver audio boxcars of approximately 20 volts for such video signals.   It also requires an input trigger from the radar set occurring at times corresponding to the transmitted radar pulse.

The video signals are put on the grid of V_{14}.   The three tubes V_{14}, V_{15}, and V_{16} constitute a wide-band video amplifier that serves to produce a negative video signal of about 60 volts in the 300-ohm plate resistor of V_{16}.   The plate of V_{16} is direct-coupled to the cathode of the special diode V_{19}, whose plate is, in turn, run at a bias voltage of about +150 volts.   This diode was chosen for its large conductivity and its small interelectrode capacitance.   Unless V_{17} is made to conduct, the diode V_{19} will not conduct even for the large video signals produced by V_{16}. However, when the gating pulse, whose generation is discussed below, is produced in the plate circuit of V_{17}, the negative video signals will cause the diode to conduct until its plate assumes the most negative value reached by the video signals in the gate interval.   This value of voltage will be maintained until a positive pulse in the grid of V_{20} returns the plate voltage of V_{19} to its original value.   The plate voltage of V_{19} therefore amounts to a stretched video pulse.   The cathode follower V_{21} reproduces the stretched pulse (perhaps 20 μsec long), and during this time the storage condenser in the cathode of V_{22} is made to assume this same potential.   This is done by the action of a positive pulse on the grids of V_{22} and V_{23} produced by V_{12} just at the end of the gate itself.   The positive pulse on V_{22} and V_{23} causes one or both of these tubes to conduct so that the cathode of V_{22} assumes the voltage of the stretched pulse on the cathode of V_{21}.   The cessation of this "clamping" pulse produced by

[1] See R. M. Ashby, F. W. Martin, and J. L. Lawson, "Modulation of Radar Signals from Airplanes," RL Report No. 914, Mar. 28, 1946.

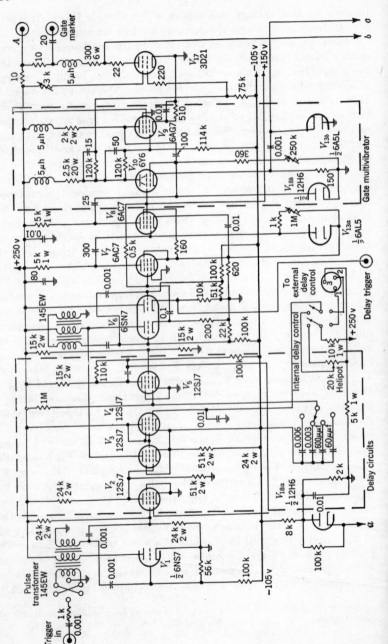

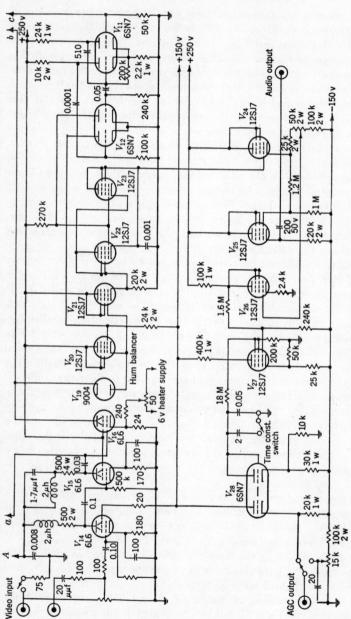

FIG. 10·1.—Wide-band boxcar and AGC circuit.

V_{12} disconnects the storage condenser until the next pulse is produced. The cathode potential of V_{22}, and hence of the cathode follower V_{24}, therefore, is the audio boxcar voltage desired. For convenience, the major portion of the d-c voltage is removed by the connection to V_{25}, whose output voltage is essentially the desired boxcar audio component. The tubes V_{26}, V_{27}, and V_{28}, serve as a direct-coupled amplifier from which the AGC voltage may be derived. The low-pass filter in this AGC link is placed in the grid circuit of V_{28}; its frequency limit can be made higher or lower than the modulation frequencies as desired.

The production of the delayed gate and associated timing pulses is accomplished by the tubes V_1 to V_{10} and their associated circuits. For any trigger pulse from the radar set that operates the blocking oscillator V_1, a standard trigger pulse of uniform shape appears on the grid of V_2. The tubes V_2, V_3, V_4, and V_5 form a high-precision delay circuit operating the blocking oscillator V_6, which, in turn, produces the delayed trigger. The amount of delay is controlled by the delay-control potentiometer that adjusts the potential on the grid of V_4. An idea of the precision available in the delay time may be obtained by noting that for a delay time of 2000 μsec a flutter, or variation in delay, of less than 0.1 μsec is ordinarily experienced. The delayed trigger operates the tubes in the monostable-state multivibrator, or "flip-flop" circuit, V_7 and V_8, which produces a small additional delay in time before operating another flip-flop circuit, composed of V_9 and V_{10}, producing the gating pulse. This small delay is helpful in observing the gate or gated signals on an external R-scope (see Sec. 2·6) operated from the delayed trigger itself. The gate-generating circuit whose output is connected to the power tube V_{17} is shunt-peaked for adequate transient response and can generate a satisfactory gate. The gate length is adjustable from 0.1 to approximately 50 μsec. The trailing edge of this gate actuates the flip-flop circuit V_{11} that generates the relatively long clamping pulse as described above. The trailing edge of the clamping pulse, in turn, generates a short pulse in V_{12}, which causes the stretched pulse, produced by the diode V_{19}, to terminate.

Several precautions have been taken to prevent hum voltages from appearing in the audio output. A "hum balancer" is shown in the cathode of V_{16}, and all hum-sensitive tubes are operated with d-c filament voltages. These tubes are V_2, V_3, V_4, V_5, V_{18}, V_{21}, V_{22}, V_{23}, V_{24}, V_{25}, V_{26}, and V_{27} and are for the most part pentodes operated as triodes. By these methods the hum appearing in the audio output has been reduced to a value less than 10 mv peak to peak.

The storage element, as can be seen, is a 0.001-μf condenser in the cathode circuit of V_{22}. To reduce the leakage from this condenser to a satisfactory value, it is necessary to operate the filaments of the tubes

V_{22}, V_{23}, and V_{24} at about one-half the rated voltage. If this is done, the boxcars will be flat to within a few per cent even for time intervals as long as 1 sec.

The charging time of the boxcar generator is governed by the video response of the circuits between the video input terminals and the cathode terminal on V_{20}. Up to the plate circuit of V_{16} the circuit is simply a conventional shunt-peaked video amplifier. However, the forward resistance of the diode V_{19}, appearing as a series element in the coupling

FIG. 10·2.—Audio-frequency reed meter.

circuit, is large enough to upset the peaking design of this network. The best value of inductance to use is most easily found by trial. With the value indicated in Fig. 10·1b the over-all video bandwidth to the half-power point exceeds 10 Mc/sec. This ensures an adequate response for video signals as short as 0.03 μsec.

The Indicator.—Many forms of indication are possible, but for the sake of brevity only one method will be discussed—that suggested by R. M. Walker, which has lent itself well to experimental work. In this indicator a bank of electrically excited reeds is incorporated with the necessary audio amplifier. Each reed is characterized by a particular resonant frequency and by a damping term that fixes its bandwidth, or equivalent Q. Inspection of the bank of reeds will provide an audio-amplitude analysis of the audio signal, provided the bandwidths of the successive reeds are roughly similar. A photograph of a set of reeds suitable for experimental analysis is shown in Fig. 10·2. The frequency range covered by this instrument is approximately 16 to 85 cps. In this photograph is shown the response of the instrument to a 70-cps audio modulation in receiver noise. Further details will be discussed in the next section.

The problem of driving such a bank of reeds from an audio source of varying amplitude is similar to the problem of making the radar receiver respond to a varying input signal. The problem of finding some method of alleviating saturation in the amplifier is solved by providing the necessary audio amplifier with an AGC that operates from the *modulation* amplitude. In this way the average audio voltage driving the reeds will be maintained essentially constant. If this audio AGC is used, the indicator system can be made to operate at maximum sensitivity.

10·2. Experimental Results.—In discussing the experimental results, it is desirable to consider controlled experiments made under four different conditions. These conditions are chosen by fixing various values of signal, noise, modulation frequency, and fractional modulation.

Behavior of a Noiseless Receiving System in the Presence of a Signal.—In the following discussion the signal-carrier amplitude will refer to the unmodulated pulse amplitude. When modulated less than 100 per cent, the average pulse amplitude is, of course, equal to the unmodulated pulse amplitude and plays the same role in this problem that the carrier plays in ordinary radio modulation. Let the signal pulse length be represented by τ, the gate length by G, the signal modulation frequency by p, and the fractional modulation by ϵ. When the signal falls within the gate, the receiver AGC adjusts the receiver gain so that the average height of the video signal and therefore the average output voltage of the peak-value boxcars are held at a constant value. Since the signal is the only voltage in the gate, the entire behavior of the system is *independent* of the gate length G and the section of the gate in which the signal is found.

The frequency analysis of the boxcar output can be found from Eq. (2·29). It is necessary in that expression only to put in a value for pulse length equal to the reciprocal of the PRF f_r. A convenient nomograph for obtaining all the output frequencies is shown in Fig. 2·12, where the vertical lines located at the PRF and its harmonics must be eliminated. In this nomograph the amplitudes of the various frequency components are unchanged by traversing the diagram in a vertical direction. It may seem strange that if two input signals of equal modulation amplitude, one at 20,100 cps and the other at 100 cps, are introduced into identical boxcar generators whose PRF is 1000 pps, the two outputs will have *the same amplitude* and the same frequency, namely, 100 cps. This, however, is the case; and if the boxcar-generator output voltages are analyzed under the two conditions, they will be found to be identical.

For a linear receiving system there are at least two interesting phenomena regarding the boxcar output worthy of discussion.

1. If the injected wave consists of several modulation frequencies, the output frequencies are represented in the diagram in Fig. 2·12 by the intersections of the lines at the modulation frequencies with the array of 45° lines. There are no cross terms due to "beats" between the input modulation frequencies. In other words, effects produced on the output by input modulating frequencies can be thought of as only the sum of the individual effects of the individual modulating frequencies. This is one very cogent reason why a linear receiving system is desirable.

2. If the input wave consists of a modulation term that is itself modulated at a slow rate (ϵ can be thought of as a very slow sinusoidal variable), the slow modulation frequency itself will not appear in the output. Only sidebands will appear in the output frequencies, separated from the main frequencies by the frequency of the slow modulation. Here again the input frequencies are p and $p \pm u$, where u is the modulation frequency of ϵ. The output frequencies are on y those given by the independent action of these three input frequencies, and u itself will not appear in the output.

These remarks apply when the input modulating function has a definite time phase. They do not apply when the injected wave is, for example, receiver noise. This case will be discussed below.

In practice the receiving system is not quite linear, and cross terms may be detected. The greatest nonlinearity appearing in the receiving system just described is in the audio amplifier, whose harmonic generation, however, is very low. The entire receiving system can be made sufficiently linear to reduce the effects of harmonic generation to negligible values.

Behavior of the Receiving System in the Presence of Receiver Noise Alone.—In the absence of a signal the audio output voltage appears to be a function of both the gate length G and the PRF f_r. Experiments have been performed varying both of these parameters, and results are depicted in Figs. 10·3 and 10·4.

The dependence of audio noise on the gate length G is shown in Fig. 10·3. An experiment was performed in which the average value of audio noise voltage in a frequency range of approximately 10 to 40 cps was measured as a function of the gate length G. A receiver whose i-f bandwidth was 2 Mc/sec was used. The experimental results are plotted in

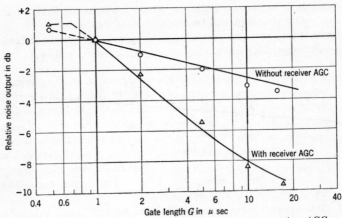

FIG. 10.3.—Noise output vs. gate length, with and without receiver AGC.

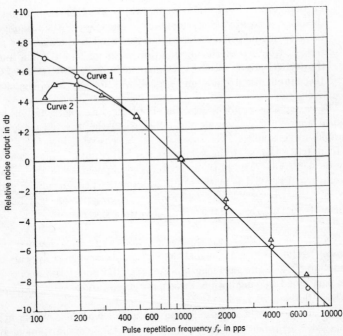

FIG. 10.4.—Noise output vs. PRF f_r. Curve 1 is for the channel covering the range from 20 to 90 cps. Curve 2 is for the channel 10 to 40 cps.

Fig. 10·3 along with a theoretical curve that will be deduced in the next section. It can be seen that the noise output falls with increasing gate length. For both cases (receiver AGC on or off) a good agreement is obtained with the theoretical results.

The dependence of noise on the PRF is depicted in Fig. 10·4. Curve 1 indicates the total noise power in the channel from approximately 20 to 90 cps, and Curve 2 shows the total noise in the channel of 10 to 40 cps. It can be seen that for both curves (normalized at a PRF of 400 pps) the noise power is inversely proportional to the frequency at a sufficiently high PRF, as predicted by the theory to be presented shortly. At a low PRF observed deviations from this law are more severe for the 20- to 90-cps channel than for the lower-frequency audio channel. These deviations are undoubtedly the result of the nonuniform spectrum of noise itself, that is, to the term

$$\frac{f_r}{(\pi f)^2} \sin^2 \frac{\pi f}{f_r}$$

in Eq. (7), where

$$\Theta_0 = \frac{1}{f_r}.$$

Behavior of the Receiving System in the Presence of Receiver Noise and Unmodulated Signals.—In this case the total output noise power is a function of three quantities: the pulse length τ, the gate length G, and the ratio of signal carrier to receiver noise power, which we may denote by z. The last two quantities are more precisely defined as follows:

1. The gate ength G may be written as $n\tau$ and is approximately equal to n/B if B is the limiting system bandwidth up to the output of the video system. This limitation may be in the i-f unit or in the video system. The quantity B is ordinarily approximately equal to $1/\tau$. If the limitation is in the video system, however, B represents twice the video-frequency bandwidth.

2. Let z be defined as the ratio of signal carrier to receiver noise power, which is measured in the i-f unit after the i-f narrowing has taken place.

Figure 10·5 shows the experimental results of noise output power as a function of z. The equipment used in obtaining these data was a linear receiver, a linear detector, and a peak-value boxcar generator using the AGC. The output noise power shown is measured in decibels relative to its value for no signal carrier. The receiver i-f bandwidth was approximately 2 Mc/sec, and the pulse length was 1 μsec. It will be noted that two curves are shown, representing the results obtained for a narrow gate ($n = 1$) and the result for a wide gate ($n = 10$). Both of these curves become identical for large values of z, as they should in a peak-value device. That is, if the signal is large enough, the gate length is unimportant. For low values of z, a maximum is obtained whose position and amplitude is a function of the gate length.

The slope of the curves for large values of z becomes -1, and the essential reason for this is the receiver AGC, which causes the output receiver noise power to be inversely proportional to the signal-carrier input power. It will be noted, however, that for the values of z larger

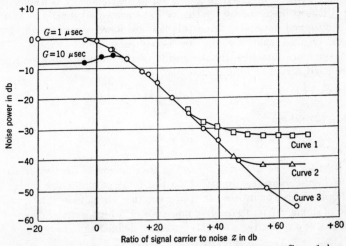

Fig. 10·5.—Dependence of noise power on the signal carrier power. Curve 1 shows the results with inadequate receiver gain control. Curve 2 shows the results with extraneous 26-cps input. Curve 3 shows results with adequate gain control. Curves 1 to 3 coalesce in regions of intermediate signal carrier power but separate into two curves at low power depending on the gate length G.

than 1000 ($+30$ db), deviations from the inverse relationship were found to occur. Three representative experimental conditions are shown in Fig. 10·5.

1. Curve 1 shows an asymptotic approach of the output noise power to a value of -33 db. This resulted from an oversight in the design of the receiver gain control that was placed in the customary position, that is, in the control-grid line of the first stages in the i-f amplifier. The residual output noise was found to be contributed by the late stages in the i-f amplifier, which were not connected to the gain control. This defect was rectified by applying the gain-control voltage to more stages in the receiver.

2. Curve 2 represents the results obtained on a trial with adequate gain control but in which the output noise was observed to

approach a constant value of -43 db. At the same time the output was observed to consist almost entirely of a 26-cps component. This was traced to a microphonic effect in the receiver. At this level of operation, microphonic difficulties were encountered in several places in the receiver, and extreme care had to be exercised to reduce them. The principal sources of difficulties were the i-f stages themselves.

3. Curve 3 represents the most satisfactory result obtained. Because of occasional microphonic difficulties, it has not always been reproducible, but it can be obtained under certain conditions. Extreme care had to be taken with the receiver power supply to achieve this result.

In any case excellent agreement was finally obtained between the experimental results and the theoretically expected results presented in the next section.

Detection of Modulated Signal in the Presence of Receiver Noise.—It may be asked why this question has not been solved by the independent analysis of signals and noise just given. The paradoxical nature of this problem can be illustrated by showing that the desired solution cannot be derived from the previous results.

It has been shown that the behavior of the system in the presence of a signal alone is *independent* of the gate length G. It has also been shown that the output noise power in a system in the absence of a signal is *reduced* by a long gate. By simple reasoning, therefore, one would come to the conclusion that a long receiver gate is desirable for a good signal-to-noise ratio, hence good sensitivity for the detection of weak modulation. This, however, is completely wrong; the actual result is that a short gate is preferable for the best sensitivity. This illustration shows that each case must be treated separately.

Fortunately the problem has been completely solved, with certain restrictions, by M. C. Wang and G. E. Uhlenbeck.[1] The solution will be given in Sec. 10·4. A simple formula may be given that expresses the percentage of signal modulation necessary for various degrees of visibility in receiver noise, namely,

$$\epsilon^2 = \frac{2Kb}{zf_r} C(z,G), \tag{1}$$

where
  ϵ = the fractional audio modulation.
  f_r = PRF.
  z = signal-carrier-to-receiver-noise power ratio.
  b = indicator reed noise bandwidth.

[1] See Appendix I in RL Report No. S-10, May 16, 1944, entitled "Detection of Propeller and Sambo Modulations," J. L. Lawson, editor.

$C(z,G)$ = a correction term that is approximately unity for values of z greater than 10. It is given explicitly in Sec. 10·4.

K = the ratio of audio signal power delivered to the reed to the average noise power on the reed.

The constant K may be set to the smallest value for consistent visibility, and under these conditions the above formula gives the corresponding value of ϵ. This will be the smallest fractional modulation that can be detected.

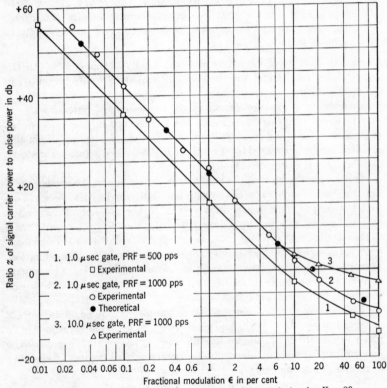

FIG. 10·6.—Dependence of signal carrier power on modulation for $K = 20$.

Complete agreement with the preceding formula is obtained experimentally, as is shown in Fig. 10·6. These curves are taken for $K = 20$, where the signal is easily visible. For the three experimental curves the following conditions apply:

1. PRF = 5000 cps, $G = 1$ μsec, $\tau = 1$ μsec.
2. PRF = 1000 cps, $G = 1$ μsec, $\tau = 1$ μsec.
3. PRF = 1000 cps, $G = 10$ μsec, $\tau = 1$ μsec.

Along with Curve 2 are shown some theoretical points for comparison. Excellent agreement is obtained both in the shape of the curve for low values of signal carrier power z and in the absolute value. The astonishing agreement in absolute value is perhaps fortuitous, but it should be mentioned that there are *no* arbitrary constants. The value of K

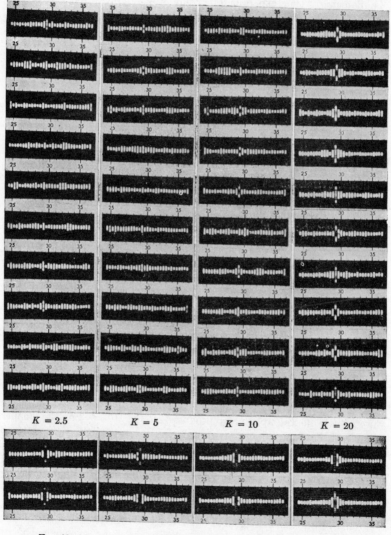

FIG. 10·7.—Photographs of reed meters at various values of K.

was measured experimentally by the reed deflections—with noise and with the audio signal added. Therefore, it appears that Eq. (1) is completely valid if the receiving system is properly designed and constructed.

One striking thing about this is the extremely low values of ϵ that can be detected. One experimental point was obtained for $\epsilon = 10^{-4}$; z itself was $+56$ db.

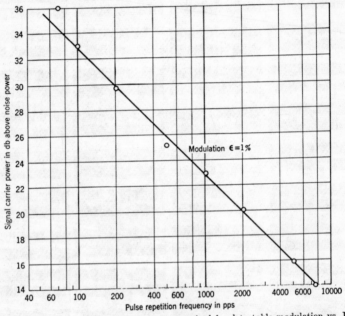

Fig. 10·8.—Variation of signal carrier power required for detectable modulation vs. PRF for $\epsilon = 1$ per cent.

The smallest value of K that permits visibility of signals in noise is a very controversial matter and takes on as many values as there are observers. For this reason a signal was photographed for various values of K; these photographs are reproduced in Fig. 10·7. For the smaller values of K, fluctuations occur from one instant to the next, and so several photographs are given that were taken at regular 15-sec intervals. The modulation signal in all cases occurs at 29 cps. It is the opinion of most observers that the photographs show up the signal slightly better than does visual observation because of the absence of time fluctuations in the photographs. Nevertheless, it will be seen that for $K = 2.5$, it would be an extremely good (and undoubtedly optimistic) operator who could point out the 29-cps signal without previous knowledge of its existence.

The effect of PRF upon visibility is illustrated in Fig. 10·8. In this experiment ϵ was fixed at a value of 1 per cent. As the repetition rate was changed, z was adjusted to maintain K at a value of 20. It can be seen that the product of z and the PRF is constant, as is predicted by the general formula [Eq. (1)].

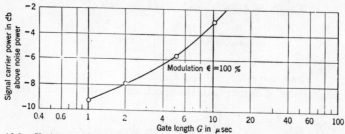

FIG. 10·9.—Variation of signal carrier power required for detectable modulation ($K = 20$) vs. gate length G for $\epsilon = 100$ per cent.

The loss in signal visibility accompanying the use of long gate lengths is noticeable only for small values of z and therefore large values of ϵ. A curve of the necessary value of z required for consistent visibility ($K = 20$) as a function of gate length G is shown in Fig. 10·9. The PRF was set at 1000 cps for this run. It can be seen that an immediate drop in signal visibility is encountered as the gate is made longer than τ. However, this represents the one set of conditions in which z is most nearly sensitive to G, namely, $\epsilon = 100$ per cent. For most values of

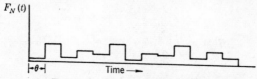

FIG. 10·10.—Boxcar output voltage.

signal intensity encountered it appears that a relatively wide gate could be employed without serious loss in signal visibility. A wide gate, however, is undesirable from an interference standpoint.

10·3. Theoretical Derivation of the Boxcar Spectrum of Noise Alone. When there is receiver noise but no signal, the boxcar generator will produce a step curve, where the heights of the steps vary in a random fashion. This is shown diagrammatically in Fig. 10·10. There will be a probability distribution $P(y)\,dy$ that the height of one boxcar will lie between y and $y + dy$. This distribution will depend on the probability distribution of a noise deflection *before* the noise enters the boxcar generator, and it will depend on the gate length of the boxcar generator. How to find $P(y)$ will be discussed later in this section [see Eq. (12)].

If it is known, the spectrum of the boxcar output can be computed according to the methods explained in Chap. 3. In fact in Sec. 3·4 the problem of finding the spectrum of a series of pulses of random height but fixed repetition interval has been considered, and the results obtained there can be immediately adapted to find the boxcar spectrum. In Sec. 3·4 it was shown that for a series of pulses of the form

$$F_N(t) = \sum_k y_k F(t - k\Theta_0),$$ (2)

where the y_k are the random heights and where $F(t)$ represents the shape of a single pulse of unit height, the spectrum is given by the expression

$$G_N(f) = \frac{2}{\Theta_0} |B(f)|^2 \left\{ [\overline{y^2} - (\bar{y})^2] + \frac{(\bar{y})^2}{\Theta_0} \sum_{n=0}^{\infty} \left(f - \frac{n}{\Theta_0} \right) \right\},$$ (3)

where

$$B(f) = \int_{-\infty}^{+\infty} dx\, F(x) e^{-2\pi i f x}$$ (4)

is the Fourier transform of the pulse shape. For the boxcar spectrum,

$$F(t) = \begin{cases} 1 & \text{for } \dfrac{-\Theta_0}{2} < t < \dfrac{+\Theta_0}{2}, \\ 0 & \text{otherwise,} \end{cases}$$ (5)

so that

$$B(f) = \int_{-\frac{\Theta_0}{2}}^{+\frac{\Theta_0}{2}} dx\, e^{-2\pi i f x} = \frac{1}{\pi f} \sin \pi f \Theta_0.$$ (6)

Since $B(f)$ is zero for $f = n/\Theta_0$, the δ-functions in Eq. (3) will not contribute for $n \neq 0$ and can therefore be omitted. Only for $n = 0$ will there be a contribution; this represents the d-c term of the spectrum. The final result for the average power spectrum can therefore be written in the form

$$G_N(f) = \frac{2 \sin^2 \pi f \Theta_0}{(\pi f)^2 \Theta_0} \left\{ [\overline{y^2} - (\bar{y})^2] + \frac{(\bar{y})^2}{\Theta_0} \varepsilon(f) \right\}.$$ (7)

This result can be described by saying that besides the d-c term $(\bar{y})^2$, the spectrum is the same as that of a single boxcar but that its intensity is determined by the fluctuation of the boxcar heights $[\overline{y^2} - (\bar{y})^2]$.

To proceed further more must be known about the probability distribution $P(y)$ of the boxcar heights. If a *linear second detector* is used, the probability distribution of the noise voltage in the video stage, i.e., before the noise enters the boxcar generator, is given by[1]

$$Q_N(r) \, dr = \frac{2r}{N^2} e^{-\frac{r^2}{N^2}} \, dr, \tag{8}$$

where N^2 is the average noise power after the i-f amplifier and r is the voltage. The cases of the short and of the long gate will be considered separately.

Short Gate.—In the case of the short gate, G is smaller than or, at most, equal to the correlation time of the video noise. Since this correlation time is of the order of $1/B$ and $B \approx 1/\tau$, where τ is the pulse length, we shall assume that

$$G \approx \tau. \tag{9}$$

The distribution function P is then identical with Q, and from Eq. (8) it follows that

$$\bar{y} = \frac{\sqrt{\pi}}{2} N; \qquad \overline{y^2} = N^2; \qquad \overline{y^2} - (\bar{y})^2 = N^2 \left(1 - \frac{\pi}{4}\right). \tag{10}$$

Long Gate.—Since the height y of the peak-value boxcar is equal to the *peak* noise voltage in the gate G when the gate is long, the probability distribution of the maximum noise voltage in G must be determined. To do this exactly is a complicated problem, but an approximate answer can be found by dividing G into n parts, each of length τ. Therefore[2]

$$G \approx n\tau. \tag{11}$$

The noise voltages in these n parts may then be considered to be independent of one another, and the probability of a maximum value y is given by

$$\begin{aligned} P(y) &= nQ(y) \left[\int_0^y dr \, Q(r) \right]^{n-1} \\ &= \frac{2ny}{N^2} e^{-\frac{y^2}{N^2}} (1 - e^{-\frac{y^2}{N^2}})^{n-1}. \end{aligned} \tag{12}$$

This gives [3]

[1] See Eq. (3·71a), where r is denoted by L and the average noise power by σ^2; N^2 has the *same* meaning as the symbol $2W$ used in Chap 7.

[2] This definition of n should *not* be taken too literally. The correlation distance in the video stage is only of the *order* of τ. For a more precise comparison with experiment, it would probably be better to introduce an adjustable constant here.

[3] The notation is such that

$$\binom{\alpha}{\beta} = \frac{\alpha!}{\beta!(\alpha - \beta)!}.$$

$$\bar{y} = \frac{\sqrt{\pi}}{2} N \sum_{k=1}^{n} (-1)^{k+1} \binom{n}{k} \frac{1}{k^{\frac{1}{2}}}, \qquad (13)$$

$$\overline{y^2} = N^2 \sum_{k=1}^{n} \frac{1}{k}. \qquad (14)$$

Numerical values of these functions for different values of n are given in Table 10·1, and their behavior is shown in Fig. 10·11.

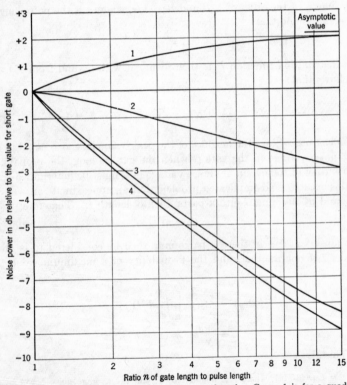

FIG. 10·11.—Dependence of noise power on gate length. Curve 1 is for a quadratic detector without receiver AGC; Curve 2, a linear detector without receiver AGC; Curve 3, a quadratic detector with receiver AGC; and Curve 4, a linear detector with receiver AGC.

Quadratic Detector.—For the sake of completeness, the results for a *quadratic second detector* are also given. The formulas used in this latter case are as follows:

Short gate:

$$\bar{y} = N^2; \qquad \overline{y^2} = 2N^4; \qquad \overline{y^2} - (\bar{y})^2 = N^4. \tag{15}$$

Long gate:

$$\bar{y} = N^2 \sum_{k=1}^{n} \frac{1}{k}; \qquad \overline{y^2} = 2N^4 \sum_{k=1}^{n} (-1)^{k+1} \binom{n}{k} \frac{1}{k^2}, \tag{16}$$

$$\overline{y^2} - (\bar{y})^2 = N^4 \sum_{k=1}^{n} \frac{1}{k^2}. \tag{17}$$

The dependence of the spectrum $G_N(f)$ on the gate length G can be computed in the following way: When *no* AGC is used, one determines $\overline{y^2} - (\bar{y})^2$ as a function of n (or of G); *with* AGC, the $(\bar{y})^2$ is always brought

TABLE 10·1.—DEPENDENCE OF CERTAIN FUNCTIONS ON n FOR A LINEAR AND FOR A QUADRATIC DETECTOR

Linear Detector

n	$\dfrac{\bar{y}}{\frac{1}{2}N\sqrt{\pi}}$	$\dfrac{\overline{y^2}}{N^2}$	$\dfrac{\overline{y^2} - (\bar{y})^2}{N^2\left(1 - \frac{\pi}{4}\right)}$		$\dfrac{\overline{y^2} - (\bar{y})^2}{(\bar{y})^2\left(\frac{4}{\pi} - 1\right)}$	
			Value	Db	Value	Db
1	1	1	1	0	1	0
2	1.29	1.5	0.875	−0.57	0.524	−2.81
3	1.46	1.83	0.786	−1.04	0.370	−4.32
4	1.57	2.08	0.726	−1.40	0.296	−5.28
6	1.72	2.45	0.651	−1.86	0.223	−6.52
8	1.82	2.72	0.600	−2.21	0.183	−7.37
11	1.92	3.02	0.553	−2.58	0.150	−8.24
15	2.02	3.32	0.512	−2.90	0.124	−9.05

Quadratic Detector

n	$\dfrac{\bar{y}}{N^2}$	$\dfrac{\overline{y^2}}{2N^4}$	$\dfrac{\overline{y^2} - (\bar{y})^2}{N^4}$		$\dfrac{\overline{y^2} - (\bar{y})^2}{(\bar{y})^2}$	
			Value	Db	Value	Db
1	1	1	1	0	1	0
2	1.50	1.75	1.25	+0.97	0.556	−2.56
3	1.83	2.36	1.36	+1.34	0.405	−3.93
4	2.08	2.88	1.42	+1.53	0.32	−4.84
6	2.45	3.75	1.49	+1.73	0.248	−6.06
8	2.72	4.45	1.53	+1.84	0.207	−6.84
11	3.02	5.34	1.56	+1.92	0.170	−7.70
15	3.32	6.29	1.58	+1.99	0.144	−8.42

down to the same level, so that then one determines $[\overline{y^2} - (\bar{y})^2]/(\bar{y})^2$ as a function of G. For the comparison with experiment see Fig. 10·3.

10·4. Theoretical Derivation of Signal-modulation Threshold.—In order to derive the minimum detectable amplitude modulation of the pulse train, one first has to obtain the boxcar spectrum when a signal is superimposed on the noise. The same procedure as in Sec. 3·4 can be followed. We can represent the modulation frequency by p and the fractional modulation by ϵ. Since in the averaging over all possible boxcar heights the average values will be different in the successive gates because of the modulation, one obtains for the boxcar spectrum, instead of Eq. (7), the following expression:

$$G_{S+N}(f) = \frac{2 \sin^2 \pi f \Theta_0}{(\pi f)^2 \Theta_0} \lim_{M \to \infty} \frac{1}{M} \left\{ \sum_{k=0}^{M-1} [\overline{y_k^2} - (\bar{y}_k)^2] + \left| \sum_{k=0}^{M-1} \bar{y}_k e^{-2\pi i f \Theta_0 k} \right|^2 \right\}. \quad (18)$$

Let us assume that again a *linear second detector* is used and again divide the discussion on the basis of gate length.

Short Gate.—The probability distribution for y, when a short gate is used, will be the same as the probability distribution for the voltage in the video stage, and this is known to be[1]

$$P(y) \equiv Q_{S+N}(y) = \frac{2y}{N^2} e^{-\frac{y^2 + S^2}{N^2}} I_0 \left(\frac{2yS}{N^2} \right), \quad (19)$$

where S^2 is the signal power and $I_0(x)$ is the Bessel function of zero order and with purely imaginary argument. For the average values the following is obtained:

$$\bar{y} = \frac{\sqrt{\pi}}{2} NF \left(-\frac{1}{2}, 1; -\frac{S^2}{N^2} \right), \\ \overline{y^2} = S^2 + N^2, \quad \right\} \quad (20)$$

where F denotes the confluent hypergeometric function.[2] To evaluate the expressions in brackets in Eq. (18), it must be remembered that because of the modulation, the signal strength S depends on k; in Eq. (20), therefore, S is replaced by

$$S_k = S_0(1 + \epsilon \sin 2\pi k \Theta_0 p). \quad (21)$$

We shall *assume* ϵ to be small. By developing in powers of ϵ up to ϵ^2 and using Eqs. (18) and (20) one finds that the spectrum is

[1] See Eq. (7·13a); one obtains Eq. (19) by replacing in Eq. (7·13a) $\alpha^2 + \beta^2$ by S^2 and by writing again for the average noise power the symbol N^2 instead of $2W$.

[2] See Eqs. (7·14a) and (7·14b); for a summary of the properties of the confluent hypergeometric function $F(a, b; z)$ and for some of the integrals, which are needed, see Sec. 7·6.

$$G_{S+N}(f) = \frac{N^2 \sin^2 \pi f \Theta_0}{2\pi f^2 \Theta_0} \left\{ \left[\frac{4}{\pi}(1+z) - F^2 + \epsilon^2 \left(\frac{2z}{\pi} - 2z^2 F'^2 - zFF' \right. \right. \right.$$
$$\left. - 2z^2 FF'' \right) \right] + \frac{1}{\Theta_0} \left[F + \frac{1}{2}\epsilon^2(zF' + 2z^2 F'') \right]^2 \delta(f)$$
$$\left. + \frac{1}{\Theta_0}\epsilon^2 z^2 F'^2 \, \delta[f - (sf_r \pm p)] + \cdots \right\}. \quad (22)$$

In this equation F stands for $F(-\frac{1}{2}, 1; -z)$ and the primes denote differentiations with respect to z, where z is defined by

$$z \equiv \frac{S_0^2}{N^2} = \frac{\text{unmodulated signal power}}{\text{noise power}}. \quad (23)$$

In this approximation the spectrum (Fig. 10·12) consists of a continuous part (given by the first term inside the braces) on which there is superimposed, besides the d-c portion (as given by the second term), the signal

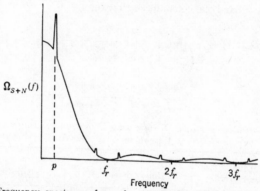

FIG. 10·12.—Frequency spectrum of a pulse, amplitude-modulated with frequency p.

spectrum, which has just the same frequencies as those given by Eq. (2·29). It can easily be shown that, in fact, for $N \to 0$, Eq. (22) gives precisely the squares of the amplitudes of the Fourier development [Eq. (2·27)]. On the other hand, for $S \to 0$ or $z \to 0$, Eq. (22) goes over into the pure noise spectrum [Eqs. (7) and (10)].

It should be emphasized that *only* when higher powers of ϵ are neglected do no new discrete frequencies appear. Developing this theory further, we should also get, for instance, the discrete frequencies $sf_r \pm 2p$; their intensities will be of the order of ϵ^4 and will go to zero when $N \to 0$.[1]

For further discussion of Eq. (22) it is well to neglect the effect of

[1] Equation (22) and the following results can therefore be trusted only when ϵ is not too large, say less than 30 per cent.

the modulation of the signal on the continuous part and on the d-c part of the spectrum, so that Eq. (21) simplifies to

$$G_{S+N}(f) = \frac{N^2 \sin^2 \pi f \Theta_0}{2\pi f^2 \Theta_0} \left\{ \frac{4}{\pi}(1+z) - F^2 + \frac{1}{\Theta_0} F^2 \delta(f) + \frac{\epsilon^2 z^2 F'^2}{\Theta_0} \right.$$
$$\left. \delta[f - (sf_r \pm p)] \right\}. \quad (24)$$

This can be checked experimentally in different ways. The depression of the continuous noise spectrum caused by the presence of a signal carrier can be determined. If an AGC receiver is used, this corresponds to measuring the function

$$D_L(z,1) = \frac{\frac{4}{\pi}(1+z) - F^2}{\left(\frac{4}{\pi} - 1\right)F^2}, \quad (25)$$

where we have fixed the constant so that for $z = 0$, $D_L = 1$. For large z we obtain

$$D_L(z,1) \approx \frac{1}{2\left(\frac{4}{\pi} - 1\right)z}\left(1 - \frac{3}{4z} + \frac{1}{8z^2} - \cdots\right); \quad (26)$$

for small z

$$D_L(z,1) \approx 1 - \frac{1}{2(4-\pi)}z^2 + \frac{2}{3(4-\pi)}z^3 - \cdots. \quad (27)$$

TABLE 10·2.—RELATIVE NOISE OUTPUT AS A FUNCTION OF THE SIGNAL CARRIER STRENGTH FOR A LINEAR OR A QUADRATIC DETECTOR

$z = \dfrac{\text{signal carrier power}}{\text{noise power}}$		$D_L(z,1)$ (linear detector)		$D_Q(z,1)$ (quadratic detector)	
Value	Db	Value	Db	Value	Db
0	$-\infty$	1	0	1	0
0.30	-5.22	0.964	-0.16	0.948	-0.24
0.75	-1.24	0.858	-0.66	0.816	-0.88
1.0	0	0.795	-1.00	0.750	-1.25
1.4	1.46	0.703	-1.52	0.660	-1.81
2.0	3.01	0.553	-2.29	0.555	-2.56
3.0	4.77	0.425	-3.36	0.438	-3.58
4.0	6.02	0.374	-4.28	0.360	-4.44
6.0	7.78	0.263	-5.79	0.266	-5.76
8.0	9.03	0.205	-6.89	0.210	-6.78
13.0	11.14	0.133	-8.78	0.138	-8.62
30.0	14.77	0.0596	-12.25	0.0635	-11.98
100.0	20.0	0.0182	-17.41	0.0197	-17.06
1000	30.0	0.00183	-27.38	0.002	-27

Numerical values of $D_L(z,1)$ are given in Table 10·2 and in Fig. 10·13. Also included are the results for a quadratic detector. The formula is then simply

$$D_Q(z,1) = \frac{1 + 2z}{(1 + z)^2}.\qquad(28)$$

Since for large z this reduces to $2/z$, on a logarithmic plot $D_L(z,1)$ and $D_Q(z,1)$ will become parallel and about 0.4 db apart.

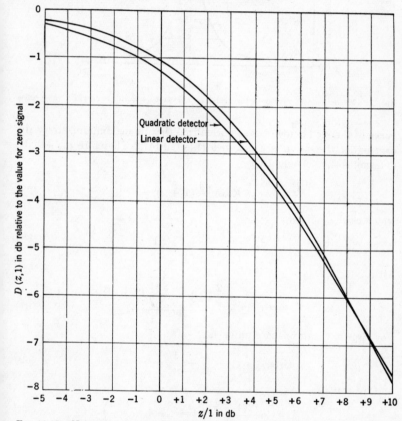

Fig. 10·13.—Noise reduction factor $D(z,1)$ caused by unmodulated signal in a short gate.

$$z = \frac{\text{unmodulated signal power}}{\text{noise power}}.$$

A more important result, which can be derived from Eq. (24), is the determination of the *minimum detectable modulation* ϵ_{min}. It may be expected that the discrete frequency p (see Fig. 10·12) will be detected when its power is a certain number, for example, K_{min}, times the power in the noise of approximately the same frequency. How large K_{min} has to be can be determined only experimentally. How much noise power the signal has to compete with depends on the bandwidth b of the final reed detector. Let us define b in such a way that when the power response

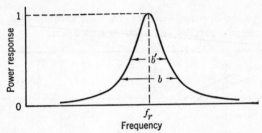

Fig. 10·14.—Schematic reed-detector response curve; $b' = 3$ db bandwidth, $b = $ noise bandwidth.

curve of the reed detector is so normalized that its maximum is unity the *area* under the curve is equal to b (Fig. 10·14). Therefore ϵ_{min} will be determined by the equation

$$\frac{\epsilon_{min}^2 z^2 F'^2}{\Theta_0} = K_{min} b \left[\frac{4}{\pi} (1 + z) - F^2 \right], \tag{29}$$

which can be written

$$\epsilon_{min}^2 = \frac{2 K_{min} \Theta_0 b}{z} C_L(z,1), \tag{30}$$

with

$$C_L(z,1) = \frac{\dfrac{2}{\pi}(1 + z) - \dfrac{1}{2}F^2}{z F'^2}. \tag{31}$$

For large z, C_L approaches unity as

$$C_L(z,1) \approx 1 + \frac{1}{4z} + \frac{1}{8z^2} + \cdots ; \tag{32}$$

and for small z,

$$C_L(z,1) \approx \frac{2(4 - \pi)}{\pi z} \left(1 + \frac{3}{2} z + \cdots \right). \tag{33}$$

In Table 10·3 and Fig. 10·15 are presented the numerical values for the correction factor $C_L(z,1)$, together with the values for the *quadratic detector*, where the formula is simply

$$C_Q(z,1) = \frac{1 + 2z}{2z}. \tag{34}$$

Long Gate.—When the gate is long, the formulas become rather complicated. First there must be determined from Eq. (19) the probability distribution of a peak value y in G; this can be done in a way analogous to the derivation of Eq. (12) from Eq. (8). We find

$$P(y) \, dy = \frac{2y \, dy}{N^2} e^{-\frac{y^2+S^2}{N^2}} I_0\left(\frac{2yS}{N^2}\right)(1 - e^{-\frac{y^2}{N^2}})^{n-1}$$

$$+ \, (n-1) \frac{2y \, dy}{N^2} e^{-\frac{y^2}{N^2}} (1 - e^{-\frac{y^2}{N^2}})^{n-2} \int_0^y \frac{2x \, dx}{N^2} e^{-\frac{x^2+S^2}{N^2}} I_0\left(\frac{2Sx}{N^2}\right). \quad (35)$$

From this must be calculated the average values $\bar{y}$ and $\overline{y^2}$; then S must again be replaced by S_k [as given by Eq. (21)] and developed in powers

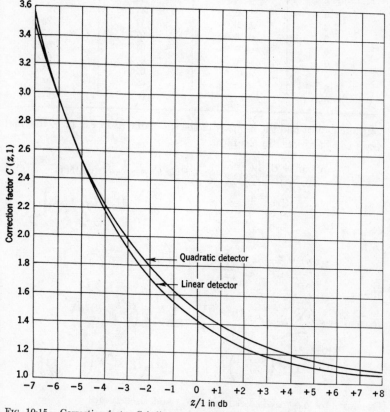

FIG. 10·15.—Correction factor $C\,(z,1)$ as a function of z, in a short gate. The minimum detectable modulation is given by

$$\epsilon^2{}_{\min} = \frac{2K\theta b}{z} \, C\,(z,1).$$

of ϵ.   An expression of the same general form as Eq. (22) is then obtained
for the spectrum, except that now the three parts (continuous spectrum,
d-c term, and signal spectrum) will depend on the gate length n cr G as
well as on z.   If one neglects the effect of signal modulation on the

TABLE 10·3.—CORRECTION FACTORS FOR A LINEAR OR A QUADRATIC DETECTOR

z		$C_L(z,1)$ (linear detector)	$C_Q(z,1)$ (quadratic detector)
Value	Db		
0	$-\infty$	∞	∞
0.2	-6.99	3.56	3.5
0.5	-3.01	1.94	2.0
1.0	0	1.41	1.5
2.0	$+3.01$	1.17	1.25
4.0	$+6.02$	1.073	1.125
6.0	$+7.78$	1.045	1.083
8.0	$+9.03$	1.034	1.063
10.0	$+10.0$	1.026	1.050
12.0	$+10.79$	1.021	1.042
30.0	$+14.77$	1.0	1.0

continuous part and the d-c part of the spectrum, as in Eq. (24), the final
result can be written in the form

$$G_{S+N}(f) = \frac{N^2 \sin^2 \pi f \Theta_0}{2\pi f^2 \Theta_0} \left\{ \frac{4}{\pi} A_L(z,n) - B_L^2(z,n) + \frac{1}{2\Theta_0} B_L^2(z,n) \delta(f) \right.$$
$$\left. + \frac{\epsilon^2 z^2}{\Theta_0} \left(\frac{\partial B_L}{\partial z} \right)^2 \delta[f - (sf_r \pm p)] \right\}, \quad (36)$$

where

$$A_L(z,n) = 1 + z + \sum_{l=1}^{n-1} (-1)^{l+1} \binom{n-1}{l} \frac{1}{l(l+1)} e^{-\frac{l}{l+1}z} \quad (37)$$

and

$$B_L(n,z) = e^{-z} \sum_{l=0}^{n-1} (-1)^{l+1} \binom{n-1}{l} \frac{1}{(l+1)^{3/2}} F\left(\frac{3}{2}, 1; \frac{z}{l+1} \right)$$
$$+ \frac{3}{2z} \sum_{l=1}^{n-1} (-1)^{l+1} \binom{n-1}{l} \frac{1}{l^{1/2}} \int_0^{2/(l+1)} dx \sqrt{1 - \frac{x}{z}} F\left(\frac{5}{2}, 1; x \right). \quad (38)$$

Of course for $n = 1$, A_L becomes $1 + z$ and B_L becomes

$$e^{-z} F\left(\tfrac{3}{2}, 1; z \right) = F(-\tfrac{1}{2}, 1; -z),$$

so that Eq. (36) goes over into Eq. (24).

Quadratic Detector.—When a *quadratic* detector is used, the same type of equation is obtained:

$$G_{S+N}(f) = \frac{2N^2 \sin^2 \pi f \Theta_0}{(\pi f)^2 \Theta_0} \left\{ 2A_Q(z,n) - B_Q^2(z,n) + \frac{1}{\Theta_0} B_Q^2(z,n)\delta(f) \right.$$
$$\left. + \frac{\epsilon^2 z^2}{\Theta_0}\left(\frac{\partial B_Q}{\partial z}\right)^2 \delta[f - (sf_r \pm p)] \right\}, \quad (39)$$

where

$$A_Q(z,n) = 1 + 2z + \frac{1}{2}z^2 + \sum_{l=1}^{n-1} (-1)^{l+1}\binom{n-1}{l}\frac{1}{l(l+1)}$$
$$\left[\frac{2l+1}{l(l+1)} + \frac{z}{(l+1)^2}\right]e^{-\frac{l}{l+1}z}, \quad (40)$$

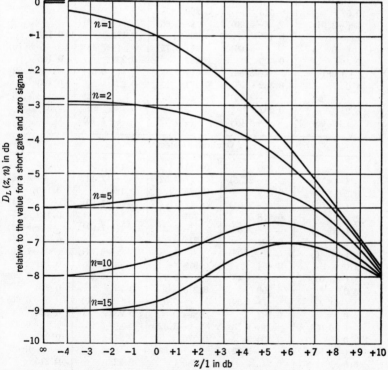

FIG. 10·16.—Noise reduction factor $D_L(z,n)$ caused by unmodulated signal, with a linear detector;

$$z = \frac{\text{unmodulated signal power}}{\text{noise power}}; \qquad n = \frac{\text{gate length}}{\text{pulse length}}.$$

and
$$B_Q(z,n) = A_L(z,n). \tag{41}$$

The results for a *short gate* follow again from this by making $n = 1$.

From Eq. (36) there can be drawn the same kind of conclusions as from Eq. (24). The depression of the noise resulting from the presence

TABLE 10·4.—DEPENDENCE OF NOISE $D(z,n)$ ON THE SIGNAL CARRIER z AND THE GATE LENGTH G

The gate length is $n\tau$; numbers in parentheses are in decibels

z	$n = 2$	$n = 5$	$n = 10$	$n = 15$
Linear Detector				
0	0.524	0.252	0.159	0.124
$(-\infty)$	(-2.81)	(-5.98)	(-8.00)	(-9.05)
0.5	0.513	0.259	0.162	
(-3.01)	(-2.90)	(-5.86)	(-7.90)	
1	0.495	0.266	0.179	0.135
(0)	(-3.06)	(-5.75)	(-7.48)	(-8.70)
2.5	0.409	0.282	0.222	0.185
$(+3.98)$	(-3.88)	(-5.49)	(-6.55)	(-7.32)
4.0	0.332	0.271	0.223	0.195
$(+6.02)$	(-4.79)	(-5.67)	(-6.52)	(-7.10)
6.25	0.247	0.223	0.195	
$(+7.96)$	(-6.07)	(-6.52)	(-7.10)	
Quadratic Detector				
0	0.556	0.281	0.181	0.146
$(-\infty)$	(-2.55)	(-5.52)	(-7.43)	(-8.36)
0.5	0.545	0.288	0.186	0.150
(-3.01)	(-2.64)	(-5.41)	(-7.30)	(-8.24)
1	0.518	0.301	0.199	0.158
(0)	(-2.86)	(-5.22)	(-7.01)	(-8.02)
1.4	0.494	0.311	0.212	0.170
$(+1.46)$	(-3.06)	(-5.08)	(-6.74)	(-7.70)
2.0	0.454	0.318	0.231	0.191
$(+3.01)$	(-3.43)	(-4.98)	(-6.37)	(-7.20)
3.0	0.390	0.313	0.251	0.216
$(+4.77)$	(-4.09)	(-5.05)	(-6.00)	(-6.66)
4.0	0.337	0.294	0.254	0.228
$(+6.02)$	(-4.73)	(-5.32)	(-5.95)	(-6.42)
5.0	0.294	0.270	0.245	0.228
$(+6.99)$	(-5.32)	(-5.69)	(-6.10)	(-6.42)
6.5	0.245	0.235	0.223	0.215
$(+8.13)$	(-6.10)	(-6.29)	(-6.52)	(-6.68)
10	0.173	0.172	0.170	0.169
$(+10)$	(-7.62)	(-7.65)	(-7.70)	(-7.73)

of the signal carrier is given by the function

$$D_L(z,n) = \frac{\frac{4}{\pi} A_L(z,n) - B_L^2(z,n)}{\left(\frac{4}{\pi} - 1\right) B_L^2(z,n)}, \tag{42}$$

which for $n = 1$ becomes equal to Eq. (25). For $z = 0$, D_L becomes equal to the relative boxcar fluctuation for pure noise as derived from Eq.

TABLE 10·5.—CORRECTION FACTOR $C(z,n)$ FOR VARIOUS VALUES OF SIGNAL CARRIER z AND GATE LENGTH G

The gate length is nr

z		$n = 2$	$n = 5$	$n = 10$	$n = 15$
Value	Db				
Linear Detector					
0	$-\infty$	∞	∞	∞	∞
0.2	-6.99	6.37	15.74	33.77	53.78
1	0	1.87	3.03	4.76	6.2
4.0	$+6.02$	1.12	1.24	1.41	1.58
30	$+14.77$	1	1	1	1
Quadratic Detector					
0	$-\infty$	∞	∞	∞	∞
0.5	-3.01	3.00	6.04	11.49	17.67
1	0	1.91	3.04	4.76	6.34
1.4	1.46	1.61	2.23	3.08	3.84
2.0	3.01	1.40	1.72	2.14	2.49
3.0	4.77	1.24	1.38	1.55	1.69
4.0	6.02	1.16	1.23	1.32	1.39
5.0	6.99	1.12	1.16	1.21	1.25
6.5	8.13	1.09	1.10	1.12	1.13
10	10	1.05	1.06	1.06	1.06
30	14.77	1	1	1	1

(13) (see Table 10·1 also); for $z \rightarrow \infty$, D_L becomes inversely proportional to z. For intermediate values of z, $D_L(z,n)$ goes through a curious maximum, which begins to appear when $n > 2$ and shifts to larger values of z when n becomes larger (Fig. 10·16). The minimum detectable modulation can again be written in the form

$$\epsilon_{min}^2 = \frac{2K_{min}\theta b}{z} C_L(z,n), \tag{43}$$

where

$$C_L(z,n) = \frac{\frac{2}{\pi} A_L(z,n) - \frac{1}{2} B_L^2(z,n)}{z\left(\frac{\partial B_L}{\partial z}\right)^2}. \tag{44}$$

Just as for the function $D_L(z,n)$, $C_L(z,n)$ can be discussed only numerically. The results can be found in Tables 10·4 and 10·5 and in Fig. 10·17.

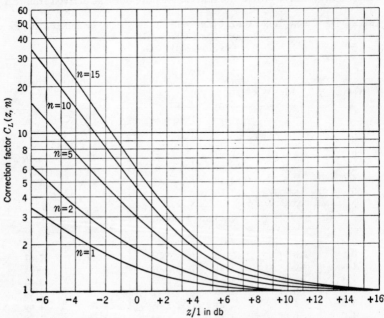

FIG. 10·17.—Correction factor $C_L(z,n)$ as a function of z for a long gate and a linear detector. The minimum detectable modulation is given by

$$\epsilon^2{}_{min} = \frac{2K\theta b}{z} C_L(z,n).$$

OTHER METHODS OF MODULATION

10·5. Propeller Modulation.—The preceding sections have shown how a receiver and indicator can be made for the detection of modulated radar pulses. One important example of their use is the detection of propeller modulation. To understand the results to be presented, the characteristic of propeller·modulation should be discussed briefly.

As the aircraft propeller rotates, the scattering cross section, or echoing area, of the aircraft varies in a cyclical fashion. The fundamental frequency of this cyclical variation is not, in general, the propeller-shaft rotation frequency but the frequency with which the individual blades pass a given point. This result is caused by the symmetry properties of the propeller, that is, each blade is exactly like its neighbor. Furthermore, the cyclical pattern is not generally sinusoidal but is usually very complicated, exhibiting many harmonics of the fundamental blade frequency. There may be 20 or 30 harmonics of sufficient ampli-

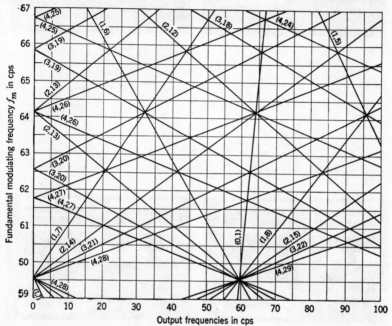

FIG. 10·18.—Output frequencies from boxcar generator at PRF = 417 pps. The (s,r) values for each line are given.

tude to be easily detectable, and these may cause extra responses at low frequency in the reed indicator by their "beats" with the PRF and its harmonics. Because of the changes in audio spectrum accompanying changes in either the PRF or fundamental blade frequency, however, the harmonic responses can be recognized. The method by which this can be done will be described below.

It is of interest to construct a sample nomograph that describes the output audio frequencies produced by a given modulating propeller-blade frequency f_m interacting with the PRF f_r. The chart shown in Fig. 10·18 was constructed for only a very limited region, since it will be used to explain some particular results; the range of frequencies can be extended if needed. Such a chart is valid for only one value of f_r.

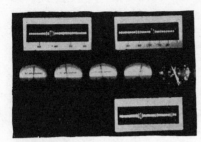

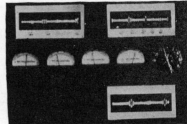

(a) Front aspect at 12 nautical miles

Modulation frequency		(s,r) values
Observed cps	Theoretical cps	
28.5	28.0	$(1,7)$
32	31.8	$(0,\frac{1}{2})$
36	36	$(1,6)$
44	43.5	$(3,19)$
64	63.65	$(0,1)$
71.5	71.2	$(2,12)$
84	84	$(3,21)$

(b) Front aspect at 12 nautical miles

Modulation frequency		(s,r) values
Observed cps	Theoretical cps	
28.0	28.0	$(1,7)$
32	31.8	$(0,\frac{1}{2})$
36	36	$(1,6)$
44	43.5	$(3,19)$
55.5	56	$(2,14)$
64	63.65	$(0,1)$
72	71.2	$(2,12)$
85	84	$(3,21)$

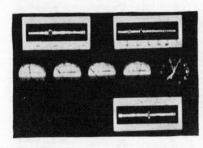

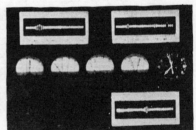

(c) Rear aspect at 10 nautical miles

Modulation frequency		(s,r) values
Observed cps	Theoretical cps	
30	30.2	$(0,\frac{1}{2})$
43	43.2	$(3,20)$
55	55	$(1,6)$
60.5	60.4	$(0,1)$
66	66	$(1,8)$
72	72	$(2,15)$
78.5	78	$(3,22)$

(d) Rear aspect at 10 nautical miles

Modulation frequency		(s,r) values
Observed cps	Theoretical cps	
30.5	30.3	$(0,\frac{1}{2})$
41	40.5	$(3,20)$
47	47.2	$(2,13)$
54	54	$(1,6)$
61	60.55	$(0,1)$
68	67	$(1,8)$
74	74	$(2,15)$
81	81	$(3,22)$

Fig. 10·19.—Four sample reed-meter displays showing the a-f spectrum of the echo of a small two-engined training aircraft (SNC) in flight. The observed frequencies can be checked by comparing with Fig. 10·2. The theoretical frequencies are those determined using Fig. 10·18 and the listed (s,r) values. Figure 10·18 is applicable, since the PRF was 417 cps.

In Fig. 10·18, f_r is 417 cps, the abscissa represents the output audio frequencies from 0 to 100 cps, and the ordinate, the values of f_m between 59 and 67 cps. The output frequencies are obtained by the intersections of a horizontal line whose ordinate is the desired blade frequency with the array of oblique lines shown. Each such line is characterized by two indices s and r. These indices define the harmonics of the PRF, which interacts with the rth harmonic of f_m to produce the particular a-f component represented by the intersection. This nomograph is similar to the one shown in Fig. 2·12, where output frequencies for a single modulating frequency are given.

In Fig. 10·18 it can be seen that for a given fractional change in the blade frequency the high harmonics of f_m and the PRF produce audio components that change frequency with relative rapidity. It is because of this fact that these components can be properly identified. Furthermore a given a-f spectrum can be "fitted" to a chart similar to that shown in Fig. 10·18, and a very precise value for f_m can be obtained. This procedure, of course, assumes a known value for the PRF.

Results of actual flight trials with an SNC type aircraft are shown in Fig. 10·19. These photographs show the responses obtained on a vibrating reed assembly similar to that shown in Fig. 10·2 except for the absence of the lowest-frequency reed meter.

A host of responses is obtained. The conditions for these tests are those for which the nomograph of Fig. 10·18 was constructed, namely, a PRF of 417 cps and a blade frequency of approximately 64 cps. Since the photographs are not very clear, a table is presented under each picture that lists the observed audio frequencies together with the "fitted" theoretical frequencies and the indices (s,r) that are assumed to be responsible for the indication. It will be noticed that a small 32-cps response is listed for the indices $(0,\frac{1}{2})$. This response is caused by a slight asymmetry in the two-bladed SNC propeller, which produces a term at the *shaft* rotation frequency, that is, one-half the blade frequency. It will also be noticed that responses of appreciable magnitude are observed from the twenty-first harmonic of the blade frequency. Furthermore, many of the high-harmonic responses are stronger than that due to the fundamental itself.

These strong harmonic responses are not at all surprising when one examines the radar intensity pattern resulting from propeller rotation, obtained for a fixed aspect of the aircraft. Such a pattern is shown in Fig. 10·20, where the ordinate represents the amplitude of returned echo and the abscissa represents time. The time required for 90° of shaft rotation of the four-blade propeller of the B-26 medium bomber used in this test is the time between the successive prominent minima. This pattern is the filtered boxcar output voltage of the receiver using a PRF of 10,000 cps to obtain the necessary detail.

The complex shape of the curve shows the presence of high harmonics of the blade frequency. The harmonic analysis of the propeller-modulation pattern of Fig. 10·20a is given in Fig. 10·20b. This analysis, which includes harmonics of the blade frequency up to the tenth, was recorded with a swept-frequency audio analyzer.[1] The harmonics of the blade

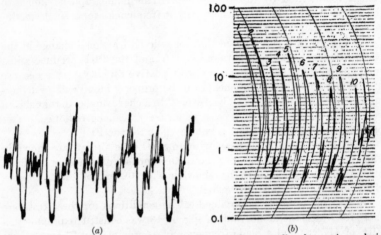

FIG. 10·20.—(a) Propeller modulation pattern. (b) Corresponding harmonic analysis. Harmonics of the blade frequency are numbered.

frequency are numbered, and the percentage of modulation in each harmonic is recorded on a logarithmic scale. The ninth harmonic is nearly 10 per cent; the tenth, nearly 7 per cent, etc. For more complete information concerning propeller-modulation studies, the reader is referred to the original reports already cited.

10·6. Theoretical Analysis of a Pulse-width Modulation System.— Besides the a-m pulse trains, which have been treated in the previous sections, there are many other types of pulse modulation, some of which have been described in Sec. 2·8. The analysis of each pulse-modulation system will follow the same general lines as the analysis given in Secs. 10·3 and 10·4 of the receiving system for a-m pulses. However, in each case, the theory must be developed separately, since it will depend essentially on the number and type of nonlinear elements in the receiver.

As a second example, we shall give a short account of the analysis of a pulse-width modulation system, in which a *slicer* (*cf.* Sec. 2·8) is used as a

---

[1] R. M. Ashby, F. W. Martin, and J. L. Lawson, "Modulation of Radar Signals from Airplanes," RL Report No. 914, Mar. 28, 1946.

noise-suppressing device.[1] The action of the slicer on a series of pulses with and without noise is shown in Fig. 10·21. Clearly, if the carrier voltage and the slicing level are both high compared to the noise, then the output of the slicer will be a series of rectangular pulses that are approxi-

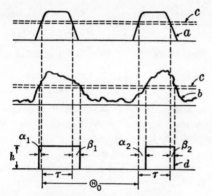

a Detector output without noise
b Detector output with noise
c Slicing level
d Rectangular pulse after slicing

FIG. 10·21.—The effect of slicing a series of pulses with and without noise.

mately at the same position as the original signal pulses. The only effects of the noise will be the small and random shifts of the two edges of the pulse, which are indicated by α and β in Fig. 10·21.

Consider now a series of signal pulses of which the width is modulated in a sinusoidal fashion. In the absence of noise the output of the slicer will be a train of rectangular pulses represented by

$$F_s(t) = \sum_j \Delta_j(t),$$

where

$$\Delta_j(t) = \begin{cases} 1 & \text{for } j\Theta_0 - \tfrac{1}{2}\tau_j < t < j\Theta_0 + \tfrac{1}{2}\tau_j, \\ 0 & \text{otherwise,} \end{cases}$$

$$\tau_j = \tau(1 + \epsilon \cos 2\pi p j\Theta_0), \tag{45}$$

and Θ_0 is the repetition period, p the modulation frequency, and ϵ the fractional modulation of the pulse length τ. Assuming commensurability of p and the PRF $f_r = 1/\Theta_0$, one finds, by a straightforward Fourier analysis,

[1] Parts of this analysis were first given by Z. Jelonek in some unpublished British reports.

$$F_s(t) = \frac{2f_r}{\pi} \sum_{k=0}^{\infty} \sum_{l=0}^{\infty} \frac{2 - \delta_{k0}}{2} \frac{2 - \delta_{l0}}{2} \left\{ \frac{J_l[\pi\tau\epsilon(lp + kf_r)]}{lp + kf_r} \right.$$

$$[\delta_{l,\ even} \sin \pi\tau(lp + kf_r) + i\delta_{l,\ odd} \cos \pi\tau(lp + kf_r)] \cos 2\pi(lp + kf_r)t$$

$$+ \frac{J_l[\pi\tau\epsilon(lp - kf_r)]}{lp - kf_r} [\delta_{l,\ even} \sin \pi\tau(lp - kf_r) + i\delta_{l,\ odd} \cos \pi\tau(lp - kf_r)]$$

$$\left. \cos 2\pi(lp - kf_r)t \right\}, \quad (46)$$

where $J_l(z)$ is the Bessel function of order l; the symbol $\delta_{l,\ even}$ is defined by

$$\delta_{l,\ even} = \begin{cases} 1 & \text{for } l \text{ even,} \\ 0 & \text{for } l \text{ odd,} \end{cases}$$

and $\delta_{l,\ odd} = 1 - \delta_{l,\ even}$. All the harmonics of f_r and p and their combination frequencies are therefore present in the spectrum of the signal.

When noise is present, the edges of the jth pulse are shifted by the random amounts α_j and β_j. By an analysis similar to the analysis used in Examples 3 and 4 of Sec. 3·4, the power spectrum of signal and noise can be written in the form

$$G_{S+N}(f) = \lim_{N \to \infty} \frac{1}{2\pi^2 f^2 N \Theta_0} \left[\sum_{j=0}^{N} (\overline{|a_j|^2} - |\bar{a}_j|^2) + \left| \sum_{j=0}^{N} \bar{a}_j e^{2\pi i f j \Theta_0} \right|^2 \right], \quad (47)$$

where

$$a_j = e^{-2\pi i f(\frac{1}{2}\tau_j + \beta_j)} - e^{2\pi i f(\frac{1}{2}\tau_j - \alpha_j)}. \quad (48)$$

In order to obtain the ensemble averages $\bar{a}_j$ and $\overline{|a_j|^2}$ the probability distribution of the α_j and β_j must be found. In Eq. (47), the assumption has been made that the α's and β's of different pulses and, therefore, the different a_j's are independent of each other. This, of course, will always be the case, since Θ_0 is always large compared with $1/B$ if B is the i-f bandwidth. For simplicity, we shall assume in addition that the α's and β's of one pulse are independent of each other. This implies that $B\tau \gg 1$, so that the original signal pulse is only slightly deformed by the i-f amplifier.

The probability distribution $P(\alpha)\ d\alpha$ follows immediately from the probability distribution of signal plus noise [cf. Eq. (7·13)]:

$$W(r)\ dr = \frac{r\ dr}{W} e^{-\frac{S^2 + r^2}{2W}} I_0 \left(\frac{rS}{W} \right) \quad (49)$$

by putting $r = h$, $S = h + \alpha tg\theta_1$, $dr = d\alpha\ tg\theta_1$, where h is the slicing level and $tg\theta_1$ is the slope of the signal pulse after the i-f amplifier and at the height h. Replacing Eq. (49) with the Gaussian approximation [cf Eq. (7·13a)], which is allowed, since $S^2 \gg 2W$, one finds

$$P(\alpha)\ d\alpha = \frac{d\alpha}{\sqrt{2\pi\sigma_i^2}} e^{-\frac{\alpha^2}{2\sigma_i^2}} \quad (50)$$

where $\sigma_1^2 = W/tg^2\theta_1$. In the same way one finds for β a Gaussian distribution with the variance $\sigma_2^2 = W/tg^2\theta_2$.

The average values indicated in Eq. (47) can now be evaluated. The results are

$$\left.\begin{array}{l} \bar{a}_j = \exp\left(-\pi i f\tau_j - 2\pi^2 f^2\sigma_2^2\right) - \exp\left(+\pi i f\tau_j - 2\pi^2 f^2\sigma_1^2\right), \\ \overline{|a_j|^2} = 2 - 2\cos 2\pi f\tau_j \exp\left[-2\pi^2 f^2(\sigma_1^2 + \sigma_2^2)\right]. \end{array}\right\} \quad (51)$$

Substitution of these results in the first sum in Eq. (47) leads to the continuous part of the power spectrum. We will neglect in this part, as we did in Sec. 10·4, the effect of the modulation of the signal. The continuous spectrum becomes therefore

$$\frac{1}{2\pi^2 f^2\Theta_0}\left(\overline{|a|^2} - |\bar{a}|^2\right) = \frac{1}{2\pi^2 f^2\Theta_0}\left(2 - e^{-4\pi^2 f^2\sigma_1^2} - e^{-4\pi^2 f^2\sigma_2^2}\right). \quad (52)$$

The substitution of Eq. (51) in the second sum of Eq. (47) leads to the discrete spectrum due to the signal. Using the expression (45) for τ_j and developing in powers of ϵ up to ϵ^2, one obtains for the discrete spectrum, when $p < f_r/2$,

$$\frac{1}{2\pi^2 f^2\Theta_0^2}\left[e^{-4\pi^2 f^2\sigma_1^2} + e^{-4\pi^2 f^2\sigma_2^2} - 2\cos 2\pi f\tau e^{-2\pi^2 f^2(\sigma_1^2 + \sigma_2^2)}\right] \sum_{s=0}^{\infty} \delta(f - sf_r)$$

$$+ \frac{\tau^2\epsilon^2}{8\Theta_0^2}\left[e^{-4\pi^2 f^2\sigma_1^2} + e^{-4\pi^2 f^2\sigma_2^2} + 2\cos 2\pi f\tau e^{-2\pi^2 f^2(\sigma_1^2 + \sigma_2^2)}\right] \sum_{s=0}^{\infty} \delta(f - sf_r \pm p).$$

$$(53)$$

If there is no noise, $\sigma_1^2 = \sigma_2^2 = 0$, and Eq. (53) goes over into the power spectrum of the signal alone, which, provided the same powers of ϵ are kept, agrees with the power spectrum that follows from Eq. (46).

According to the power criterion (*cf.* Sec. 7·3), the detectability of the modulation ϵ depends on the ratio of the power of the signal peak at the frequency p to the power of the continuous noise spectrum with which the signal has to compete. Suppose that a narrow audio filter of width b is used; it follows from Eq. (53) that the power of the signal peak at the frequency p is

$$\frac{\tau^2\epsilon^2 f_r^2}{8}\left[e^{-4\pi^2 p^2\sigma_1^2} + e^{-4\pi^2 p^2\sigma_2^2} + 2\cos 2\pi p\tau e^{-2\pi^2 p^2(\sigma_1^2 + \sigma_2^2)}\right]$$

whereas it follows from Eq. (52) that the power of the continuous noise spectrum is

$$\frac{bf_r}{2\pi^2 p^2}\left(2 - e^{-4\pi^2 p^2\sigma_1^2} - e^{-4\pi^2 p^2\sigma_2^2}\right).$$

The minimum detectable modulation is therefore given by

$$\epsilon_{min}^2 = \frac{4kb}{\pi^2\tau^2 p^2 f_r} \cdot \frac{2 - \exp(-4\pi^2 p^2\sigma_1^2) - \exp(-4\pi^2 p^2\sigma_2^2)}{\exp(-4\pi^2 p^2\sigma_1^2) + \exp(-4\pi^2 p^2\sigma_2^2) + 2\cos 2\pi p\tau \exp} \\ [-2\pi^2 p^2(\sigma_1^2 + \sigma_2^2)], \quad (54a)$$

where k is a constant, which has to be determined experimentally, just as in Sec. 10·2.

For further discussion we shall assume that the i-f amplifier (band-width B) deforms the pulses in a symmetrical fashion, so that $\sigma_1 = \sigma_2 = \sigma$. Assume further that $p\sigma$ and even $p\tau$ are much smaller than unity. Then Eq. (54a) reduces to

$$\epsilon_{min}^2 \cong k\,\frac{8b\sigma^2}{f_r\tau}. \quad (54b)$$

For a Gaussian pulse and a Gaussian i-f pass band, σ^2 and τ can be calculated exactly, and Eq. (54b) becomes

$$\epsilon_{min}^2 \cong k\,\frac{b}{4f_r}\,\frac{1}{z}\left(\frac{\dfrac{S_0}{h}}{\log\dfrac{S_0}{h}}\right)^2, \quad (55a)$$

where S_0 is the pulse amplitude before the i-f amplifier, h is the height of the slicing level, and $z = S_0^2/2W$. For the case of a square pulse and a Gaussian i-f pass band, one obtains in the same way

$$\epsilon_{min}^2 \cong k\,\frac{1.78b}{f_r}\,\frac{1}{zx^2}\,e^{-2[1-(2h/S_0)]^2}, \quad (55b)$$

where $x = B\tau_0$ is the product of the i-f bandwidth and the original pulse length. In both Eqs. (55a) and (55b) x is assumed to be large compared with unity. For a Gaussian pulse ϵ_{min}^2 is independent of x, whereas for a square pulse ϵ_{min}^2 goes to zero when $x \to \infty$. This difference can easily be understood. The influence of the noise decreases for increasing slope of the pulse at the slicing level. For a square pulse the slope increases indefinitely when $x \to \infty$; whereas for the Gaussian pulse the slope will, of course, remain finite.

CHAPTER 11

THRESHOLD PULSED SIGNALS IN CLUTTER

INTRODUCTION

11·1. Comparison between Clutter and Noise.—In many ways noise and "clutter" are similar. In the following pages are discussed some of the similarities as well as the differences between them. The similarities have given rise to the argument that both types of interference have similar effects, but this conclusion is not a valid one.

The frequency spectrum of receiver noise is essentially uniform at the input of the i-f amplifier; the frequency spectrum of the clutter is influenced by the transmitted pulse itself. For practical purposes all frequencies in the neighborhood of the transmitter frequency are, on the average, equally reflected by clutter. Hence the long-time-average power spectrum of the clutter will be just that of the transmitted pulse, that is, usually $a(\sin^2 x/x^2)$ spectrum, where x is the frequency deviation from the center radio frequency. Thus noise and clutter would be expected to behave differently with respect, for example, to a variation in receiver bandwidth.

The amplitude probability distributions of clutter and noise at the receiver second detector differ only with respect to a multiplicative constant. This property comes about because both phenomena are random; they are produced by the random interaction of many small processes. The *average values* of the amplitudes at the second detector of noise and clutter behave differently, however. In noise the average value is constant in time, but for clutter it varies in time, i.e., radar range, not only with geometrical factors but also with the different scattering properties of the illuminated medium. This varying average amplitude of clutter causes much difficulty since, without special circuits, saturation in the receiver will not be avoided in regions of strong clutter return. For receiver noise, however, a setting of the receiver gain control can be found where saturation by receiver noise can be easily avoided. In addition to the total variation in clutter amplitude, possibly requiring some form of receiver AGC for satisfactory operation, the rate at which this clutter-amplitude variation occurs, i.e., as the range changes, will be important. This rate of change will determine the speed with which the AGC must act to be effective.

One other important property of clutter is the rate at which the clutter *configuration* changes in time.   If the radar return from a single transmitted pulse is examined, a complicated time pattern will be obtained that contains all frequencies up to very high ones, a pattern that is similar, except for spectrum differences, to receiver noise.   This pattern, or configuration, will remain essentially unchanged, however, if a second pulse is used shortly afterward.   The configuration is therefore relatively stable in time, perhaps for as long as a second, although its shape may be complicated.   The reason for this stability is that the returned signal depends on the physical positions of the reflecting objects.   Changes in relative position and therefore in the signal amplitude occur comparatively slowly.   The consequences of this fact will be discussed more fully in Secs. 11·9 and 11·10, where it will be shown how this phenomenon can be used to reduce the effects of clutter.

11·2. Threshold Signal in the Absence of Saturation.—In the absence of saturation, problems connected with the perception of signals in clutter are similar to signal-perception problems in noise.   Even though clutter is relatively stable, the configurational changes are usually sufficiently rapid to be visually somewhat similar to normal noise fluctuations. Clutter has a somewhat coarser and more grainy appearance than ordinary noise, however.   Nevertheless, as with receiver noise, the desired signal must be of the order of magnitude of the average clutter (plus noise) power to be recognizable.   These remarks apply exclusively to clutter in which the configurational changes are relatively rapid, for example, sea return and rainstorm echoes.   They do not apply, however, to ground return, where the clutter configuration is virtually stable.   In the case of ground clutter, a satisfactory criterion for signal perception is all but impossible.   A small desired target may produce an echo large enough to be clearly seen, but it will not, in general, be *recognized* as the desired target because of confusion with other similar echoes in the neighborhood.   Consideration of ground clutter will for this reason be reserved for Sec. 11·9, where it will be shown that the desired signal may have properties differing from those of clutter, for example, velocity properties.

The problem posed by the perception of a desired signal in fluctuating clutter, for example, rainstorm clutter, is complicated by several factors. First, unlike the case for receiver noise, the average amplitude of clutter return depends not only upon transmitted pulse power but upon the total volume of rainstorm illuminated at any given instant by the pulse. In other words, at any given instant the receiver input is collecting from a region of rainstorm reflectors power that is as large as the packet of r-f energy sent out by the transmitter in one-half the pulse length.   Therefore an increase in transmitted pulse length by a factor of α produces an α-fold increase in the scattering cross section for the clutter.   For the perception in clutter of a desired discrete target, one whose cross section or echoing area is independent of the pulse length, short pulses should be used. This argument makes it clear that the signal threshold power in clutter should be directly proportional to the pulse length, provided, of course, that the receiver i-f bandwidth is as wide as or wider than optimum for the pulse length (see Chap. 8) and that the intensity of clutter is sufficient to override all receiver noise.

This reasoning was confirmed by an experiment in which the output pulse of a signal generator was introduced into the r-f receiving section of a radar system. The power of the pulse was known and variable, and its phase adjustable so that it could be made to coincide with the radar echoes of a local rainstorm. When the lengths of the radar pulse and of the signal generator pulse were changed from 5 to 0.05 sec, the observed threshold signal was 18 db less as compared with the theoretical 20-db difference. This proportionality between pulse length and signal threshold in clutter can also be qualitatively confirmed by studying the effect of antenna beamwidth on the perception of discrete targets in clutter. One would expect that the cross section of clutter extended in three dimensions would be proportional to the antenna-beam solid angle, since the illuminated part of the clutter is proportional to it. For clutter on a plane surface, such as sea return, the clutter cross section is proportional to the width of the antenna beam. No exact quantitative information is available on this point, but it is a well-known fact that narrow-beam, high-discrimination radar sets are much less affected by extended clutter than are radar sets having an equivalent wavelength but a broad antenna-beam pattern. One of the complicating features in the quantitative determination of the effect of the beamwidth is the difficulty of securing clutter that is essentially uniform over the large areas likely to be illuminated by a broad radar beam. Furthermore, when the discrimination of the radar set is very high, that is, when it has very narrow beamwidth and small pulse length, the clutter itself is no longer uniform but generally breaks up into a number of distinct reflecting volumes. This characteristic is particularly true of sea clutter, where the discrimination of the set may be made high enough to resolve individual reflecting sea waves. When this happens, the experimental determination of the minimum detectable signal is difficult, not because of insufficient signal amplitude or clutter fluctuation but because of confusion with other clutter peaks that appear to be discrete. Nevertheless, for the perception of a discrete signal in clutter, high-discrimination radar sets have proved much more useful than low-discrimination sets.

One point should be emphasized: As long as there is sufficient radar power for the clutter echoes to be much stronger than receiver noise, *the signal threshold power in clutter is independent of transmitted power but varies directly with pulse length.* This situation is markedly different from the problem of signal threshold in receiver noise (see Chap. 8).

For a given pulse length, the effect on signal threshold power in clutter of the various receiver parameters, such as i-f bandwidth, video bandwidth, presentation sweep speed, etc., could be investigated. These variables would be found to have a somewhat different effect from that observed in the presence of receiver noise because, as was shown in the preceding section, the spectrum of clutter, as viewed in the i-f amplifier, differs from that of receiver noise. For the same returned power the clutter spectrum is, in fact, the same as that of the desired discrete echo, except that all components of the spectrum of clutter are, in general, independent or noncoherent; for the discrete echo, the various components are coherently related. Since the spectra of the signal and clutter are the same, it might be argued that changes of i-f or video bandwidths would have no effect on the signal threshold power. Because of the difference in coherence, however, this is not true. For very narrow i-f bandwidths, it is the *amplitude* of the *signal* response and the *power* of the *clutter* response that will be proportional to bandwidth. This situation is analogous to that for receiver noise; obviously, therefore, the signal threshold power will vary inversely with the i-f bandwidth in this region. For wide i-f bandwidths the situation is different, however. The responses to both clutter and signal approach asymptotic values, and the signal threshold power becomes independent of i-f bandwidth. Thus there is no optimum i-f bandwidth, although a receiver is usually required whose bandwidth is nearly optimum for noise, since both types of interference are usually encountered. No good experimental information is available on this point, however, although rough experiments have shown that the argument is probably correct.

As for noise, video bandwidth has a less pronounced effect than i-f bandwidth on signal threshold in clutter. For receiver noise at optimum i-f bandwidth the signal threshold power is increased when the video pass band is narrowed from either the high side (low-pass filter) or the low side (high-pass filter or differentiator). This characteristic is not necessarily true of clutter. Because of the difference in coherence between signal and clutter, a low-pass video filter increases the threshold signal. The video clutter components are essentially independent; hence for small video bandwidths the average amplitude of clutter response is proportional to the square root of video bandwidth, whereas the amplitude of signal response is directly proportional to the video bandwidth. In contrast to this situation, Middleton and Sutro[1] have shown that when a

---

[1] D. Middleton and P. J. Sutro, "Analysis of a Possible A/J System Against Window," RRL Report No. 411-128, Dec. 9, 1944.

high-pass filter is employed, an improvement in signal perception is to be expected, especially when the i-f bandwidth is increased. The reason for this improvement may be seen by considering the action of a high-pass filter or differentiator. From a wide-band i-f amplifier a pulse from the desired discrete signal will have relatively steep edges. These sharp transient voltages will be passed through the differentiator and will therefore act much like *shortened* pulses. For each signal pulse, two shortened pulses will be manufactured, one positive in sign and the other negative. Were it not for the extra negative pulse, which contributes a factor of 2 to clutter fluctuations, the signal threshold would be just the same after differentiation as for the case in which a short transmitted pulse is used. If sufficiently rapid differentiation is provided, therefore, a net improvement in signal perception will occur. It should be emphasized, however, that a greater improvement could be obtained by using a short transmitted pulse, since this would avoid the extra negative pulse produced by the differentiator.

Attempts to prove experimentally the desirable effect of the differentiator have usually been disappointing, partly because of the unavoidable *low-pass* filter characteristics of the human eye and brain pointed out in Sec. 8·7 and partly because of the lack of contrast between highly differentiated signals. The low-pass characteristics of the eye appear to override the action of any differentiator and therefore reduce the effectiveness of the latter. This is true, of course, only where the presentation sweep speed is slow enough to make the "eye bandwidth" important. This condition, however, is universally met in any presentation that is being used for long-range search, the one function for which the avoidance of clutter is so important. These difficulties will be clearly evident from the results presented in Sec. 11·8.

One important point should be noted regarding the effect of a low-pass filter. It might be argued that because of the low-pass effect of the human eye and brain, an additional low-pass filter located in the video system should not be serious. This argument is true if there is no nonlinearity between the two filters—a condition that rarely exists. Although the screen of the cathode-ray tube used for intensity-modulated presentation is nonlinear, nonlinearity of this type is not usually of importance. The most troublesome effect of a narrow video system results from the *video-limiting* action necessary for intensity-modulated displays. The average value of clutter (d-c term) causes limiting and consequent loss of all signals long before clutter *fluctuations* are large enough to mask a desired echo. This situation is also true of receiver noise, but here a blocking condenser can eliminate the d-c term. The variable value of the d-c term makes this solution impossible for clutter. A differentiator can be used, however, to remove the d-c term and its sidebands, which fluctuate at a low frequency; this explains why radar operators usually report an improvement in operation when they use a video-differentiating circuit.

It should now be clear that the use of fast sweeps or expanded-range oscilloscopes such as the R-scope (see Sec. 2·6) will improve signal perception in clutter. This device, enabling the eye to perceive more of the fine signal detail, i.e., the higher video frequencies, will constitute a video filter with a higher h-f cutoff. Experiments have qualitatively confirmed this.

No good data have been gathered showing the effects of signal-presentation time and over-all system integration on signal threshold power in clutter. It seems reasonable, however, to suppose that the effects are similar to those for receiver noise (see Chap. 8); qualitative observation is in agreement with this supposition.

11·3. Threshold Signals in the Presence of Saturation.—Signal perception in clutter is greatly reduced if saturation exists in the receiver. In the presence of saturation the response of the receiver to incremental input signals is essentially zero. Saturation is most likely to occur in the video system as a result of limiting; but as was pointed out in the preceding section, its occurrence can be largely avoided by using a high-pass filter or differentiator between the second detector and video system. Even with such a device, however, saturation may still occur in the i-f amplifier itself. The i-f amplifier tubes may be driven into an overload region by the clutter signal. An obvious (but in practice inadequate) palliative is the use of larger tubes; the customary device used to alleviate this overload effect is an AGC, which regulates the gain of the receiver in accordance with the total voltage appearing in the output of the second detector. The possibility of sudden changes in clutter amplitude makes it imperative that this AGC have a rapid action, but its action must not be so rapid that it causes serious distortion of discrete echoes. This form of gain control has been referred to as *instantaneous automatic gain control,* or IAGC, to distinguish it from the more conventional AGC operated from a third detector and having a relatively slow response (see Sec. 2·7). More will be said about practical circuits and optimum adjustment for the IAGC in the next section.

The major cause of signal loss in clutter is saturation in either the video or i-f amplifier and not any of the causes mentioned in the preceding section. Saturation is in many ways extremely unsatisfactory, since virtually no quantitative information can be given on its effects. The conditions for saturation in either the i-f amplifier or video system vary enormously from one receiver design to the next; they depend upon many factors beyond the scope of this discussion, such as tube characteristics and stability. About all that can be said is that once saturation occurs, the desired signals are completely lost. Before saturation occurs, signal perception will depend upon the factors discussed in the preceding section.

METHODS FOR THE REDUCTION OF CLUTTER SATURATION

There are in current use two general means of reducing i-f amplifier saturation in the presence of clutter. The first is to use IAGC to keep the average clutter amplitude at the second detector essentially constant. The second is to use an i-f amplifier whose response is logarithmic, that is, whose output i-f voltages are proportional to the logarithm of the input i-f voltages. Both schemes require additional circuits to alleviate the effects of video saturation. When the clutter is essentially uniform

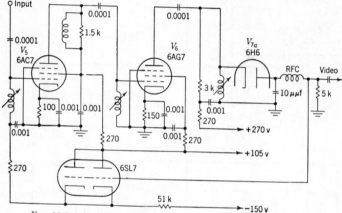

FIG. 11·1.—An IAGC circuit, which protects the last two i-f stages.

at the various azimuths and monotonic in range, a third method has proved useful, that is, the use of a *time-varied gain* control. This device generates a simple time-dependent wave shape that varies the gain of the receiver in such a way as to compensate for spatial variations in clutter amplitude.

11·4. Instantaneous AGC.—Bell and Ashbrook[1] have developed an IAGC circuit in which the average negative d-c component of the rectified second detector voltage is applied to the control grid of the next-to-the-last i-f amplifier tube. To maintain low impedance from the grid of the i-f tube to ground, this connection is made through a cathode follower. The circuit is then similar to that shown in Fig. 11·1. The circuit is operated in the following way: As soon as a strong video signal appears at the second detector, whether produced by clutter or by the desired

[1] P. R. Bell and F. Ashbrook, "Some General Microwave Anti-jam Design Considerations and Performance of a Special Receiver," RL Report No. S-8, Feb. 24, 1944.

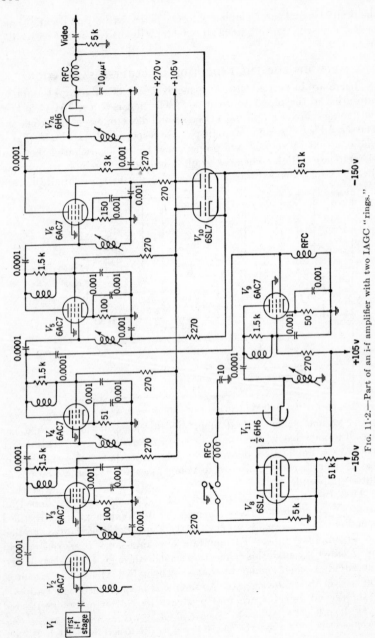

Fig. 11·2.—Part of an i-f amplifier with two IAGC "rings."

echo, the i-f amplifier acquires a bias voltage that increases until the video voltage at the second detector is reduced to some equilibrium value. This equilibrium value is such that it equals the bias voltage on the i-f amplifier needed to reduce the gain of the latter to a point where the incoming signal or clutter voltage produces the indicated output equilibrium voltage. This circuit is a standard degenerative loop used for AGC whose novel feature is the speed of response. The tightness of control is the ratio of the output amplitude change to the input amplitude change.

An IAGC circuit of this type has two drawbacks: (1) The tightness of control is usually not sufficient to prevent video saturation; (2) the total dynamic range of input voltages that can be handled before saturation of preceding stages occurs is limited. The second disadvantage can be overcome by adding another IAGC "ring," as shown in Fig. 11·2, complete with another second detector operating from an earlier stage. The addition of the second ring aids considerably in the handling of input voltages varying over wide dynamic limits; but because of relatively loose control, it does not permit the operation of the video system with the small limit level desirable for the rejection of c-w interference (see Chap. 12).

A new type of IAGC circuit with almost ideal characteristics has been developed by Josephson, Lawson, Linford, and Palmer.[1] This circuit makes possible extremely tight control, extreme speed of response without instability, and economy of components. A single degenerative ring is shown schematically in Fig. 11·3. Each ring is applied around only one i-f stage to avoid possible complications arising from phase shift in the i-f amplifier. This phase shift is troublesome if rapid response is required, since oscillations may develop at certain frequencies. Tests have shown that with the ordinary design of i-f amplifiers, protective bias should be applied to each of the last few amplifier stages and not to alternate stages if all amplifier tubes are to be operated in the optimum part of their characteristics. Failure to do this will cause an unnecessary loss in pulse gain.

Each ring consists of a double-triode tube and associated elements; one section of the tube acts as a diode rectifier, the other as a "bootstrap" cathode-follower amplifier, so named because of the feedback through the diode rectifier from cathode to grid. With the switch closed, the total voltage appearing on the diode load resistor R_3 is the sum of the rectified i-f voltage and the cathode potential of tube V_{2b}, the latter being reduced by a small factor by the potential divider R_4 and R_5. It can be

[1] V. Josephson, J. L. Lawson, L. B. Linford, and C. H. Palmer, Jr., "Anticlutter Circuits for AEW," RL Report No. S-52, Aug. 1, 1945.

shown that the actual voltage appearing on the cathode of tube V_{2b} under these conditions is *larger* than the rectified diode voltage by a factor of approximately $(R_4 + R_5/R_4)$. This ratio can easily be made of the order of 100; therefore, the tube V_{2b} acts as a high-gain amplifier and cathode follower. The speed of response can be controlled by R_2 and C_3 and can be easily varied from a fraction of a microsecond to several

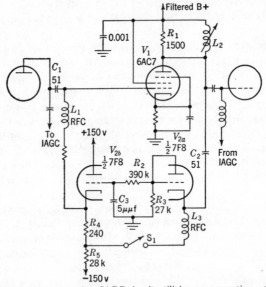

FIG. 11·3.—Schematic diagram of an IAGC circuit utilizing a regenerative cathode-follower amplifier.

hundred microseconds. The total range of bias voltage available is adequate to bias the i-f amplifier to cutoff. Because of the gain of the cathode follower, the tightness of control is excellent.

These IAGC rings can be applied to as many i-f stages as desired. The first ring is probably best applied to the last i-f stage, then to each preceding stage in turn until an adequate over-all dynamic range is available. Figures 11·8 and 11·9 illustrate the behavior of such IAGC circuits. Satisfactory prevention of saturation requires proper design not only of the IAGC but also of other circuits, which will be described in the following pages.

11·5. Logarithmic I-f Amplifier.—Another scheme used to reduce i-f saturation[1] is the so-called "logarithmic i-f amplifier." Such an amplifier exhibits a video output voltage essentially proportional to the logarithm of the input i-f envelope voltage. This characteristic can be achieved

[1] See Vol. 23, Radiation Laboratory Series, p. 583.

in at least two ways. L. Belleville has built this type of amplifier by connecting separate diode second detectors (envelope detectors) to each i-f stage, then adding linearly the resulting separate video signals. For small i-f voltages the last i-f stage will make almost the sole contribution to the video signal, and the video response will be essentially proportional to the input voltage; this condition will persist until the i-f voltage becomes large enough to saturate this last stage. For larger input voltages the last i-f stage will contribute nothing to the output, but the next-to-the-last i-f stage will make a contribution up to input voltages for which *it* saturates, etc. This procedure can, if desired, be continued for all i-f stages in the receiver. The final result will be a receiver whose video output voltage is approximately proportional to the logarithm of the input voltage; the approximation to the smooth logarithmic curve consists of a number of straight lines (representing linear response) of varying slope (the slope depending on the over-all gain up to the particular contributing detector). For such a receiver the video response is always finite for incremental changes in input voltage; hence saturation in the sense described in the preceding section is not possible.

R. A. McConnell has suggested another method of constructing such a logarithmic receiver. This one also depends upon successive saturations in the i-f stages to secure a logarithmic over-all response, but the voltage addition for successive stages is made in the i-f amplifier rather than in the detector or video sections. Only two additional points must be noted in connection with a receiver of this type: (1) The i-f voltages from stage to stage are usually in phase opposition; and in adding i-f voltages in appropriate phase, reversal must therefore be made in all odd-numbered stages; (2) i-f buffering must generally be used to prevent feedback from the output to an antecedent part of the i-f amplifier. Both conditions are easy to bring about, and some satisfactory logarithmic receivers have been constructed in this way.

In the two types of receivers discussed the logarithmic characteristic extends over a limited region of input voltages. Up to voltages that begin to saturate the last i-f stage, the response is essentially linear. From this point up to voltages that saturate all stages the response is essentially logarithmic, and above this point the dynamic gain is zero. Therefore these receivers are most commonly referred to as linear-logarithmic receivers. The crossover point between a linear and logarithmic characteristic is determined by the saturation of the last i-f stage; in terms of the input voltage the crossover point can be adjusted to any desired value by an appropriate setting of the over-all gain of the receiver.

Unfortunately, adequate trials of a logarithmic receiver for use in clutter have not yet been made. Although such receivers have, qualitatively, shown promise, results comparable to those shown in Figs. 11·11 to

11·13 are not available. It is not yet known whether the logarithmic characteristic is more or less suitable than IAGC; circuits for IAGC appear to offer a greater variety of adjustments, but the results are difficult to evaluate. Linear-logarithmic receivers have been extensively used in connection with the moving-target-indication schemes described in Secs. 11·9 and 11·10.

11·6. Video Saturation.—Both the logarithmic receiver and the IAGC-protected receiver require additional means of preventing video saturation. In the logarithmic receiver the d-c value of video output voltage continually rises with increasing input voltage, but the output *fluctuations* remain nearly constant. It is therefore customary to remove the d-c term by means of a high-pass filter or differentiator before injection into the limited video amplifier. In this way video saturation can be almost avoided.

In the IAGC, however, not only the d-c term but the *fluctuations* increase with input voltage. The d-c term rises because of some looseness of control; the fluctuations increase because of the nonlinear amplification of i-f stages near their cutoff bias. Most of the video saturation can usually be removed by the use of a high-pass filter between the second detector and the video system. This procedure is of great value only where a relatively loose IAGC circuit is used. However, to reduce in the detector output the amplitude of clutter *fluctuations*, which are troublesome only where the i-f amplifier becomes nonlinear, a circuit called the detector balanced bias, or DBB, has been developed by Josephson, Lawson, Linford, and Palmer.[1] The circuit, shown schematically in Fig. 11·4, is in many ways similar to the IAGC circuit shown in Fig. 11·3. Instead of biasing the *same* i-f stage degeneratively, however, the rectified output voltage from the last i-f stage is used to bias the following second detector. The amount of applied bias is controlled by the gain of the bootstrap amplifier V_{2a}, which is controlled, in turn, by the potential divider R_1 and R_2. With certain approximations (low internal impedance of the diode V_{1b}) the gain of the bootstrap amplifier can be shown to be R_2/R_1; this gain is simply the ratio of video voltage produced on the cathode of V_{2a} to the rectified diode voltage produced by V_{1b}. The cathode video voltage of tube V_{2a}, which is applied to bias the cathode of the second detector V_{1a}, can therefore be made smaller than, equal to, or larger than the peak i-f voltage also appearing on the second detector cathode. The adjustment is usually made so that the appearance of clutter on the indicator is only slightly more intense than receiver noise background; that is, the second detector is nearly biased off by clutter.

[1] V. Josephson, J. L. Lawson, L. B. Linford, and C. H. Palmer, Jr., "Anticlutter Circuits for AEW," RL Report No. S-52, Aug. 1, 1945.

The operation of a simple circuit such as that illustrated in Fig. 11·4 leaves much to be desired. Several useful modifications are shown in Fig. 11·5. Unless a slow action or delay in time is provided, desired echoes as well as clutter will be removed. To eliminate this difficulty a delay line can be inserted between the diode V_{1b} and the cathode follower V_{2a}, as shown in Fig. 11·5. If the total delay is made of the order of the pulse length, there will be little distortion of desired discrete echoes. The delay line must be electrically matched at both ends to prevent "ringing."

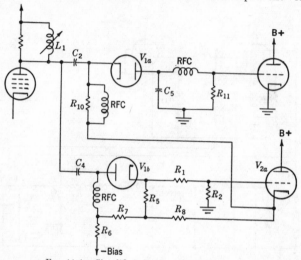

FIG. 11·4.—Simplified circuit of a DBB amplifier.

This matching is effected by making the characteristic impedance equal to R_1, which can be shown to provide a match at the output end, and by placing a resistor R_5, also equal in magnitude to R_1, across the input terminals of the line. A line-delay mechanism of this kind is not feasible in the IAGC circuits previously described because of the IAGC feedback characteristics. The circuit would oscillate violently at a frequency for which the phase shift in the line is approximately 180°.

The purpose of the combination C_1 and R_3 is to provide different bias amplifications for rapid transients and for steady i-f voltages. A larger gain in tube V_{2a} is required for clutter than for c-w interference (see Chap. 12). The arrangement shown in Fig. 11·5 allows the gain for each type of interference to be adjusted separately. The gain for clutter is essentially R_2/R_1; that for c-w interference is essentially $R_2/(R_1 + R_3)$. The purpose of C_1 is to provide an appropriate time constant making possible maintenance of transient gain throughout a typical clutter area on the one hand, and, on the other, reducing the effect of c-w interference modulated at a low a-f rate. With the addition to the circuit of R_3 and C_1, the grid circuit of V_{2a} must be provided with a d-c restorer to obtain proper d-c voltages after a large section of clutter. This d-c restorer is the diode V_{2b}.

The resistors R_{12} and R_{13} provide appropriate grid bias to tube V_{2a} in its quiescent state; this bias is adjusted in such a way that the second detector V_{1a} is barely nonconducting. The diode V_{1b} is operated

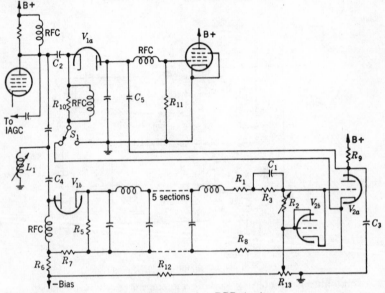

Fig. 11·5.—Complete DBB circuit.

normally somewhat past cutoff, with the result that normal noise level in the receiver will not operate the DBB circuit. This adjustment is made by proper choice of R_7, which carries the normal current passed by the cathode follower V_{2a}. The resistor R_8 is initially adjusted so that its voltage drop just equals the normal grid-cathode potential of tube V_{2a} and thus ensures nearly zero potential difference around the loop comprising R_5, R_1, R_3, and R_2. With this arrangement proper operation of the circuit for normal variations in the electrical characteristics of the tubes can be secured; R_{13} must be adjusted each time V_2 is replaced, however.

The bias voltage is applied to the second-detector cathode through an r-f choke and parallel damping resistor R_{10}. The capacitor C_2 must be small enough to present a high video impedance to the cathode of tube V_{2a}, yet large enough to pass the r-f voltages appearing on the plate of the last i-f tube directly to the cathode of the second detector. For the same reasons C_4 must be of a compromise size. The inductance L_1 tunes the i-f circuit to the appropriate value.

One more circuit detail should be noted. When relatively sharp video voltages are applied to the cathode of the second detector, some effect of these voltages is ordinarily seen in the detector output load resistance R_{11}. This effect is produced by the small interelectrode capacitance of the second detector V_{1a}, which, together with R_{11}, acts as a high-pass filter or differentiator for the biasing video voltages. This differentiator action can be nullified by the neutralizing arrangement shown. A voltage of sign opposite to that of the biasing voltage is obtained from the plate of V_{2a} through the plate load resistor R_9 and is applied to R_{11} through a small capacitor C_5. As a result, the effect of the biasing voltage appearing through the interelectrode capacitance C_{pk} of V_{1a} is approximately neutralized if the product of R_9 and C_5 is made equal to the product of R_6 and C_{pk}. The capacitor C_3 is necessary to make the plate-recovery characteristic of the cathode follower V_{2a} similar in form to its cathode-recovery characteristic. This similarity is achieved if C_3 is made approximately equal to $(C_2 + C_4)R_6/R_9$.

The final circuit shown in Fig. 11·5 can be made to perform very well. In response to pulsed signals it behaves much like a "line" differentiator, that is, one that preserves satisfactorily the shape of the leading edge of the pulse. Areas of clutter can be made nearly invisible on an intensity-modulated display, such as the PPI (see Sec. 2·6), by proper adjustment of R_2, that is, the gain of the biasing amplifier. Interfering c-w signals can be handled smoothly even without a subsequent video high-pass filter, provided R_3 is appropriate. The circuit possesses two important features not available in the simpler video high-pass filter—the adjustable gain of the biasing amplifier and the delay time of the line. Both features should be helpful in final operation; therefore, the circuit is in principle more satisfactory than a simple high-pass filter. This superiority is not often easily demonstrated, as evidenced in Figs. 11·11 to 11·13, but the circuit has been found helpful under many conditions.

11·7. The Time-varied Gain Control.—The time-varied gain, TVG, control is used to vary the gain of a receiver as a function of the time after the transmitted radar pulse. It is sometimes called a "sensitivity-time control," STC, or a "temporal gain control." The desired gain pattern is ordinarily accomplished by generating a voltage wave of a prescribed form, initiated by each transmitted pulse. This voltage wave is applied to the i-f amplifier gain control lead, and it thus varies the receiver gain with time according to the shape of the applied voltage wave. If this voltage wave is properly shaped to conform with the clutter pattern, receiver saturation may be avoided. The essential difficulty with this scheme is producing an appropriate wave shape.   For simplicity's sake, it is convenient to consider only simple waveforms, such as step functions or an exponential curve.   Simple waveforms will match only those clutter patterns which are relatively uniform in azimuth and which change *relatively smoothly* in range; therefore, they are not generally useful in rainstorm clutter.   The TVG control has proved to be successful in operation with sea return (see Figs. 11·11 to 11·13 for photographs illus-

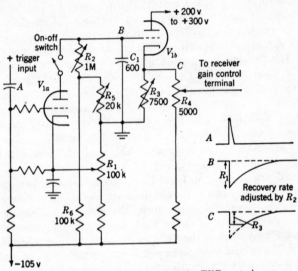

F<small>IG.</small> 11·6.—Schematic diagram of a TVG control.

trating its efficacy).   The circuit of the particular TVG used for these photographs is shown in Fig. 11·6.   The circuit is interesting because, although characterized by simplicity and economy of components, it will produce an easily variable wave shape.

When the switch is closed, the operation is initiated by a trigger pulse from the transmitter; the output waveform consists of an initial, step-like, flat segment followed by an exponential return to the initial voltage level.   The depth and length of the step are controllable, and the time constant of the exponential curve is adjustable.   In addition, the d-c level of the entire wave, that is, its quiescent level in the absence of triggers, is adjustable.   This last adjustment amounts to the usual receiver gain control.

Typical waveforms at selected points in the circuit are indicated.   At *A* the trigger input waveform is shown.   The tube V_{1a} charges the condenser C_1 to a potential governed by the potentiometer R_1 during the applied trigger pulse.   The potential across C_1 decays exponentially at the rate determined by the time constant R_2C_1. Thus the waveform at B is similar to that depicted in Fig. 11·6, where the initial height of the exponential function is controlled by the potentiometer R_1. This waveform would ordinarily be faithfully reproduced at point C because of the cathode follower V_{1b}, but the presence of R_3 prevents the cathode from following the grid potential during a part of the voltage wave. A sufficiently large negative voltage swing on the grid of tube V_{1b} will produce only a limited negative swing in its cathode; this swing is, in fact, the product of R_3 and the normal quiescent current flowing through the tube V_{1b}. Thus a flat section to the output wave will occur when the input voltage drops to a critical value. The depth of the flat section is controlled by R_3, and its length by R_1 (and, of course, R_2). The d-c level of the output wave is controlled by R_4. One other circuit peculiarity should be noted: the potential divider R_5 and R_6. This divider is used to fix the quiescent grid bias on V_{1b} at such a value that the cathode of V_{1b} is at ground potential; in this way the interaction between the controls R_3 and R_4 is eliminated.

The four parameters of the waveform, namely, the d-c level, depth of step, recovery time constant, and length of step, are therefore adjustable by means of the four controls R_4, R_3, R_2, and R_1, respectively. If adjustment is made in this order, little difficulty is experienced in arriving at final settings; this procedure usually requires only two or three successive approximations.

11·8. Efficiency of Circuits Used for Reduction of Clutter Saturation. Results are now available that show graphically the improvement obtained by the use of IAGC, DBB, and a high-pass video filter of the simple RC-type. To obtain beneficial results, however, these circuits must be designed with particular values of time constants and operating potentials.

The following general conclusions may be derived from results presented in Figs. 11·7 to 11·13:

1. The time constant of a simple high-pass filter is not critical; a value equal to the reciprocal of the pulse length appears satisfactory.
2. The time constant (product of R_2 and C_3) of the IAGC circuit shown in Fig. 11·3 should be much larger than the radar pulse length; a value of approximately 50 μsec has been found desirable. Probably more important than the pulse length in determining this time constant is the rapidity with which the average value of clutter (or other) echoes changes in time.
3. Proper operation of the DBB circuit in clutter is obtained with a transient gain probably from three to four times as high as the d-c gain. This adjustment is best made in actual trials.

4. For sea return the TVG is helpful; it is possibly more satisfactory than any other single circuit.

5. The beneficial effects of various circuits are usually additive. Experience has shown the use of IAGC to be advisable when either DBB or a high-pass filter is employed. The combined results are superior to the results of either circuit alone. It has not been found helpful, however, to use both DBB and a high-pass filter. The TVG is always helpful in sea return; it may greatly reduce the load the other circuits must carry. Its adjustment requires considerable skill, however, and its use for actual field operation may therefore be viewed with some misgivings.

These conclusions were derived from data obtained in trials in which an airborne radar set was used for the study of the effect of sea return. The radar set employed a beam pattern whose main lobe measured approximately 8° vertically and 3° horizontally. The wavelength was approximately 10 cm, and the pulse length approximately 2 μsec. Enough sensitivity was available to obtain clutter from sea return out to ranges often in excess of 100 miles. The intensity of sea return was usually sufficient to cause video saturation out to ranges of 40 miles, provided no special circuits were employed. Typical PPI photographs taken at an elevation of 7000 ft are shown in Figs. 11·7a, 11·9a, 11·10a, and 11·11a. The concentric circles are described by electrical range marks separated by time intervals each representing 10 miles. As can be seen, the total area represented in the photographs exceeds 3×10^4 square miles, yet it is possible to obtain strong echoes in most of this area. These pictures were taken in the region of Boston, Mass.; the pattern of Cape Cod, Martha's Vineyard, and Nantucket can easily be seen. The central portion of the photograph, however, is for the most part a uniform white region within which it is not possible to see any detail. This is the region where video saturation has taken place for both sea clutter and land return, as well as for such desired discrete targets within the clutter as ship echoes. In this region even such prominent features as the shore line between Massachusetts and the ocean immediately to the east cannot be recognized.

The improvement effected by the use of a simple high-pass filter is shown in Fig. 11·7b, c, and d. Each photograph was obtained using a different time constant in the filter. The white portion in the center extending out to the 20-mile range mark is an unfortunate addition to the photographs; it is caused by a marker introduced for reasons not pertinent to this discussion. It can be seen, however, that some improvement is made possible by the use of the high-pass filter; the region of complete saturation is smaller than that in the normal case (see Fig. 11·7a). The value of the time constant is not critical; careful inspection of the original photographs shows that a value equal to the pulse length is probably most desirable.

The improvement shown in Fig. 11·7 is not marked; this is explained by the presence of i-f saturation and some residual video saturation.   The

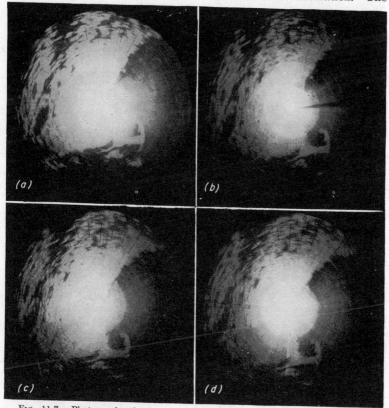

Fig. 11·7.—Photographs showing the effectiveness of a high-pass video filter: (a) results with a normal receiver and (b), (c), and (d) results of varying the values of the product RC of the filter. (b) $RC = 0.25$ μsec. (c) $RC = 1$ μsec. (d) $RC = 2$ μsec. The pulse length τ was 2 μsec.

great improvement in results obtained by using the IAGC, is shown in Fig. 11·8. Four photographs are shown; each one is taken for different values of the IAGC time constant (R_2 times C_3 in Fig. 11·3). For each of these photographs a high-pass filter was also employed because the IAGC used was not sufficiently effective to prevent video saturation. As can be seen, the proper IAGC time constant is much longer than the radar pulse length; a value of 30 to 60 μsec has been found most satis-

factory. A single photograph illustrating the use of IAGC alone is
shown in Fig. 11·9b; for this photograph a time constant of 60 μsec was
used in the IAGC circuit. Considerable video saturation still remains,
and the result obtained by the combined use of the IAGC and the high-
pass filter is far superior to that obtained by the use of either circuit alone.

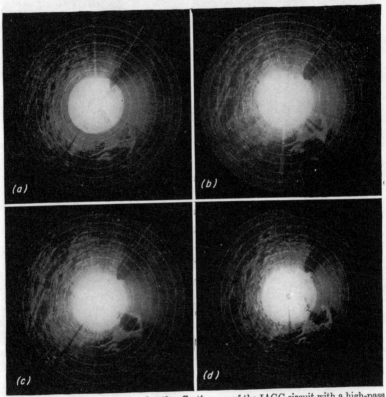

FIG. 11·8.—Photographs showing the effectiveness of the IAGC circuit with a high-pass
video filter. They show the effect of varying the time constant of the IAGC circuit.
(a) $R_2C_3 = 0.20$ μsec. (b) $R_2C_3 = 1.2$ μsec. (c) $R_2C_3 = 6$ μsec. (d) $R_2C_3 = 60$ μsec.
Compare with Figs. 11·7a or 11·9a for normal operation.

The operation of the DBB circuit is illustrated in Fig. 11·10. The
three photographs (Fig. 11·10b, c, and d) were taken with different values
of transient gain. As can be seen, the use of too much gain results in a
"reversal" of the land areas. Too little gain fails to effect the desired
improvement. When the proper gain is used, the land areas are easily
recognized, yet sea clutter is kept below strong saturation. For these

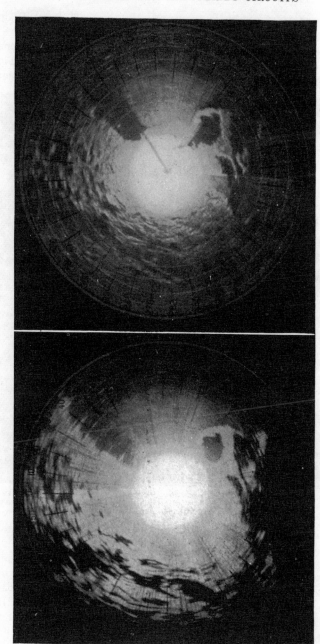

(a)

(b)

FIG. 11·9.—Photographs showing the effectiveness of the IAGC alone. (a) Receiver normal; (b) the IAGC set as in Fig. 11·8d, with no high-pass video filter.

photographs IAGC was used to prevent i-f saturation. The proper gain setting lies between the values used in Fig. 11·10b and c.

The TVG is extremely effective, as can be seen in Fig. 11·11b. Strong sea-clutter saturation is completely prevented, although there remain a few completely black areas, which represent a more than sufficient

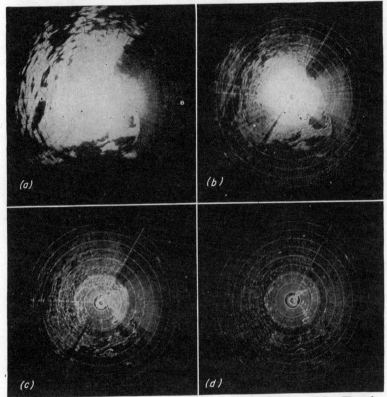

Fig. 11·10.—Photographs showing the effectiveness of IAGC and DBB. They show the results of varying the gain of the DBB circuit. The IAGC circuit is set the same as in Fig. 11·8d. (a) Receiver normal; (b) gain = 3; (c) gain = 5; (d) gain = 7.

receiver gain reduction and therefore a lower system sensitivity in those areas than would have been desired in principle.

The six photographs of Figs. 11·11 to 11·13 illustrate the final results obtained by the use of the various circuits described. A normal picture is shown, together with one showing the evident improvement obtained by the use of IAGC and either a high-pass filter or DBB circuit. In addition are shown the results obtained by the use of the TVG and, finally, by the use of both the TVG and the proper combinations of IAGC,

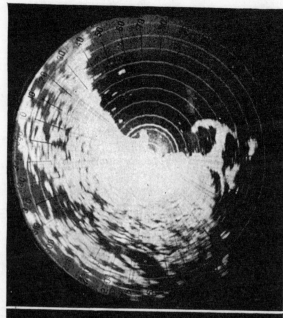

(a)

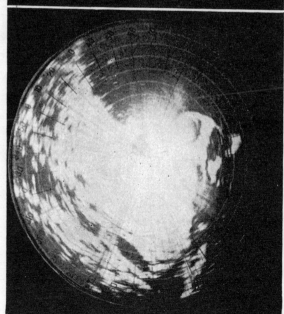

(b)

FIG. 11·11.—Photographs showing the effectiveness of a TVG control. (a) Receiver normal; (b) with TVG.

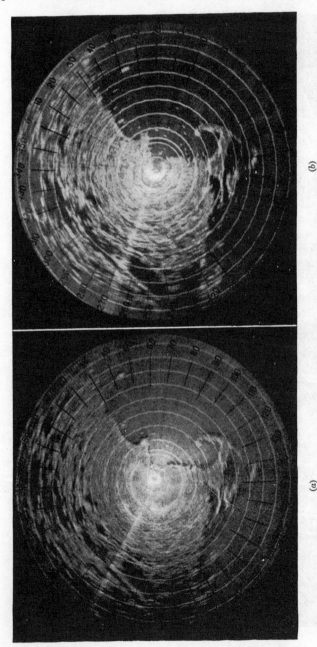

(a)

(b)

FIG. 11·12.—Photographs showing the effectiveness of IAGC circuits and a high-pass video filter (a) without TVG and (b) with TVG. For comparison with normal receiver see Fig. 11·11a.

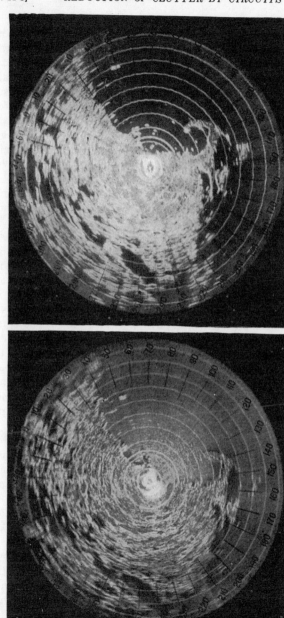

(a)

(b)

Fig. 11·13.—Photographs showing the effectiveness of IAGC and DBB circuits (a) without TVG and (b) with TVG. For comparison with a normal receiver see Fig. 11·11a.

high-pass filter, and DBB.   It is evident that the use of either combination of three circuits as shown in Figs. 11·12b and 11·13b gives the best results; sea return is nearly invisible, yet many ship echoes can be clearly seen.

It should be clearly understood that only some of these circuits will be effective for other forms of clutter.   The dramatic improvement effected by the use of TVG as shown in Fig. 11·11 readily suggests that this circuit alone would suffice for all practical needs, but this assumption does not obtain in cases of clutter originating in storm areas.   The complicated spatial pattern of such storm areas makes TVG useless, and reliance must therefore be placed on the other circuits.   Figure 11·14 shows how effective appropriate circuits can be.   Figure 11·14b shows a PPI whose radius represents approximately 20 miles.   The faint concentric circles are range marks separated by intervals representing 5 nautical miles. The strong circle at a range of 8 miles is an artificial echo from a test signal generator injected directly into the receiver.   Since this signal is not collected by the antenna, it has no dependence on azimuth; hence it appears on the PPI as a circle.   The echoes seen in the photograph are, for the most part, produced by objects on the ground.   The ground return is confined mainly within a radius of 10 miles because the radar set was located at an elevation of about 100 ft.   Some discrete ground targets are still noticeable out to the edges of the PPI, however.   In the photograph are also shown the echoes from some storm areas; they are recognized by the extended nature of the returned pattern and the undefined, fuzzy edges characteristic of such clutter.   These clutter areas are noticeable in the left-hand and in the lower right-hand sectors of the photograph. There is also a clutter area at the lowest part of the signal generator circle sufficiently intense to obliterate the signal generator echo in this region, as well as many discrete land echoes.

The improvement afforded by the use of proper IAGC and DBB circuits is shown in Fig. 11·14a.   The clutter from the storm areas is practically removed, and the underlying discrete ground echoes can be seen.   Furthermore. the signal from the test generator can be seen in its entirety, with the exception of three or four small breaks; these are due to the small recovery time of the IAGC, operated by an intense preceding land echo.   These breaks do not represent poor performance of the IAGC circuit; they occur in regions for which the test signal was already invisible in the original photograph.   Ordinarily *no desired signals are lost* when the clutter circuits are used properly and in the proper combination; Fig. 11·14 bears out this statement.   Furthermore, the improvement in operation resulting from the use of clutter circuits is substantial, provided the circuits are properly designed.

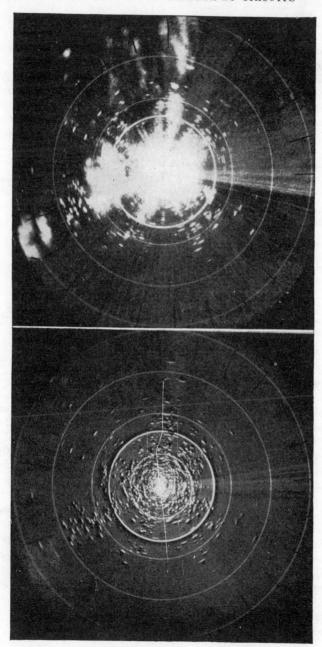

(a)

(b)

FIG. 11·14.—Photographs showing the effectiveness of anticlutter circuits on storm clutter. (a) Receiver with IAGC and DBB circuits; (b) receiver normal.

MOVING-TARGET INDICATION

11·9. General Description.—In the preceding discussion of signal threshold in clutter most of the properties of clutter were shown to be similar to those of the desired signal; hence conventional methods of signal separation do not yield spectacular results. The fundamental purpose of all the clutter circuits mentioned is to reduce the saturation likely to occur in various parts of the receiver. After the saturation is removed,

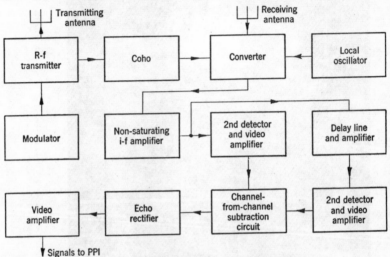

Fig. 11·15.—Block diagram of an MTI system.

these circuits may not be able to select preferentially the desired signal from strong clutter echoes or from other interfering discrete echoes, for example, those coming from objects on the ground, for the reason that a reflecting object on the ground has been assumed to yield a signal of the same type as that given by the desired target. This assumption may not be correct. Most of the time the desired object differs from a ground object in one important respect: It is usually *moving*. This fact may be utilized in devising a method of discriminating between the desired target and interfering fixed objects. Many schemes for making this discrimination have been suggested, and at least one or two have been developed to a highly successful degree. One such scheme, developed by R. A. McConnell and his colleagues, is explained in the following discussion.

The essential differences between the scheme for moving-target indication, or MTI, and the conventional method of radar operation lie in the form of reception and in the way the video signals are handled before they are presented on the PPI. A typical system is shown in block form in Fig. 11·15. The transmitted pulse is produced in the conventional way by the action of a pulse-forming modulator on the r-f transmitter. The received echo signal is injected into the superheterodyne converter along with the local oscillator, but in addition there is injected the output of a coherent r-f oscillator, or "coho." This oscillator is restarted at each pulse with a phase defined by the transmitted r-f pulse and delivers into the receiver a constant r-f voltage larger than any desired echo voltage. Therefore the *signal* voltage from the desired echo, added to the coherent-oscillator voltage, will produce a change in r-f voltage; either an increase or a decrease will result, depending upon the relative phases of the echo and the coho. This scheme is therefore one in which the output voltage in the i-f amplifier not only is a function of echo amplitude but is dependent on the phase of the echo return relative to the coho and hence relative to the main transmitted pulse. Since the total echo phase relative to the transmitted pulse is dependent only on the distance from transmitter to reflecting target and is, in fact, a measure of this distance in terms of the r-f wavelength, phase variations will occur only by radial target movement. One wavelength change in radial distance will result in a 4π change in r-f phase of the echo and hence, because of the local oscillator and converter, in a 4π change in i-f phase relative to the i-f coho voltage.

The i-f amplifier that follows the superheterodyne converter is of a nonsaturating variety, protected either by IAGC or by linear-logarithmic construction. The i-f amplifier output is split into two channels; one of these channels produces a conventional video signal, and the other produces an exact replica of this signal except that it is delayed in time. The delay in time is made to correspond precisely with the interval between the initiation of successive transmitted pulses, that is, the reciprocal of the PRF. In this way two video outputs, obtained from successive transmitted pulses, are available. These two video channels are then put into a circuit that takes their *difference*. In the output line of this channel-from-channel subtraction circuit will appear only signals whose phases have changed appreciably in the time between pulses. Echoes from fixed objects will have a fixed phase and amplitude from pulse to pulse; hence they will give identical video signals in the two channels and therefore be completely canceled out in the subtraction circuit. The complete system up to the output of the subtraction circuit therefore represents a scheme by which echoes from moving targets are made visible and echoes from fixed targets are completely removed. The moving target, to be visible, must move an appreciable fraction of a wavelength in the time between successive pulses.

If the cancellation is to be effective, the two video channels must have exactly equal signal amplitudes and shapes; this can be effected if the i-f bandwidth at the input of each second detector is the same and if the over-all gain through the delay line and post-delay amplifiers is properly set. These conditions are not especially difficult to obtain. The delay line itself has usually assumed the form of a liquid transmission medium in which supersonic waves are propagated. Quartz crystals are generally used to convert electric energy into sound energy and vice versa. The over-all attenuation of such a delay line depends upon the bandwidth desired and for the usual case is of the order of magnitude of 60 db. Thus the amplifier following the delay line must have an over-all gain in excess of 60 db with adequate bandwidth and negligible noise. Such an amplifier is, however, easy to construct and adjust.

Another scheme devised to obtain delayed video signals uses a cathode-ray storage tube. It has not, however, been so highly developed as the one using a supersonic delay line. In this system the video signals are stored on a suitable cathode-ray-tube screen and are later taken off again for purposes of comparison. This system has generally suffered by comparison with the supersonic line for two reasons: (1) The signal definition is usually not so satisfactory because of the finite area of the electron beam and possibly the "graininess" of the storage surface; (2) the time over which adequate storage can be maintained is limited because of charge leakage in the screen material. It appears, however, that these limitations are not too serious; already storage tubes that show adequate length of storage time have been built.

The output from the subtraction circuit invariably contains signals of both polarities depending upon the change in phase of the signal from pulse to pulse. It is customary to convert these signals into signals of one polarity by means of an echo rectifier. The operation with an intensity-modulated display, such as the PPI, is thus made considerably more satisfactory. A video amplifier between the echo rectifier and the PPI, as shown in Fig. 11·15, is used to bring the signals to a satisfactory value for easy visibility.

The construction of an actual system similar to that shown in Fig. 11·15 has shown up certain difficulties that have necessitated minor changes. To ensure an adequate coho, whose r-f voltage is larger than that produced by the largest desired echo, enough i-f voltage from the coho and local oscillator must be produced to overload even a carefully designed i-f amplifier. It has therefore become customary to inject the coho as an *i-f voltage* directly into the second detector input, as shown in Fig. 11·16. In this case the coho is an *i-f oscillator*, which is started at the time of the transmitted pulse but is locked in phase to the i-f pulse produced by the conversion of the r-f transmitted pulse. This scheme, like the one shown in Fig. 11·15, is sensitive to the phase of the echo, but the coho voltage itself never goes through the i-f amplifier and cannot therefore cause i-f overload.   The i-f amplifier itself is made nonsaturating either through IAGC or through linear-logarithmic construction.

Stability throughout the MTI system must usually be very high, and special precautions must often be taken with various components.   The local oscillator and coho must be stable to a small fraction of a cycle in phase, even at very long ranges, that is, for a very large number of cycles.

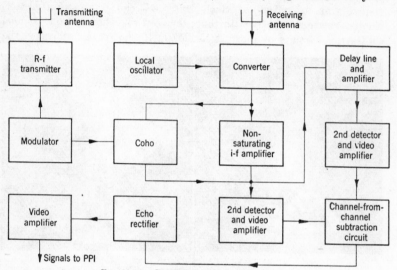

Fig. 11·16.—Block diagram of an MTI system.

The transmitted pulses must be formed at precise time intervals, determined essentially by the delay time of the delayed video channel. An elegant scheme, attempted in various forms, is to trigger the modulator for the transmitter from pulses derived from the delay line itself.   These may be obtained in several ways, but care must be taken not to interfere with the usual video operation of the delay line.   In any case the time difference between the delay in the delayed video channel and the interval between transmitted pulses must not be greater than a small fraction of a pulse length.

In spite of the many requirements for stability, however, systems have been built that perform exceptionally well.   An example of the efficiency of the device is shown in Fig. 11·17, where the PPI pictures are shown. In each of these photographs an easily recognized sector slightly larger than 90° displays normal system operation and normal ground clutter. Within the ground clutter not only is it impossible to recognize desired signals, such as those from aircraft, but even land configuration is lost in the intense saturation.   Outside the sector showing normal system operation the MTI system is in effect and shows the phenomenal success achieved in suppressing ground clutter. Several signals are visible, all due to aircraft, in the MTI sector.

Although the MTI was originally developed to combat the effects of ground clutter, its effectiveness in counteracting most other forms of clutter was soon appreciated. It was pointed out in Sec. 11·1 that the configuration of reflectors, which causes sea clutter or storm clutter, changes relatively slowly with time; therefore the channel-from-channel subtraction circuits of Figs. 11·15 and 11·16 should almost cancel the

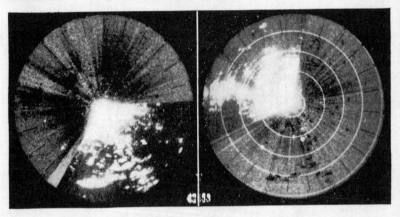

Fig. 11·17.—Photographs showing the effectiveness of MTI in removing ground clutter. Several aircraft signals are visible in the sectors covered when MTI was operating.

clutter echoes, and they actually accomplish this. An example of the effectiveness of cancellation is shown in Fig. 11·18. The first photograph shows a normal PPI picture with a 30-mile sweep. Return from storm areas is easily visible at azimuths of about 15° and 150° and near 30 miles range and at 60° azimuth and 15 miles range. The second photograph is an MTI picture, taken approximately at the same time, and shows almost no evidence of storm clutter.

It has become customary to express the effectiveness of MTI operation in terms of the *subclutter visibility*. This term specifically expresses, in decibels, the ratio of the strength of the echo that, produced by a signal generator of random phase, is barely detectable on a PPI in clutter with which it coincides in range during normal system operation, to the strength of the echo barely detectable when the MTI is in operation, and the adjustments are such that the clutter itself is not visible. In ground clutter a subclutter visibility of −20 db in the field or perhaps −30 db in the laboratory can be achieved at a wavelength in the 10-cm region and a PRF of approximately 2000 pps. Storm clutter can be reduced as much as 10 to 15 db, the figure depending on the spatial velocity and, presumably, the turbulence of the storm.   There are instances where little or no reduction of clouds has been observed.   Nevertheless these figures represent an improvement by an order of magnitude over the usual radar detection capability, even when the radar is equipped with the special circuits previously described.   There is no improvement, however, for slow-moving targets.

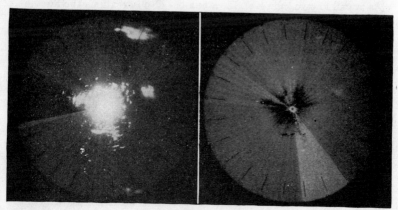

Fig. 11·18.—Photographs showing the effectiveness of MTI in removing clouds, particularly those in the upper right-hand quadrant.

11·10. Threshold Signals in the MTI System.—The MTI system just described makes use of two general principles: (1) the production of a *coherent video* signal, (2) a *delay and cancellation* principle.   Threshold signals in the over-all system can best be analyzed by considering the two parts separately.   An exhaustive treatment of the subject will not be attempted here, but it is hoped that the discussion will give some insight into the mechanism of signal perception.

Coherent Systems.—The analysis of threshold signals follows much the same pattern as that used in Chap. 8 for the ordinary system.   Certain striking differences are noted in the quality of the output signal, however. The appearance of the signal depends upon its phase relative to the coho and especially upon whether the phase is unchanging, continuously increasing, or continuously decreasing.   The case for a fixed target whose phase is optimum, that is, in phase with the coho will be considered first.

Fixed Target.—In this case the signal is recognized by an amplitude deflection that exceeds random noise deflections.   These deflections can all be measured relative to the amplitude of the coho voltage since this latter voltage is the amplitude that exists in the absence of both noise and signal.   Since the signal is in phase with the coho, the signal deflection is simply given by the signal voltage. The noise, however, has a random phase with respect to the coho and therefore produces a zero-average deflection amplitude, whether the signal is present or not. Nevertheless the noise produces chance fluctuations in the total voltage that depend upon the rms value of the noise voltage itself. Therefore for a single observation the threshold signal voltage will be of the order of the equivalent noise voltage.

As is well known, however, for a number of observations the fluctuations are reduced to a value that is inversely proportional to the square

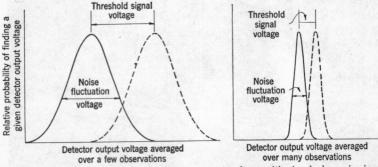

FIG. 11·19.—Schematic behavior of detector output voltage with signal plus noise in a coherent system.

root of this number. This follows from the Gaussian nature of the noise amplitude distribution and is the same consideration that has been applied to noise in the usual noncoherent system (see Chap. 8). We can therefore write the conditions for threshold signal in the following form:

$$V_{S_{90}} \approx \frac{V_N}{\sqrt{N_S}}, \qquad \text{or} \qquad P_{S_{90}} \approx \frac{P_N}{N_S}, \tag{1}$$

where $V_{S_{90}}$ and $P_{S_{90}}$ are the voltage and power of the threshold signal respectively, V_N and P_N are the rms voltage and power of the noise, respectively, and N_S is the total number of observations.

It has been assumed in the preceding discussion that a coho voltage, large compared with either the signal or the noise, and a linear second detector are used. In the comparison between signal power and noise power, the linearity of the second detector need not be assumed provided the coho voltage is large. The usual quadratic detector will be essentially linear under this condition; it is the same kind of condition that makes the superheterodyne converter linear in its action.

An illustration of the quantities involved is shown in Fig. 11·19. In the first drawing a plot is made of the relative probability of finding a given detector output voltage as a function of the given output voltage averaged over a few observations. The bell-shaped curves are produced by the Gaussianlike noise fluctuations; the threshold signal is one that shifts the average output deflection by an amount approximately equal to the width of the noise distribution. For a large number of observations the average noise fluctuation is reduced in accordance with Eq. (1); and as the second diagram of Fig. 11·19 shows, the threshold signal voltage can be reduced by a like amount.

It will be noticed that the dependence of signal threshold power on the number of observations, that is, integration time, differs from that noted in the noncoherent system. This difference was first pointed out by Emslie,[1] who showed that in the coherent system the total threshold signal energy is independent of the number of observations. This conclusion means that for fixed targets the sensitivity of the coherent system may be far higher than that of the noncoherent system. The improvement is accounted for by the better integration from pulse to pulse arising from the linear form of signal deflection, even though the signal is smaller than noise itself.

A better criterion than Eq. (1) could be obtained; in fact, from accurate curves of the type shown in Fig. 11·19 betting curves similar to those shown in Chap. 8 could be constructed. This is beyond the scope of this chapter, however. It is sufficient here to point out that apart from these refinements, Eq. (1) must be interpreted properly. The total noise power is, of course, essentially proportional to the i-f bandwidth; the signal deflection is proportional to the i-f bandwidth for small values of the latter and independent of bandwidth for large values. Thus the signal deflection will depend on i-f bandwidth and will have a maximum in the neighborhood of $B\tau = 1$, where B is the i-f bandwidth and τ is the pulse length. This is the same situation that was found in Chap. 8; therefore Eq. (1) should be used only where the signal deflection is, in fact, not seriously affected by insufficient i-f bandwidth. The complete dependence on i-f and video bandwidths could be calculated, if desired, by methods similar to those used in Chap. 8.

Unfortunately, there are at the present time no good experimental results that confirm Eq. (1). The dependence on the total number of observations N_S has been checked qualitatively, however. The results obtained show that the signal threshold power is inversely related to a power of N_S; the power was found to be greater than $\frac{1}{2}$ but less than unity. This conclusion is not entirely unexpected; for signals very small with respect to noise, that is, for a large number of observations, the effect of *contrast limitations* was anticipated. It is believed therefore that Eq. (1) probably holds only where N_S is small and fails when N_S is large because

[1] A. G. Emslie, "Coherent Integration," RL Report No. 103-5, May 16, 1944.

of the finite contrast required for perception by the human eye and brain mechanism.

For fixed targets not at optimum phase with respect to the coho, the same arguments apply, except that the signal deflection is not given directly by the signal voltage. It is simply the product of the signal voltage and the cosine of the phase angle between the coho and the signal.

Moving Targets.—For moving targets the signal deflection averaged over a large number of cycles is zero. This is because the time spent in any particular phase is the same as the time spent in the opposite phase; therefore the signal is not recognized by an average deflection in output

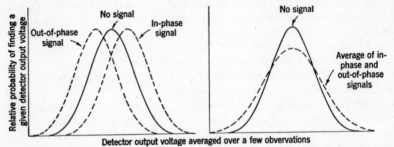

FIG. 11·20.—Schematic behavior of detector output voltage for in-phase and out-of-phase signals in a coherent system.

voltage. The signal, however, acts in such a way as to broaden the output amplitude distribution. This can be observed qualitatively by averaging the distributions of signal and noise for both in-phase and out-of-phase signals; this process is indicated in Fig. 11·20. The first diagram indicates in dotted lines the distribution of in-phase and out-of-phase signals added to noise. The second diagram indicates by a dotted line the average value of these two conditions and compares the resulting distribution with that in the absence of a signal. The signal can be seen to broaden the distribution. It can be shown analytically that with signals small with respect to noise power, this broadening is proportional to the *square* of the signal voltage. A signal will be recognized when the broadening is of the order of magnitude of the noise fluctuation; therefore the threshold condition will occur if

$$V_{S_{90}}^2 \approx \frac{V^2}{\sqrt{N_S}} \quad \text{or} \quad P_{S_{90}} \approx \frac{P_N}{\sqrt{N_S}}, \tag{2}$$

where $V_{S_{90}}$ and $P_{S_{90}}$ are the voltage and power of the threshold signal, respectively; V_N and P_N are the rms voltage and power of the noise respectively; and N_S is the total number of observations. It can be seen, therefore, that for noncoherent signals the threshold power varies inversely with the square root of N_S; this is the same dependence on N_S

that is observed to hold for signals obtained on the usual noncoherent system. Equation (2) is, like Eq. (1), subject to limitations of i-f bandwidth and contrast; these quantities have not been carefully investigated either experimentally or theoretically. Since the dependence on N is the same as for the usual noncoherent case, however, it is convenient to know how the threshold signal depends upon the introduction of the coho. This dependence has been checked experimentally, and the introduction of the coho found to increase the threshold signal power by approximately 3 db. It is believed, therefore, that, with the introduction of this correction factor, the problem of the perception of a moving target in a coherent system is essentially the same as that solved in Chap. 8.

For the sake of completeness, the statement just made requires one reservation. In principle the starting phase of the coho can be changed at a rate that makes its phase relative to the moving target stationary. Under this condition the moving target echo will behave like the fixed echo previously described, and Eq. (1) will be valid. However, this requires that the radial velocity of the moving target be known or found quickly; this condition is not generally found in practice and may therefore be neglected.

Delay and Cancellation.—The principle of delay and cancellation used in MTI alters the signal and noise responses. The signal response will first be considered, then the noise response, and finally the signal response in the presence of noise.

1. *Signal response.* The signal is essentially a series of pulses whose amplitude is varied sinusoidally at a frequency determined by the rate of phase shift brought about by target motion. This frequency f is, in fact, the Doppler shift in returned radio frequency produced by target movement and is given by

$$f = \frac{2v}{\lambda},\tag{3}$$

where v is the radial target velocity and λ is the r-f wavelength. The amplitude of an output signal pulse in the delay-and-cancellation scheme is essentially the *difference* between the amplitude of a given pulse and the amplitude of the preceding pulse. The *maximum* signal output deflection will occur at the point of maximum difference in the sinusoidal signal-amplitude curve. For a signal of unity peak amplitude (each side of the no-signal amplitude) the maximum amplitude of the output signal will be given by

$$A_{max} = \left| 2 \sin 2\pi \frac{f}{f_r} \right|,\tag{4}$$

where f_r is the PRF. A plot of A_{max} vs. f, as shown in Fig. 11·21, shows that the signal response has maxima at a frequency of half the PRF and at all odd harmonics of this frequency. Likewise, at a frequency of the

PRF itself or its harmonics, the system will give no output indication whatsoever. For very low frequencies, $f \ll f_r$, the system is relatively unresponsive; this is the feature which permits the system to reject fixed ground clutter and also relatively slow-moving sea or storm clutter.

The curve shown in Fig. 11·21 is a bit disturbing because there appear to be regions in f and hence in radial target velocity v where the system is "blind." This is indeed the case, but the situation is not so serious as it seems. Because of the presence of propeller modulation, as discussed in Chap. 10, these blind speeds are not actually observed when the target is an airplane. The propeller modulation prevents the envelope of the returned series of pulses from assuming a simple sinusoidal form; the blind speed regions are thereby "filled in," and the signal loss within these regions is considerably less.

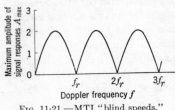

FIG. 11·21.—MTI "blind speeds."

2. *Response to noise.* The video noise that appears in the output of the cancellation network is easily calculated. Since the noise distribution in the coherent video system has a symmetrical shape about the axis, the addition of two independent noise channels will give the same average noise distribution as will the subtraction of these channels. Thus the noise fluctuation voltage in the output of the cancellation circuit will be larger than the voltage in each channel by a factor of $\sqrt{2}$ and will have approximately the same Gaussian shape.

3. *Response to a signal in the presence of noise.* In the presence of noise, the signal will consist of a series of pulses modulated by a sinusoid of frequency f. The amplitude of this sinusoid is governed both by the input signal amplitude and by the PRF, shown graphically in Fig. 11·21. The *average value* of the signal output voltage is zero; therefore for signal visibility a broadening of the noise distribution must be effected in a way similar to that for which Eq. (2) is valid. Therefore the threshold signal power will vary inversely with the square root of N. The various system parameters are expected to have effects similar to those described in Chap. 8 for parameters in a conventional noncoherent system. It is necessary, however, to normalize the threshold power for two effects: the first is the action of the coho, the second, the effect of target velocity. As was mentioned previously, the effect of the coho is to increase the signal threshold power by about 3 db; the effect of the target speed is shown in Fig. 11·21. In a practical case in which aircraft are used as targets, the average signal threshold increase produced by various target velocity blind spots does not appear to be serious. Either the blind regions are so small that they are seldom encountered, or they are filled in satisfactorily by propeller modulation.

CHAPTER 12

THRESHOLD SIGNALS IN ELECTRONIC INTERFERENCE

As is pointed out in Secs. 6·6 to 6·8, the different varieties of electronic interference can be roughly classified as simple and complex. In each of these categories the effects of the particular interference and the methods for its alleviation depend upon the detailed structure of the interference. This chapter will treat the question of pulsed-signal threshold power for three types of interference: (1) unmodulated c-w interference, (2) noise-modulated c-w interference, and (3) pulsed interference. Pulsed interference may be of either the simple or the complex variety discussed in Secs. 6·7 and 6·8; cases of both varieties are presented together, since methods for their alleviation are similar. In all cases treated it is assumed that the interference has been allowed to reach the i-f terminals of the receiver; that is, no r-f measures have been taken to minimize interference.

THRESHOLD SIGNALS IN UNMODULATED CONTINUOUS-WAVE INTERFERENCE

12·1. Effect of C-w Interference.—A description of the c-w interference itself is almost unnecessary; it consists essentially of a constant-amplitude, constant-frequency voltage, which we assume exists at the input terminals of the i-f amplifier. The signal pulses and equivalent noise also appear on these terminals, however. Our problem is to consider the interaction effects of all three voltages in an attempt to evaluate the threshold signal. Because many receiver and indicator characteristics are involved that do not lend themselves to easy analysis and measurement, the task is a difficult one. Wherever possible, however, quantitative results will be given.

Interaction of C-w Interference with Signal.—Let us assume, for simplicity's sake, that the c-w voltage is large compared with the pulse voltage. The signal will cause a change in the output voltage of the second detector. As the pulse and the c-w interference may occur with any relative phase and with any difference in frequency, the video signal will consist of a small element of length proportional to τ (the pulse duration); this element has an amplitude that differs from the video voltage (produced by the interference) by an amount proportional to the pulse voltage. The video frequency during this element is the difference between the pulse and c-w frequencies. The situation is shown in Fig.

12·1.   Because the phase relationships are not, in general, maintained from pulse to pulse, the video signals from many pulses take on all possible phase combinations.

If the c-w interference is at the same frequency as the pulse, i.e., on-frequency c-w interference and the i-f bandwidth is sufficiently wide, the video signal will evidently consist of a number of video pulses of duration

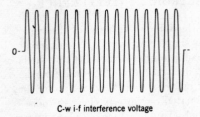

τ and of varying amplitudes, depending upon the phase relationship of the c-w interference and the signal.   On the average it is equally likely for the c-w interference to be in phase with the signal as to be out of phase; there-

C-w i-f interference voltage

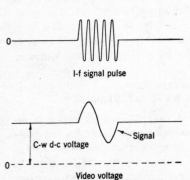

0 —

I-f signal pulse

0 — — — — — — — — — — — —

C-w d-c voltage — — Signal

Video voltage

Fig. 12·1.—Voltage waveforms when signal pulse and c-w interference are mixed.

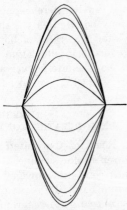

Fig. 12·2.—Voltage waveforms of video signal in presence of on-frequency c-w interference.

fore the *average* video deflection over a large number of pulses is zero. (We still assume that the signal deflection is the *change* in video deflection caused by the signal.)   The appearance of the signal on an A-scope, however, will be similar to that when no c-w interference is present, except that the signal is "filled in" and extends both sides of the baseline (see Fig. 12·2).   It is already clear that the signal threshold power probably will not depend upon the *average* video deflection.   The peak deflection of this video signal depends upon the type of second detector: for a linear detector the peak deviation from the baseline is unchanged by the interference, whereas for a quadratic detector the amplitude of the video signal depends markedly on the intensity of the c-w interference.   For this reason the linear detector is generally pref-

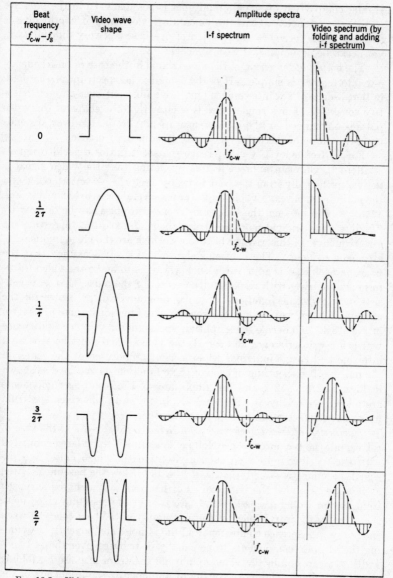

Beat frequency $f_{c\text{-}w} - f_s$	Video wave shape	Amplitude spectra	
		I-f spectrum	Video spectrum (by folding and adding i-f spectrum)
0			
$\frac{1}{2\tau}$			
$\frac{1}{\tau}$			
$\frac{3}{2\tau}$			
$\frac{2}{\tau}$			

FIG. 12·3.—Video wave shapes and spectra for symmetrical signals (cosine functions).

erable; comparison of signal amplitudes is possible even in the presence of the interference. (These statements are valid only if overloading is avoided in the receiver. Prevention of overload is a very difficult task, yet it can be accomplished with some success.)

The *amplitude spectrum* of the video signal in the case of on-frequency c-w interference is simple. It is the same as the spectrum of the pulse in the absence of c-w interference but with a different over-all multiplicative constant. For a single pulse it is clear that the shape of the video pulse is unchanged by the interference; its amplitude, however, depends upon the phase of the pulse relative to the c-w interference.

For off-frequency c-w interference the spectrum of the video signals is altered. One can appreciate this by noting that the video signal is derived principally from the beat tones between the c-w interference and the pulse frequencies. Typical spectra for several cases are shown in Fig. 12·3. As can be seen, the spectrum for a given pulse can be derived by "folding" the original pulse spectrum about an axis that represents the c-w frequency; in this way the beat tones, which are the video frequencies, are made evident. The diagrams shown in Fig. 12·3 assume that the phase in each case is adjusted in such a way as to make the video waveform symmetrical with respect to the center of the pulse, that is, it consists only of cosine functions. Similar diagrams can be drawn for the antisymmetrical waveforms representing sine functions; these are shown in Fig. 12·4. To derive the amplitude spectrum for any phase difference between c-w interference and signal, the video signal must be separated into sine and cosine functions whose origins are located at the center of the pulse. The spectrum of each of these functions is obtained as shown in Figs. 12·3 and 12·4, and the amplitudes of the resulting components are added vectorially at right angles. In this way the video spectrum for any specific case can be rapidly computed.

Interaction of C-w Interference with Receiver Noise.—As in the case of the signal, the c-w interference voltage is assumed to be large compared with the receiver noise. In such a situation the video noise, like the signal, becomes two-sided, that is, it "beats" below the baseline as often as it appears above the baseline. Furthermore, as might be surmised from the preceding discussion, the spectrum of the resulting video noise is altered by the interference; it consists simply of the beat tones between the i-f c-w interference component and the i-f noise components. Assuming the i-f noise components to be equally distributed over the i-f bandwidth, we can obtain the video amplitude spectrum of noise by folding the amplitude response curve of the i-f amplifier at the frequency of the c-w interference in much the same way as was done for the signal frequency components in Figs. 12·3 and 12·4. In this case, however, no relationship exists between the noise components of the two folded halves;

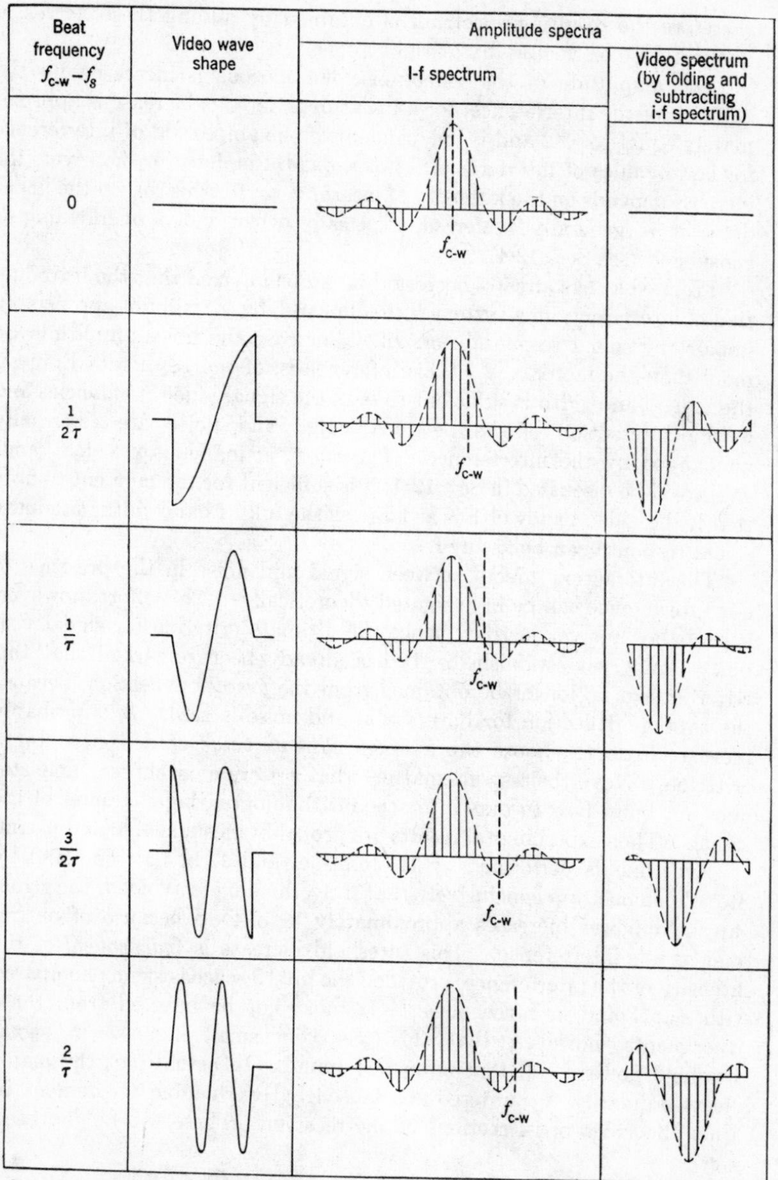

FIG. 12·4.—Video wave shapes and spectra for antisymmetrical signals (sine functions.)

therefore the resulting spectrum is obtained by adding these halves in quadrature, i.e., vectorially at right angles.

The amplitude of the video-noise fluctuations is increased by the addition of the interference; for a linear detector this increase is approximately equal to $\sqrt{2}$ and is independent of the amplitude of interference for large values of interference. For a quadratic detector, however, the increase depends on the intensity of interference; for this reason the linear detector is generally preferred, especially when video overloading is considered (see Sec. 12·4).

From what has already been said it can be inferred that the introduction of interference in a system with a linear detector will not appreciably impair the signal response, nor will it increase the noise amplitude by more than the factor $\sqrt{2}$. This inference is, of course, justified only if the video bandwidth is sufficient to pass the signal video frequencies and if the interaction effects between signal and noise are essentially unchanged by the interference. The effect of inadequate video bandwidth will be discussed in Sec. 12·4; it is sufficient for the moment to note that if the video bandwidth is as large as the full i-f bandwidth, adequate signal response can be assured.

The interaction effects between signal and noise in the presence of c-w interference can be investigated theoretically. This effort, however, is probably not yet justified, since the ultimate criterion for signal visibility is not yet established. It has already been remarked that this criterion can no longer be obtained from the *average* deflection, because the average deflection for both signal and noise is zero. It is probably more realistic to choose the average *absolute value* of deflection for a criterion. Nevertheless, no matter what criterion is chosen, one still does not know how to take into account the fluctuating character of the signal. Thus experimental results are probably most reliable and useful.

Experiments performed by H. Johnson, and J. L. Lawson,[1] and by Stone[2] demonstrate conclusively that if overloading is avoided, the signal threshold power increases approximately 3 to 4 db because of on-frequency c-w interference. This threshold increase is *independent* of the intensity of the interference, provided the interference is strong compared with signal and/or noise power. It must not be inferred from these experiments, however, that this relatively small increase in signal threshold power is all that is usually found. In actual fact the major effects ordinarily encountered are caused by overloading phenomena in either the video or i-f sections of the receiver. These will be discussed later.

[1] Unpublished, but see RL Report No. 910, Mar. 22, 1946.

[2] A. M. Stone, "Synthetic Radar Echoes in the Presence of Jamming," RL Report No. 708, June 22, 1945.

12·2. Video Overloading.—Overloading or saturation in some part of the video system is the most common and most serious effect produced by c-w interference. The severity of the effect varies with the type of indicator, the intensity-modulated indicator, such as the PPI, being in

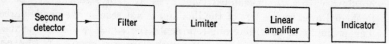

Fig. 12·5.—Block diagram of typical video system.

general most easily affected. The reason for this is the necessarily increased limiting that must be employed with this type of indicator to prevent defocusing, or "blooming," with strong signals.

A block diagram of a typical video system is shown in Fig. 12·5. The output voltage from the second detector is first filtered by an appropriate high-pass filter whose purpose will be described below. The filtered voltage is amplified by an essentially linear amplifier before it is applied to the indicator system. The peak output voltage that can be applied to the indicator is *limited* to some chosen value. The limiter can follow or precede the linear amplifier; for convenience it usually precedes the amplifier and does, in fact, usually involve merely the cutoff bias of the first amplifier tube.

In the absence of c-w interference the filter indicated in Fig. 12·5 is not needed; the output of the second detector may be direct-coupled to the grid of the first amplifier stage. In this condition, however, as soon as the c-w interference produces a d-c second-detector voltage sufficient to bias the amplifier tube to cutoff, i.e., to the assigned limit level, nearly all signal information will be lost. Signal information will occur only for signal pulses out of phase with the interference and of an amplitude approximately equal to that of the interference. It is only under this condition that the second-detector voltage will be small enough to permit conduction in the first amplifier stage and hence make possible the conveyance of signal information. The signal is recognized on

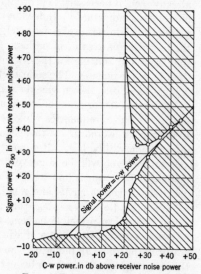

Fig. 12·6.—Signal threshold power in presence of c-w interference. Direct coupling in video amplifier.

the A-scope by a *negative* deflection from the baseline.   It is to be expected that for very large intensities of c-w interference the signal will make its appearance only for values of signal nearly equal to the c-w voltage. This is actually found to be true; Fig. 12·6 shows an experimental curve obtained with a direct-coupled video system.   The signal is seen in the unshaded area to the left of the line and is not seen in the shaded area. The ordinate in this diagram represents the signal power in decibels relative to the receiver noise power; the abscissa represents the c-w interference power in decibels relative to the receiver noise power.   As is shown in the diagram, for large values of c-w interference power the threshold signal power is almost equal to the c-w power.

It is clear from Fig. 12·6 that a relatively small amount of c-w interference is enough to remove virtually all traces of the signal, a result of the saturation, or limiting, in the receiver.   (This limiting, we have already seen, is necessary to prevent defocusing, or blooming, on intensity-modulated indicators.)   Indeed, even with the A-scope, the limiting voltage level, in terms of noise level, cannot be made indefinitely large; in the best designs a value of perhaps 100 can be realized.   The problem is, then, to avoid limiting for the c-w voltage and yet to maintain the proper limit level for pulses.   The solution to this problem is fortunately simple: A high-pass filter, shown schematically in Fig. 12·5, is employed between the second detector and the video system to pass the major part of the important pulse frequencies while removing the deleterious d-c term due to the c-w interference.   If this is done *before* limiting, virtually no signal information will be lost.   If a linear detector is used, the resulting signal and noise level will be relatively unaffected by the interference.   A quadratic detector is much less favored because of the interference-dependent levels of signal and noise, which have been mentioned.

Since the d-c term arising from the c-w interference is the main difficulty, it could in principle be removed by an RC-filter, even though the l-f cutoff were set to a value of a few cycles per second.   This, however, is true if the video amplifier uses no d-c restorers.   (D-c restorers prevent the coupling condensers from being charged by pulses of polarity opposite to that of the conventional video pulse.)   Ordinarily, however, a large pulse of opposite sign, i.e., pulse and c-w interference out of phase, will, by means of d-c restoring action (possibly caused by grid current in one of the amplifier tubes), reinstate the d-c potential on the coupling condenser, thereby nullifying the action of the filter.   For this reason a high-pass filter, whose l-f cutoff is perhaps $1/2\tau$, where τ is the pulse length, is usually preferred.   Strong pulses will not affect the filter operation for subsequent desired pulses, nor will an appreciable increase of threshold signal be required in the absence of c-w interference.   Furthermore, should the c-w interference be slowly modulated in amplitude, the high-pass filter will successfully remove the slow modulation components as well as the d-c term.

It is desirable at this point to consider briefly the action of a high-pass filter in receivers that are supplied with a "gate" and that subsequently employ a third detector (see Chap. 2). If the "gating" is done in the i-f amplifier, the operation of the gate on the c-w voltage will obviously convert the d-c second-detector output to pulses. The high-pass filter will "differentiate" these pulses in the same fashion as desired signal pulses. To avoid this added difficulty in discernibility the gating should be done in the video section *after* the high-pass filter; in this way the *RC*-filter will remove the c-w voltage before it can cause a "gate pulse."

The use of a high-pass filter in the video system can successfully eliminate video saturation provided a linear second detector is used. With a quadratic detector, on the other hand, the rise in signal and noise amplitudes due to the interference voltage is usually sufficient to cause by itself serious video limiting. Therefore, whenever c-w interference is expected, as has been repeatedly emphasized, a quadratic detector should not be used.

Even when a suitable high-pass filter and linear second detector are used, serious limiting effects may be noticeable in the receiver. These are all traceable to saturation in the i-f amplifier. The next section considers what methods can be employed to alleviate this situation.

12·3. Intermediate-frequency Overloading.—When an i-f amplifier is subjected to strong c-w interference, several undesired effects may be encountered. For example, the entire amplifier may be thrown into oscillation; this phenomenon, however, is usually due to inadequate shielding and filtering, a condition generally easily remedied. Nevertheless to avoid this difficulty special precautions with regard to amplifier stability must be taken. Nearly all amplifiers are considerably more unstable in the presence of strong c-w interference because the various tubes are forced to operate in regions of higher mutual conductance. It is perhaps easiest to recognize this form of instability by obtaining a curve of the kind shown in Fig. 12·7. In this figure the curves indicate the threshold signal power as a function of c-w interference power. A stable amplifier yields a monotonic curve; irregular behavior usually denotes instability. The latter condition is depicted in the first curve of this diagram; the second curve shows the result when no instability appears. This type of plot is one of the best criteria of receiver stability in the presence of c-w interference.

It will be noticed, however, that in Fig. 12·7 even though the receiver is made stable and video saturation is eliminated by the use of a high-pass filter, ultimately a large increase in signal threshold occurs. The knee of the curve is observed always to occur at the point where receiver noise is no longer visible on the A-scope. What appears to happen is simply a reduction in the "pulse gain," that is, the incremental gain, of the receiver. Eventually this pulse gain of the receiver turns out to be approximately inversely proportional to the c-w in'erference power. In general, all i-f amplifiers exhibit this behavior; the saturation properties of the amplifier can be measured either in terms of the knee of the curve

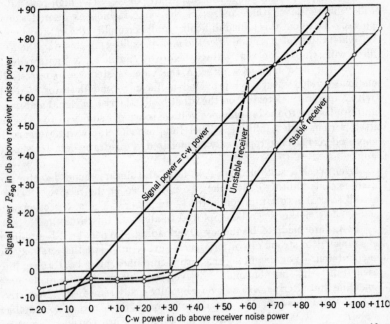

FIG. 12·7.—Signal threshold power in presence of c-w interference. High-pass video coupling.

or in terms of the ratio of interference to pulse power in the region above the knee of the curve. Obviously, in comparing receivers standard conditions must be used throughout.

Many factors contribute to i-f saturation. Before these are considered, however, a brief calculation will indicate why the kind of results shown in Fig. 12·7 need not be surprising. For an *unchanged* gain over the range of c-w power indicated on the abscissa, let us roughly calculate the undistorted output power required of the i-f amplifier. Let us assume that in the absence of c-w interference, the average noise level at the second detector is about 1 volt, measured across 1000 ohms; this is a fairly representative figure. An unchanged gain for a c-w power 100 db above this level would require a *continuous* power output of 10^7 watts from the second detector, or more than ten times the output power of the most powerful present-day broadcasting transmitter. Thus the power-output capability of the i-f amplifier and second detector is an important criterion. In general, the gain reduction observed in an i-f amplifier subjected to c-w interference is caused either by *plate saturation* in the amplifier tubes or by *grid loading* or by both. Intermediate-frequency grid conduction loads the preceding i-f stage, hence reducing its gain. Because of transit-time effects i-f loading can easily occur *without* d-c grid current.

Two types of amplifier gain have been mentioned. The conventional gain is defined by the c-w output voltage divided by the c-w input voltage; the "pulse gain," by the output pulse signal relative to the input pulse. At first glance these two definitions of gain might appear to be identical. The circuits can be so arranged, however, that the "pulse gain" is far higher than the c-w gain—by automatic biasing of the i-f tubes in accordance with the c-w power so that only the very tips of the c-w voltage oscillations appear in the conduction region of the tube. In this way the *incremental* gain of the amplifier is almost maintained, while the c-w gain is reduced to unity. The foregoing procedure is illustrated in Fig. 12·8. In the conventional scheme strong c-w oscillations swing the tube over the entire characteristic; the output voltage will be saturated, containing no signal intelligence. If automatic biasing is used, however, only the tips of the i-f input voltage wave appear in the operating region of the tube and signal intelligence appears in the output voltage wave. Automatic biasing can easily be made to eliminate plate saturation and grid loading entirely. It does not, however, maintain pulse gain unchanged because the duty ratio or "mark-to-space" ratio in the plate-current impulses is reduced. Figure 12·8 shows that if strong c-w interference is encountered, the plate-current impulses, while still changing amplitude in accordance with the signal by an amount that is independent of c-w power, become very thin "spikes" whose width depends (inversely) upon the c-w power. The i-f components of these current impulses falling within the i-f pass band, therefore, diminish as the c-w power is increased. In spite of this duty-ratio factor, however, automatic biasing can greatly improve the operation of a receiver. In Fig. 12·9 three curves are shown, all of them taken with the same receiver and under the same standard conditions. The first curve was obtained with no i-f biasing and no video high-pass filter; the second curve shows the improvement afforded by the use of the high-pass filter. These two curves are the same as those shown in Figs. 12·6 and 12·7. The third curve shows the very substantial improvement brought about by automatic biasing of the i-f amplifier. The automatic biasing is accomplished by means of the *instantaneous automatic gain control* circuit, or IAGC, of Fig. 11·3 and described in Sec. 11·4. It is of particular significance that this circuit, developed primarily for the prevention of saturation by clutter, is so effective in its suppression of c-w interference effects

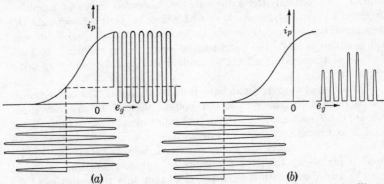

FIG. 12·8.—Intermediate-frequency waveforms illustrating automatic biasing. (*a*) Waveforms without automatic biasing; (*b*) waveforms with automatic biasing.

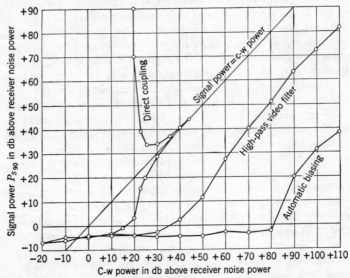

FIG. 12·9.—Signal threshold power in presence of c-w interference.

Besides automatic biasing, *rejection filters* in the i-f amplifier can be used to reduce the effects of c-w interference. These filters are designed to provide infinite attenuation at some adjustable frequency made, in practice, to coincide with the frequency of the offending c-w interference. A typical circuit of such an infinite-rejection filter is shown in Fig. 12·10.

In the absence of the variable resistor shown, the circuit is simply a conventional "wave trap"; the variable resistor may, however, be adjusted to provide infinite attenuation at the resonant frequency. Its effect is to compensate for the coil losses in the resonant circuit.[1]

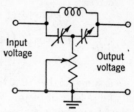

In practice, the infinite-rejection filter is not satisfactory, especially for receivers in the microwave region. The principal difficulty is the necessity for continual frequency adjustment. Furthermore, even though the frequency were properly adjusted, it is rare to find a source of c-w interference whose stability is adequate to "stay in the notch." Usually l-f sidebands are present that are not properly attenuated by the filter.

Fig. 12·10.—Infinite-rejection filter.

12·4. Dependence of Threshold Signal upon C-w Interference Frequency.

—The effects of c-w interference have been briefly discussed, both in the region where no saturation occurs and in the region of video or i-f saturation. These effects have been treated largely for on-frequency interference, however, and for adequate video bandwidth. In this section a theoretical analysis will be attempted of the effects connected with other interference frequencies and video bandwidths. The analysis will be carried out with the assumption of no overloading; the variables with which we are concerned are therefore (1) the c-w power, (2) the video bandwidth, and (3) the difference between the c-w and signal frequencies $f_{cw} - f_s$. For simplicity's sake, it will be assumed that the signal frequency is centrally located in the i-f pass band[2] and that the i-f pass band is symmetrical and Gaussian in shape. Assuming in addition a square pulse shape, the signal can be represented as

$$S(t) = \begin{cases} S \sin (2\pi f_s t + \theta_s) & \text{for } |t| < \dfrac{\tau}{2}, \\ 0 & \text{otherwise,} \end{cases}$$

while the continuous wave can be written as

$$E(t) = E \sin (2\pi f_{cw} t + \theta_{cw}).$$

The total input is the sum of the signal and the c-w voltages and can be written in a form analogous to Eq. (1) of Sec. 7·2:

$$S_{\text{in}}(t) = S(t) + E(t) = \alpha_0(t) \cos 2\pi f_s t + \beta_0(t) \sin 2\pi f_s t,$$

---

[1] A. M. Stone and J. L. Lawson, "Infinite Rejection Filters," *J. Applied Phys.*, **18**, 691 (1947). See also A. M. Stone and J. L. Lawson, "Infinite Rejection Filters," RL Report No. 72-6, June 1, 1943; A. M. Stone, "A Note on Pulse Distortion by Rejection Filters," RL Report No. 422, Sept. 16, 1943.

[2] In the notation of Sec. 7·2 this means that f_s is equal to the carrier frequency f_c.

where

$$\alpha_0(t) = \begin{cases} E \sin\left[2\pi(f_{cw} - f_s)t + \theta_{cw}\right] + S \sin\theta_s & \text{for } |t| < \frac{\tau}{2}, \\ E \sin\left[2\pi(f_{cw} - f_s)t + \theta_{cw}\right] & \text{otherwise}, \end{cases}$$

$$\beta_0(t) = \begin{cases} E \cos\left[2\pi(f_{cw} - f_s)t + \theta_{cw}\right] + S \cos\theta_s & \text{for } |t| < \frac{\tau}{2}, \\ E \cos\left[2\pi(f_{cw} - f_s)t + \theta_{cw}\right] & \text{otherwise}. \end{cases}$$

If we assume further that the i-f bandwidth B is much larger than $1/\tau$, so that the pulse will be practically not deformed, we obtain for the output of the i-f amplifier

$$S_{out}(t) = \alpha(t)\cos 2\pi f_s t + \beta(t)\sin 2\pi f_s t,$$

where

$$\alpha(t) = \begin{cases} E \exp\left[-\frac{a^2(f_{cw} - f_s)^2}{B^2}\right]\sin\left[2\pi(f_{cw} - f_s)t + \theta_{cw}\right] \\ \qquad\qquad + S \sin\theta_s \quad \text{for } |t| < \frac{\tau}{2}, \\ E \exp\left[-\frac{a^2(f_{cw} - f_s)^2}{B^2}\right]\sin\left[2\pi(f_{cw} - f_s)t + \theta_{cw}\right] \\ \qquad\qquad\qquad\qquad \text{otherwise}, \end{cases} \quad (1a)$$

$$\beta(t) = \begin{cases} E \exp\left[-\frac{a^2(f_{cw} - f_s)^2}{B^2}\right]\cos\left[2\pi(f_{cw} - f_s)t + \theta_{cw}\right] \\ \qquad\qquad + S \cos\theta_s \quad \text{for } |t| < \frac{\tau}{2}, \\ E \exp\left[-\frac{a^2(f_{cw} - f_s)^2}{B^2}\right]\cos\left[2\pi(f_{cw} - f_s)t + \theta_{cw}\right] \\ \qquad\qquad\qquad\qquad \text{otherwise}, \end{cases} \quad (1b)$$

and $a = 1.18$.

As in the previous sections of this chapter, for the case of actual interest, the original c-w power is much larger than either the signal or the noise power. Assuming a *linear* second detector, the detector output of the c-w plus signal plus noise will be a nearly Gaussian distribution of the form given by Eq. $(7\cdot13a)$ and with an average value

$$\bar{r} = (\alpha^2 + \beta^2)^{1/2} = \begin{cases} E \exp\left[-\frac{a^2(f_{cw} - f_s)^2}{B^2}\right] \\ \qquad + S \cos\left[2\pi(f_{cw} - f_s)t + \varphi\right] \quad \text{for } |t| < \frac{\tau}{2}, \\ E \exp\left[-\frac{a^2(f_{cw} - f_s)^2}{B^2}\right] \quad \text{otherwise}, \end{cases} \quad (2)$$

where $\varphi = \theta_{cw} - \theta_s$ and where terms proportional to S^2 have been neglected. One sees from Eq. (1) that the average value of the detector output will oscillate inside the pulse because of the beat frequency between the c-w and the signal. In addition the average value $\bar{r}$ will vary from pulse to pulse, because the phase difference φ will vary and will assume any value between zero and 2π. Clearly, as a result of this phase fluctuation, the introduction of the signal will only widen somewhat the original Gaussian distribution without changing the average value $E \exp\left[-a^2(f_{cw} - f_s)^2/B^2\right]$. Because of these reasons the detectability criteria of Sec. 7·3 are *not* applicable, and to proceed further additional assumptions have to be made.

First, we shall consider only the case of a very narrow video bandwidth; for this case the variations of r inside the pulse will not be significant. Therefore for the detection of the signal only the average value of r over the pulse length τ will play a role. This leads to

$$\tilde{\bar{r}} = \begin{cases} E \exp\left[-\dfrac{a^2(f_{cw} - f_s)^2}{B^2}\right] + \dfrac{S}{2\pi(f_{cw} - f_s)\tau} \\ \quad \{\sin\left[\pi(f_{cw} - f_s)\tau + \varphi\right] + \sin\left[\pi(f_{cw} - f_s)\tau - \varphi\right]\} \\ \hspace{6cm} \text{with signal,} \\ E \exp\left[-\dfrac{a^2(f_{cw} - f_s)^2}{B^2}\right] \qquad \text{without signal} \end{cases} \quad (3)$$

Second, in order to take into account the phase fluctuations, we shall assume that the observer will average over *one-half* of the widened (but symmetrical) distribution resulting from the variations of the phase φ. All values of φ will be assumed to be equally probable, or in other words the probability for the phase to be between φ and $\varphi + d\varphi$ will be assumed to be $d\varphi/2\pi$. With all these assumptions, the quantity that determines the detectability of the signal and that we denote as in Sec. 7·3 by $\bar{r}_{S+N}$ is given by

$$\bar{r}_{S+N} = \frac{2}{\sqrt{2\pi W}} \int_0^{2\pi} \frac{d\varphi}{2\pi} \int_0^\infty dx\, x \exp\left\{-\frac{[x - (\tilde{\bar{r}}_{cw+s} - \tilde{\bar{r}}_{cw})]^2}{2W}\right\}, \quad (4)$$

where $\bar{r}_{cw+s}$ and $\bar{r}_{cw}$ are the two values of the average deflection given by Eq. (3). The integrals in Eq. (3) cannot be carried out exactly, but one can develop in powers of $S^2/2W$; keeping only the first two terms, one obtains

$$\bar{r}_{S+N} = \sqrt{\frac{2W}{\pi}} \left\{1 + \frac{S^2}{4W}\left[\frac{\sin \pi(f_{cw} - f_s)\tau}{\pi(f_{cw} - f_s)\tau}\right]^2\right\}. \quad (5)$$

As in Sec. 7·3 we will assume that the detectability of the signal will depend on the ratio of $(\bar{r}_{S+N} - \bar{r}_N)$ to the fluctuation of the output when no signal is present.

The assumption of a very narrow video bandwidth b implies a further reduction in the output signal by the familiar factor $b\tau$. Hence one obtains

$$\bar{r}_{S+N} - \bar{r}_N = \frac{S^2 b\tau}{4W} \sqrt{\frac{2W}{\pi}} \left[\frac{\sin \pi (f_{cw} - f_s)\tau}{\pi (f_{cw} - f_s)\tau} \right]^2. \tag{6}$$

The fluctuation of the video output in the absence of the signal can be computed by means of Eq. (7·20b). The α's and β's there are given by Eq. (1) with $S = 0$. Since $E \gg W$, the main contribution to the continuous spectrum of the linear detector output comes from the term proportional to ρ. Retaining only this term, one obtains for the correlation function of the c-w plus noise

$$\overline{r_1 r_2} = W\rho(t_2 - t_1) \frac{\alpha_1\alpha_2 + \beta_1\beta_2}{[(\alpha_1^2 + \beta_1^2)(\alpha_2^2 + \beta_2^2)]^{1/2}}$$
$$= W\rho(t_2 - t_1) \cos [2\pi(f_{cw} - f_s)(t_2 - t_1)], \tag{7}$$

from which follows the spectrum in the usual way. Using Eq. (7·21) and (7·26) of Sec. 7·2, one finds for the spectrum of the linear detector

$$G_L(f) = W[Q(f_{cw} - f_s + f) + Q(f_{cw} - f_s - f)], \tag{8}$$

where

$$Q(f) = \sqrt{\frac{2}{\pi}} \frac{a}{B} \exp\left(-\frac{2a^2 f^2}{B^2}\right) \tag{9}$$

is the normalized spectrum of the intermediate frequency, which we had assumed to be of Gaussian shape. For a narrow video bandwidth b the fluctuation of the video output will be simply $G_L(0)b$. Using again the notation of Sec. 7·3, we obtain therefore, from Eqs. (8) and (9) for the fluctuation of the video output, the expression

$$\overline{r_N^2} - (\bar{r}_N)^2 = \sqrt{\frac{2}{\pi}} \frac{2aWb}{B} \exp\left[-\frac{2a^2(f_{cw} - f_s)^2}{B^2}\right]. \tag{10}$$

In analogy to the deflection criterion of Sec. 7·3, we shall assume that the minimum detectable signal power is determined by the equation

$$\frac{\bar{r}_{S+N} - \bar{r}_N}{[\overline{r_N^2} - (\bar{r}_N)^2]^{1/2}} = C, \tag{11}$$

where C is a constant, which may still depend on the observation time. Combining Eqs. (6) and (10), one then finds for the minimum detectable average signal power

$$\bar{P}_{\min} = \frac{S^2\tau}{\Theta_0} = \frac{4\sigma^2 C}{\Theta_0} \left(\frac{\pi aB}{2b}\right)^{1/2} (2\pi)^{1/4} e^{-\frac{a^2(f_{cw} - f_s)^2}{B^2}} \left[\frac{\pi(f_{cw} - f_s)\tau}{\sin \pi(f_{cw} - f_s)\tau}\right]^2, \tag{12}$$

where in order to put the dependence of $\bar{P}_{\min}$ on the bandwidth B in evidence we have expressed W in terms of the noise power σ^2 before the intermediate frequency and the bandwidth B according to

$$W = \sigma^2 \int_{-\infty}^{+\infty} df\, e^{-\frac{2a^2f^2}{B^2}} = \frac{\sigma^2 B}{a}\sqrt{\frac{\pi}{2}}.$$

Before discussing Eq. (12) and comparing it with experiment, one should remember that Eq. (12) holds only if $(f_{cw} - f_s) < B$, since we have assumed that the c-w power is large compared with the signal and noise power. For very large detuning, one may clearly consider the c-w to be absent. In this case the average of the linear detector output is [see Eq. (7·14a)]

$$\bar{r}_{s+N} = \sqrt{\frac{\pi W}{2}}\, F\left(-\frac{1}{2}, 1; -\frac{S^2}{2W}\right) \cong \sqrt{\frac{\pi W}{2}}\left(1 + \frac{S^2}{4W}\right)$$

if $S^2/2W \ll 1$. For a narrow video bandwidth one obtains therefore, instead of Eq. (6),

$$\bar{r}_{s+N} - \bar{r}_N = \sqrt{\frac{\pi W}{2}}\, \frac{S^2 b\tau}{4W}. \tag{13}$$

For the continuous noise spectrum of the detector output we get, using Eqs. (7·20a) and (7·26) of Sec. 7·2,

$$\begin{aligned}
G_L(f) &= \frac{\pi W}{4} \int_{-\infty}^{+\infty} df_1\, Q(f_1)Q(f + f_1) \\
&= \frac{\sqrt{\pi}\, aW}{4B}\, e^{-\frac{a^2f^2}{B^2}}.
\end{aligned}$$

The fluctuation of the video output with which (13) has to be compared is as before $G_L(0)b$ or

$$\overline{r_N^2} - (\bar{r}_N)^2 = \frac{\sqrt{\pi}\, aWb}{4B}. \tag{14}$$

For large detuning, the minimum detectable average signal power will therefore be given by

$$\bar{P}_{\min}(\infty) = \frac{4\sigma^2 C}{\Theta_0}\left(\frac{\pi aB}{2b}\right)^{\frac{1}{2}} (4\pi)^{-\frac{1}{4}}. \tag{15}$$

These results can be compared with some experiments performed by A. L. Gardner and C. M. Allred with apparatus specially constructed for this purpose. In these experiments the injected c-w power was 40 db above receiver noise power, the i-f bandwidth was rather wide ($B\tau \cong 2.2$), and the video bandwidth was quite narrow. It was first noted that with the frequency of the continuous wave in the middle of the i-f pass band (on-frequency interference) the signal threshold was about 3.5 db higher than with no continuous wave present. This can be compared with Eqs. (12) and (15), from which follows

$$\frac{\bar{P}_{\min}(0)}{\bar{P}_{\min}(\infty)} = (8\pi^2)^{\frac{1}{4}}, \tag{16}$$

or 4.75 db. Detuning the continuous wave increases the signal threshold still further until the detuning has gone so far that the continuous wave is practically not present any more. The experimental results are shown

TABLE 12·1.—EXPERIMENTAL AND THEORETICAL VALUES OF SIGNAL LOSS WITH DETUNING

$f_{cw} - f_s$	Signal threshold, db, relative to threshold at $f_{cw} - f_s = 0$	
	Experimental	Theory*
0.5	5.5	3.6
1	13.5	∞
1.5	11	10.75
2	15	∞
2.5	9	10.3
3	5	
3.5	0	
4	−2.5	
4.5	−3.5	

* For $(f_{cw} - f_s)\tau$ larger than 2.5, Eq. (12) is no longer applicable; hence, no theoretical values are given.

in Table 12·1 together with the theoretical values calculated from the equation

$$\frac{\bar{P}_{\min}}{\bar{P}_{\min}(0)} = e^{-\frac{a^2(f_{cw}-f_s)^2}{B^2}} \left[\frac{\pi(f_{cw} - f_s)\tau}{\sin \pi(f_{cw} - f_s)\tau} \right]^2, \tag{17}$$

which follows from Eq. (12). The agreement between theory and experiment is as good as can be expected. The theoretical infinities for integral values of $(f_{cw} - f_s)\tau$ are due to the neglect of the terms proportional to S^2 in Eq. (2). However, the experiments give exceptionally large values for the signal threshold for these values of $(f_{cw} - f_s)\tau$, so that the first-order theory seems qualitatively justified.

In the case of a wide video bandwidth it is not the *average value* but the *envelope* of the pulse that is significant. Since the envelope is not sensitive to detuning, no increase in signal threshold with detuning is expected. This is confirmed by experiment. An experimental curve showing the effect of detuning when a relatively wide-band video system is used is given in Fig. 12·11. It can be seen that the signal threshold varies little and remains a few decibels above the value when no continuous wave is present. It is fortunate that a great improvement in signal perception can be obtained by employing a video system whose bandwidth is approximately as large as the i-f bandwidth, since this condition is

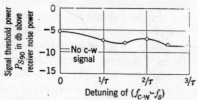

Fig. 12·11.—Signal threshold power vs. the detuning of the c-w signal with a wide video amplifier. The threshold in the absence of c-w interference is indicated.

desirable for proper signal perception even in the absence of c-w interference (see Chap. 8).

THRESHOLD SIGNALS IN
NOISE-MODULATED CONTINUOUS-WAVE INTERFERENCE

It has just been shown that given proper video bandpass characteristics and absence of i-f or video overload, the effect of unmodulated c-w interference is not very serious. Even for very large amounts of interference a maximum rise in signal threshold power of only 3 or 4 db occurs. The essential reason for this is that the interference contains no *fluctuations* which would tend to mask the signal. It is almost an accident that any deleterious effect occurs at all; the experimentally observed values come about principally because of a change in form of signal and noise brought about by the interference. The next step is to consider interference effects produced by modulated c-w power. That an infinite variety of modulating functions exist is clear; in the following treatment, however, discussion will be limited to "noisy" functions, that is, those which are nonrepetitive and of a statistical nature. The random nature of noise has been shown repeatedly to be principally responsible for the efficiency with which it is able to mask signals; therefore we can expect that "noisy" interference will most readily mask desired signals.

Noisy interference can be produced in a variety of ways; perhaps the most obvious way is simply to amplify r-f thermal noise. The properties of this type of noise have been described in Chap. 4; it has a uniform power spectrum (in which the frequency components are unrelated) and a Gaussian amplitude distribution. From an interference point of view the problem has already been solved; the noise has the same characteristics as internal receiver noise whose effect on signal threshold power has been described in Chaps. 8 and 9.

Radio-frequency thermal noise interference of large power is usually hard to produce because of the usual difficulties with r-f amplification;

consequently, it is generally expedient to modulate an r-f c-w carrier with an appropriate video noise function. This modulation can be applied to the carrier amplitude, frequency, or phase. Frequency and phase modulation are shown in Chap. 2 to be similar; one can proceed from frequency to phase modulation and vice versa by the use of appropriate filters. We may therefore consider *amplitude* and *frequency modulation* as the two fundamental operations. Although it is quite possible to consider in detail the effects of each type of modulation, only the a-m case will be presented in the following discussion.

12·5. Continuous-wave Interference Amplitude Modulated by Noise. Let us assume for simplicity that the video-voltage noise function produces corresponding changes in the r-f amplitude within the limitations of the r-f amplifier. Ideally these limitations are felt in two ways: (1) The r-f amplifier has a minimum power output (zero) that the modulating function must not try to cross, and (2) the r-f amplifier has a definite peak output-power capability. These limitations mean that any of the noise functions which we are likely to consider will not be immediately applicable to modulation; these functions must first be passed through limiters to prevent overdriving the r-f amplifier on large noise peaks and to prevent cutoff of the r-f amplifier on large negative peaks. This limiting action may, of course, be provided by the r-f amplifier itself; however, in computing the spectrum and amplitude distribution of r-f noise it is convenient to think first of limiting the video noise function, then of applying purely linear amplitude modulation to the r-f carrier.

The problem confronting us, then, is essentially the c-w interference case discussed in Secs. 12·1 through 12·4, except that in addition to the c-w carrier we now must consider the r-f noise sidebands. The properties of these noise sidebands depend upon the properties of the video noise function as well as on the degree of limiting, or "clipping." That this problem is complex is proved by the complicated effects of even the unmodulated c-w carrier. Consideration of the general case will not be attempted. Discussion will be limited to the behavior of the system under the following set of conditions:

1. The receiver is fitted with an adequate i-f filter and has an adequate video bandwidth.
2. The noise modulating function is to be video thermal noise with Gaussian amplitude distribution and bandwidth defined by b_n. This bandwidth is ordinarily determined by the video amplifier characteristics.
3. The limiting, or clipping, is symmetrical about the average value of the Gaussian noise function. This implies that the r-f amplitude is modulated about a value equal to one-half the peak value.

With these restrictions in mind we are in a position to discuss qualitatively the effects to be expected. The signal threshold power will depend essentially on three factors: (1) the amount of receiver noise present, (2) the r-f interference *carrier*, and (3) the spectrum and amplitude of the interference noise. The first two factors have already been discussed in Chaps. 8 and 9 and in Secs. 12·1 through 12·4; let us therefore consider the interference noise itself.

We shall be concerned with two properties of the interference-noise sidebands: (1) the *power spectrum* that incidentally will give the total sideband power relative to the carrier power and (2) the *quality* of the noise, which must be measured in terms of the efficiency with which it is able to mask a desired signal. The first property has been calculated by Van Vleck.[1] He has assumed symmetrical limiting, or clipping, of the video noise function. If one defines the fractional modulation resulting from the noise as m, where m is the ratio of rms video noise voltage *before* limiting to the limiting level itself, then Van Vleck has shown that clipping has little noticeable effect on the spectrum for values of m less than unity. Furthermore, the total noise sideband power in terms of the carrier power is given simply by $\frac{1}{2}m^2$ again for values of m less than unity. For values of m greater than unity the spectrum is modified appreciably by the clipping, and the total noise sideband power is not a simple function of m. Where m becomes infinite, a condition Van Vleck describes as "super clipping," he has shown that the total sideband power is just equal to the carrier power. Representative spectra and amplitude distributions for $m = 1$ are shown in Fig. 12·12. In this diagram the video noise function is assumed to have a uniform spectrum out to the bandwidth limit b_n.

In what is to follow the region of particular interest is that for which the fractional modulation m is less than unity. Therefore we can easily calculate the total noise sideband power and its spectrum from the modulating video bandwidth b_n and the fractional modulation m. The problem might appear at this point to be nearly solved; this would be true if one knew precisely how efficiently the clipped interference noise (compared with unclipped noise) masks the desired signal. Unfortunately this property of the interference noise is not easily susceptible to calculation. Figure 12·12 makes it clear that the noise-amplitude distribution is profoundly altered by the clipping. The apparent "ceiling" produced by the limiting action provides a more or less definite amplitude baseline over which a relatively small signal can be noticed. Therefore the ceiling produces a qualitative change in the noise that may

[1] J. H. Van Vleck, "The Spectrum of Clipped Noise," RRL Report No. 411-51, July 21, 1943.

outweigh considerations of total noise power. The ceiling effect, as shown in Fig. 12·12, is dependent upon the sharpness with which limiting takes place and upon the fractional modulation m. This would also be the ceiling effect as seen on the A-scope provided the receiver r-f bandwidth B were sufficiently large to pass the entire spectrum shown in Fig. 12·12. If the receiver i-f bandwidth B is less than the total interference-noise bandwidth $2b_n$, however, the output noise of the receiver will lack some of the frequency components needed to reestablish the well-defined ceiling; therefore the ceiling effect will be less pronounced than that shown

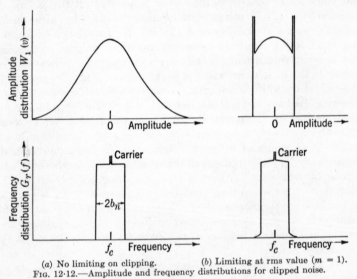

(a) No limiting on clipping. (b) Limiting at rms value ($m = 1$).
FIG. 12·12.—Amplitude and frequency distributions for clipped noise.

in the diagram. We may expect the ceiling effect to vanish completely when $B \ll 2b_n$. Therefore according to this reasoning the ceiling effect depends upon two parameters, the fractional modulation m and a quantity β equal to $2b_n/B$, that is, the ratio of interference-noise bandwidth to receiver i-f bandwidth. A clipping factor F_c is introduced, representing a measure of the loss in interference-noise effectiveness caused by clipping. This factor is most conveniently expressed as the logarithm of the ratio of actual interference-noise sideband power to the equally effective unclipped noise power. A clipping factor F_c of 3 db therefore represents a condition where the clipped noise power falling within the receiver i-f bandwidth is equivalent in effectiveness to unclipped noise of approximately one-half the power. The clipping factor $F_c(m,\beta)$ is most readily determined by experiment; its limiting value when m is small and β is large approaches 0 db.

In an elaborate series of experiments Stone[1] has shown that the foregoing conclusions appear to be valid; he has obtained empirical values for the clipping factor as a function of m and β and has plotted them in a most convenient form.   This plot is reproduced in Fig. 12·13; m is shown as ordinate, and β as abscissa.   The contour lines represent different clipping factors; these lines do not appear in an area near the left-hand edge of the diagram because in this region self-consistent results were not obtained.   Stone's results, however, clearly show the clipping factor to be extremely important, especially when the fractional modulation exceeds unity and the

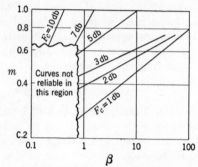

Fig. 12·13.—Fractional modulation m as a function of $\beta = 2b_n/B$ for various values of the clipping factor F_c.

interference-noise bandwidth $2b_n$ is comparable to the receiver i-f bandwidth B.

For large values of interference power the rise in threshold signal caused by the interference can be evaluated as follows:

1. Calculate the total interference-noise sideband power falling in the receiver i-f bandwidth in comparison with receiver noise itself. The calculation is made from a knowledge of the ratio of the interference-carrier power to the receiver-noise power, the fractional modulation m, and the value of β, which is the ratio of total interference-noise bandwidth to receiver i-f bandwidth. This interference-noise power (in terms of receiver noise power) is most conveniently expressed in decibels.

2. Add about 3 db to Item 1 to account for the effect of the carrier.

3. Correct for the clipping factor F_c by means of the curves in Fig. 12·13.   This correction in decibels is to be subtracted from Item 2.

4. The final answer represents the increase in signal threshold power caused by the interference.

This procedure appears to be valid as long as $m \leq 1$ and as long as the interference is strong compared with receiver noise.   It is also assumed that no overload or saturation effects occur in the receiver; this can be assured by methods discussed in Secs. 12·2 and 12·3.

One additional point is worth mentioning.   For a fixed interference-noise bandwidth the clipping factor F_c is a function of i-f bandwidth B.

[1] A. M. Stone, "Synthetic Radar Signals in the Presence of Jamming," RL Report No. 708, June 22, 1945.

Therefore, in measuring threshold signals as a function of B, in a way similar to that shown in Fig. 8·7, the smallest threshold signal energy will be found at a value of $B\tau$ somewhat *higher* than the value determined for receiver noise.   A. M. Stone[2] has found that under certain conditions the optimum value of $B\tau$ could be shifted by a factor of as much as 3 or 4. It does not appear, however, that this situation should alter the design of receivers, for the wider bandwidth generally gives a greater opportunity for off-frequency interference.

THRESHOLD SIGNALS IN PULSED INTERFERENCE

12·6. Description of Pulsed Interference.—In the first two parts of this chapter an attempt was made to analyze the deleterious effects of c-w interference even though modulated in amplitude by a complicated noise function.   Other forms of electronic interference exist, one of the most common of which may be termed *pulsed interference*.   Here, the interfering wave may consist of a train of r-f pulses whose repetition frequency may or may not be constant and whose radio frequency and pulse length may or may not correspond to that of the desired signal.   In radar reception, pulsed interference will very likely arise from other near-by radar sets operating on nearly the same radio frequency.   Such interference will appear on the radar A-scope as a series of intense saturated signals, which usually differ from genuine echo signals in their nonsynchronized positions and in their relatively great intensities. Because of the resulting fencelike appearance on the A-scope, the interference is usually known as "railing" interference.   Several interfering radar units produce several sets of interspersed railings whose relative positions continually change.   A discussion of railing interference and methods of suppressing its effect is given in Sec. 12·7.

Because of the relatively large peak powers that can be produced with pulse techniques the possibility of producing damaging interference by this means should be considered.   It can be shown that no power is "wasted" in a carrier and that a "noisy" function can be produced by random variations in the interval between successive pulses.   The conditions determining threshold signal power for this situation are discussed in Sec. 12·8.

12·7. Railing Interference.—In railing interference one must consider not only the effect of the main interfering pulse but also the trailing interference echoes produced by near-by reflecting objects.   These echoes, though very weak in comparison with the main interference pulse, may still be large enough to exceed a desired signal.   In practice these trailing echoes can be detected for perhaps 100 μsec after the main pulse.

[1] *Ibid.*

In spite of these trailing echoes there is generally a considerable period during which the receiver is not affected at all by the interference; in these time intervals signal detection can be maintained at nearly normal sensitivity. For this reason railing interference of low-duty ratio does not materially affect threshold signals; the effect of interference duty ratio is to alter the fraction of time during which the signal may be seen. In a sense this is equivalent to an alteration of PRF, shown in Chap. 8 to have only a mild effect on threshold signal. According to this argument, one would expect to find a rise in threshold signal power of 1.5 db when the interference duty ratio is as large as 50 per cent. In actual practice a somewhat larger rise in signal threshold power is obtained because one does not completely neglect the time elements occupied by the interference. In an intensity-modulated indicator the bright spots produced by the interference are annoying and fatiguing to the observer; they are, however, more of an annoyance than a real hazard to signal perception.

General methods of alleviating the pulsed interference effects consist in causing the interference to operate some device that, for the duration of the interfering pulse, desensitizes the receiver or indicator. In this way there is no perceptible indication of the interference; the desired signals can be seen under nearly normal conditions in the free intervals between interfering pulses. To remove only the interference so that the desired signal still remains, one must utilize some special characteristic of the interference. The three common characteristics of the interference that may differ from the characteristics of the desired signal are (1) the amplitude, (2) the radio frequency, and (3) the shape or length. These three characteristics suggest corresponding methods for interference suppression.

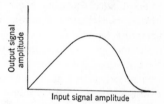

FIG. 12·14.—Response characteristic of typical pulse-amplitude discriminator.

Amplitude Discrimination.—Several devices have been developed to provide pulse-amplitude discrimination and selection. All of them have operated on the same principle, but the applications to receivers have differed. In all these devices a modification to the over-all receiver response characteristic has been made. The resulting characteristic is similar to that shown in Fig. 12·14: the response to input voltage larger than a given input amplitude is made zero. Thus if the receiver gain is so adjusted that all desired signals are of a size to give a satisfactory output, all interfering pulses of high intensity will be eliminated. Although it is true that an interfering pulse occurring simultaneously with a desired signal pulse will remove the signal, the fraction of time in which this happens is only the duty ratio of the interfering pulse.

The response characteristic shown in Fig. 12·14 can be produced in a number of ways. The normal video output of the receiver can be "swamped" by a video signal of opposite polarity, which at low signal level is made inoperative by an appropriate bias voltage. This swamping action can, if desired, be accomplished directly in the output of the second detector; in this case it is derived from a biased second detector of opposite polarity. Perhaps the simplest technique, however, is to use a video signal derived from one of the i-f stages to bias the grid of the following i-f stage; in this instance a strong input signal will bias the i-f stage to cutoff, and no output voltage will occur.

The principal difficulties with any of these schemes are of two kinds. (1) The desired signals actually have a large range in amplitude, and the amplitude-selection "slot" must therefore be made extremely wide. Under these conditions satisfactory removal of railing interference is not usually possible. (2) As was mentioned previously, railing interference consists of an intense leading pulse followed by a train of reflection echoes lasting for a number of microseconds. These trailing pulses, usually of much longer duration than the original interfering pulse, are nearly always of the same general size as the desired signal pulse and cannot therefore be removed by this procedure. These two difficulties can be overcome by a slightly different form of interference suppressor developed by Lawson. This suppressor, designed to combat railing interference, was required to remove completely the railing pulse together with its trailing echoes, without removing any desired (radar) pulse.

To remove the railing pulse and echoes, a "blanking gate" of controllable length was supplied; this gate was initiated by the interfering signal and could then be made long enough to remove the trailing echoes as well as the interfering pulse. To make sure desired radar pulses were not removed, a new system was devised. It is clearly desirable to trigger the gate from video signals in which the interfering pulses are enhanced by comparison with the desired signals. This enhancement can be assured by receiving the interfering pulses on a separate non-directional antenna. The scheme offers no improvement if the interference comes from the same direction as the desired signal; otherwise the improvement is proportional to the directional gain of the receiving antenna used for signal reception (radar antenna).

In spite of the separate nondirectional antenna and interference receiver the main transmitted radar pulse and close radar echoes will be strong enough to trigger the blanking gate unless a gate "deadener" is applied. This deadener can take the form of a multivibrator triggered from the main radar pulse, preventing operation of the blanking gate for a certain time after the transmitted radar pulse. This time can, of course, be controlled by the multivibrator time constant and can be adjusted so that the interference suppressor removes no radar echoes.

The interference suppressor system is shown in block form in Fig. 12·15. As shown in this diagram the interference receiver is of the superheterodyne type, using the same local oscillator as the signal receiver; this connection is desirable to obtain comparable sensitivity and selectivity in the two receivers. The other elements shown in this

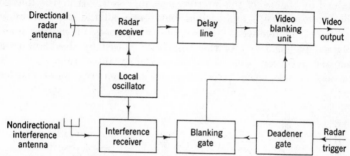

Fig. 12·15.—Elements of interference suppressor.

diagram are self-explanatory, with the exception of the delay line. The actual production of the blanking gate requires a small but finite time; the purpose of the delay line is to assure arrival of the blanking gate *before* the interfering pulse arrives through the signal channel. In this way all traces of the interference can be removed.

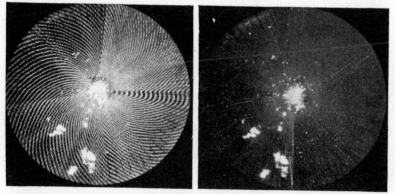

(*a*) PPI, 100-mile sweep; normal operation   (*b*) PPI, 100-mile sweep; suppressor in operation

Fig. 12·16.—Photographs illustrating the performance of the interference suppressor.

Typical results that can be obtained by the use of this interference suppressor are illustrated by the PPI photographs shown in Fig. 12·16. In these photographs the PPI sweep length represents 100 miles. The first photograph shows railing interference striations normally present as a result of the presence of many near-by radar sets, one of them located less than 100 ft away. Radar ground signals, i.e., signals from targets on the ground, are visible out to ranges of about 20 miles; some thunderstorm patches can be seen out to 90 miles. Several discrete aircraft echoes can be seen at various ranges.

The second photograph in Fig. 12·16 shows the great improvement obtained by the use of the interference suppressor. It is true that some railing interference is still visible, but nearly all the original annoying interference is removed. These remaining spots of interference are explained by inactivity of the suppressor caused by the blanking-gate generator recovery time after a preceding interfering pulse. This situation occurs when interfering pulses from two nonsynchronous

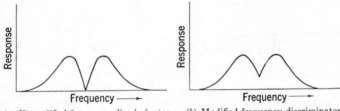

(a) Unmodified frequency discriminator   (b) Modified frequency discriminator
Fig. 12·17.—Frequency discrimination response curves.

transmitters nearly coincide in time and can be avoided by using a gate generator with extremely short recovery time.

No radar echoes need be lost by the use of this device. Echoes may be lost with the pulse-length-selection devices to be described shortly because a radar echo has a length that depends upon the nature and extent of the target under surveillance.

Frequency Discrimination.—We can discriminate between desired signal and interfering pulse by means of the radio frequency itself. The easiest way is to enhance the response of the interference receiver shown in Fig. 12·15 to off-frequency signals by using, for example, an ordinary frequency discriminator with subsequent pulse rectification. The pulse response of the over-all receiver to incoming pulses of various frequencies will be as shown in Fig. 12·17a. In this arrangement no blanking of (radar) echoes or interfering pulses exactly at the radar frequency will occur. If, however, the response is altered as shown in Fig. 12·17b, by adding to the response indicated in Fig. 12·17a the output from the unmodified receiver, blanking of on-frequency interference can be effected. The ratio of on-frequency interference to radar echo will be as high as in the unmodified receiver; this ratio will increase for off-frequency interference, thus providing more complete interference suppression. Hence frequency discrimination may be received as an additional aid and not as an alternative scheme to amplitude discrimination.

Pulse-shape Discrimination.—Radar echoes from discrete point targets have the same shape as the transmitted radar pulse. It is natural to inquire whether or not this information can be utilized to reduce the effect of interference with a different characteristic shape or even to reduce the signal threshold power in receiver noise. In the following discussion the radar pulse will be assumed to be of rectangular shape; the important "shape factor" is in this case simply the length of the pulse. A circuit can be constructed that will satisfactorily pass rectangular pulses of a critical length; pulses of a substantially different length will be completely rejected.

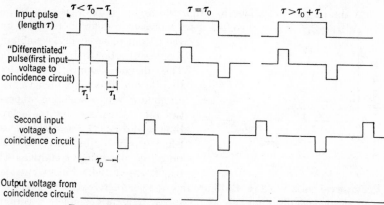

Fig. 12·18.—Waveforms illustrating pulse-length selection.

Let us consider the input video pulse of length τ applied to a "delay-line differentiator," whose function is to add to the input voltage wave an equal wave of opposite sign, which, however, is slightly delayed by a time τ_1. The output voltage from such a device will consist of two pulses, each having a duration τ_1 equal to the slight delay in time previously mentioned. These pulses will be of opposite sign and separated by the original input pulse length τ; they have an appearance suggested by the derivative of the input pulse. This two-pulse wave is next applied to a coincidence circuit; the other input voltage to the coincidence circuit is a replica of the two-pulse wave but reversed in sign and delayed by a fixed amount τ_0. The coincidence circuit is of a type in which the output voltage is the product of the two input voltages. With the arrangement just described the output of the coincidence circuit will register a pulse only if the original pulse length τ is close to τ_0; no output pulse will be registered at all if $\tau < \tau_0 - \tau_1$ or if $\tau > \tau_0 + \tau_1$ (see Fig. 12·18). The preceding result can be formulated in mathematical terms. Let the input video voltage function be represented by $f(t)$. The output of the line differentiator will be given by the expression $f(t) - f(t - \tau_1)$. The voltage output of the coincidence circuit can then be expressed as

$$E_{out} = [f(t) - f(t - \tau_1)][-f(t - \tau_0) + f(t - \tau_1 - \tau_0)]. \quad (18)$$

If we now insert the value of $f(t)$, we can evaluate E_{out}. Let us assume the input pulse to start at $t = 0$, to end at $t = \tau$, and to have an amplitude A. For this particular function one finds by means of Eq. (18) that

$$E_{out} = A^2 \begin{cases} \text{for } \tau_0 < t < \tau + \tau_1 & \text{if } \tau_0 - \tau_1 < \tau < \tau_0 \\ \text{for } \tau < t < \tau_0 + \tau_1 & \text{if } \tau_0 < \tau < \tau_0 + \tau_1. \end{cases} \quad (19)$$

Thus the output pulse length within the proper interval is seen to be simply $\tau_1 - |(\tau - \tau_0)|$; therefore if we represent the circuit response by

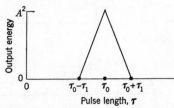

FIG. 12·19.—Response for pulse-selection circuit for input pulses of length τ.

the output pulse energy, we obtain the result shown in Fig. 12·19. This diagram shows graphically that the circuit is a pulse-length discriminator whose selection properties are determined by the delay time τ_0 and τ_1. These delay times being easily adjustable, a wide range of operating conditions is readily produced. Pulses outside the interval shown in Fig. 12·19 are rejected completely; this property of the pulse-length discriminator would appear to permit complete rejection of an interference pulse of length substantially different from the desired signal pulses.

In practice the rejection is not complete with respect to railing interference, nor is there the ideal response to all desired radar echo pulses shown in Fig. 12·19. This apparent failure of pulse-length discrimination is caused by two different effects. (1) Even though the input pulse to the receiver may have a defined length τ_0, the output video pulse has a different length, because of the finite rise time (or bandwidth) of the receiver and the video limiting action. For a nonlimited pulse, the video pulse length at one-half amplitude is approximately equal to the input pulse length; however, as soon as limiting sets in, the video pulse broadens. For very large input signals the broadening will generally be sufficient to cause complete rejection of the pulse. (2) The signals with which one deals are not necessarily discrete pulses; the interference also does not consist of rectangular pulses. In this event the desired signals will be largely rejected and some of the interference will be passed. This situation can be quantitatively calculated by using the proper voltage function $f(t)$ in Eq. (18); the output voltage will then usually not be zero for arbitrary interference voltage functions. Nevertheless, in spite of these difficulties, a pulse-length discriminator built by Ashby and Neher[1] has proved to be of the same order of effectiveness as the amplitude discriminator of Fig. 12·18. In this particular pulse-length discriminator the relatively narrow pulses from the coincidence unit were subsequently lengthened somewhat to permit easy visibility; and to avoid the pulse-broadening produced by limiting, a wide-band i-f amplifier was used.

The type of pulse-length discriminator just described is only one of many forms of shape-discriminators that can be considered; nevertheless it serves to illustrate the general effect expected. One can shape the signal pulse in special ways; for example, a series of pulses is often generated with a fixed sequence of lengths and intervals. A suitable pulse-shape discriminator can be made by using various appropriate delay lines; this type of discriminator is usually called a decoder; that is, it serves to decode the relatively complicated signal message. For any of these decoders the response can be calculated for any input voltage function by methods similar to that by which Eq. (18) was derived.

At the beginning of the discussion on pulse-shape discrimination an interesting question was raised regarding the possibility of reducing signal threshold power in receiver noise by the use of pulse-shape discrimination. At first sight it would appear that pulse-length discrimination would permit one preferentially to select desired signals from noise (which itself has no defined "length"). Unfortunately this does not seem to be the case, at least in the region where signals are not larger than noise itself. The reason is that when pulsed signals and noise become mixed, the mixture distorts the signal shape. This distortion is so severe that the pulse-length discrimination is of little value. In an actual experiment by R. M. Ashby and J. L. Lawson the signal threshold power measured on an A-scope was not perceptibly changed by the use of a pulse-length discriminator. This result might be different if the initial conditions were such as to cause the threshold signal to be considerably larger than noise, but this case was not investigated experimentally.

12·8. Randomly Spaced Interference Pulses.—In Sec. 12·7, a discussion was undertaken of railing interference, characterized chiefly by intense pulses of relatively low duty ratio. To combat the effects of this interference some form of discrimination between interference and desired signal is used to desensitize the indicator during periods of interference. The free time between interference pulses is then used for signal observation. None of the interference-suppression methods proposed are suit-

---

[1] R. M. Ashby and L. Neher, "Pulse Lengths Selector and Multiple Pulse Decoder." RL Report No. 917, Mar. 21, 1946.

able when the duty ratio of the interference becomes high and where the time interval between successive interference pulses becomes comparable to the signal pulse length (strictly, the reciprocal of the i-f bandwidth). In the limit where the interference pulse interval is extremely small compared with the reciprocal of i-f bandwidth, the interference is handled by the receiver just like c-w interference; in such circumstances methods for c-w interference suppression are often found helpful (see Secs. 12·1 to 12·4).

If the interference pulses are randomly spaced in time, one might expect a relatively large rise in signal threshold power because of the "noisy" appearance. This is only partially true. If the average pulse spacing is large compared with the reciprocal of the i-f bandwidth, many free intervals are available for signal detection. This form of interference is like railing interference and can be handled accordingly. If the average interference-pulse spacing is small compared with the reciprocal of i-f bandwidth, however, the output of the receiver will show amplitude noise fluctuations. This noise depends among other things upon the function that determines the interference-pulse spacing; whatever this function is, one finds the greatest similarity to nonlimited noise if the reciprocal of i-f bandwidth is extremely large compared with the average pulse spacing. For this condition the interference energy is spread over a relatively great band; the fraction falling within the receiver bandwidth is relatively small. Hence the interference is not generally so effective as some other forms of noisy interference.

CHAPTER 13

THRESHOLD MODULATIONS FOR AMPLITUDE-MODULATED AND FREQUENCY-MODULATED CONTINUOUS-WAVE SYSTEMS

13·1. Introduction.—In this chapter we shall discuss the problem of determining the minimum detectable modulation for a-m and f-m c-w systems. The problem has been investigated by Crosby[1] both experimentally and theoretically for the case that the carrier power is large compared to the noise power. Our main purpose is to extend the theoretical results of Crosby and to show how the application of the general methods of Chap. 7 lead to a unified treatment of the problem. For a description of the main parts of the receiver we refer to Chap. 2. For amplitude modulation only the superheterodyne receiver will be considered, whereas for frequency modulation only the case of complete amplitude limitation will be discussed in detail.

The modulation will be assumed to be sinusoidal, so that for amplitude modulation the signal will be represented by

$$S_A(t) = S_0(1 + \epsilon \cos 2\pi pt) \cos 2\pi f_c t, \tag{1}$$

where S_0 is the carrier amplitude, f_c the carrier frequency, p the modulation frequency, and ϵ the fractional modulation (*cf.* Sec. 2·1). The spectrum consists of the carrier and the two sidebands of amplitude $\epsilon S_0/2$.

For frequency modulation (*cf.* Sec. 2·3) the signal is represented by

$$S_F(t) = S_0 \cos \left(2\pi f_c t + \frac{\epsilon f_c}{p} \sin 2\pi pt \right). \tag{2}$$

The modulation index $\epsilon f_c/p$ will be assumed to be large, so that of the sidebands (frequencies $f_c \pm np$) only those which lie within the frequency excursion interval have appreciable intensity. The half width of the i-f amplifier will be assumed to be larger than the frequency excursion ϵf_c, so that the i-f amplification of the signal will not give rise to any appreciable deformation of the signal.

The main problem is to find the minimum detectable fractional modulation ϵ_{min} when the signal is disturbed by the presence of noise. To determine ϵ_{min} the *power criterion* will be used just as in Sec. 10·4. In the power spectrum of signal plus noise there will appear a signal peak at the

[1] M. G. Crosby, "Frequency Modulation Noise Characteristics," *Proc. I.R.E.*, **25**, 472 (1937).

frequency p and with power $\sim \epsilon^2$ superposed on a continuous background of noise. The signal peak will be just detectable if its power is of the same order of magnitude as the power of a segment of the continuous noise spectrum around the frequency p. The application of this power criterion will lead to ϵ_{min} expressed as a function of system parameters and of the ratio z of the unmodulated signal power to the noise power (*cf.* Sec. 7·3). The establishment of this function constitutes the main result of the theory.

13·2. The Minimum Detectable Amplitude Modulation.—For amplitude modulation all the necessary formulas have been derived already in Sec. 7·2. Only the case of the *linear* detector will be considered. The starting point is then Eq. (7·18), in which one has to substitute

$$\alpha_1 = S_0(1 + \epsilon \cos 2\pi pt), \qquad \beta_1 = 0,$$
$$\alpha_2 = S_0(1 + \epsilon \cos 2\pi p(t + \tau)), \qquad \beta_2 = 0.$$

The first term of Eq. (7·18) is developed in powers of ϵ. Keeping only terms up to ϵ^2, one obtains after averaging over the time t

$$\widetilde{I_1(1)I_2(2)} = \frac{\pi W}{2}[F^2 + \epsilon^2 zF(F' + 2zF'') + 2\epsilon^2 z^2 F'^2 \cos 2\pi p\tau + \cdots],$$

where $z = S_0^2/2W$, $F = F(-\frac{1}{2}, 1; -z)$, and the primes denote differentiations with respect to z.

In the further terms of Eq. (7·18), which are proportional to $\rho(\tau)$ and $\rho''(\tau)$, the modulation of the signal can be neglected. Using the recurrence relations for the hypergeometric function F (*cf.* Sec. 7·6), one obtains finally for the correlation function of signal plus noise

$$R(\tau) = \frac{\pi W}{2}\left(F^2\left(-\frac{1}{2}, 1; -z\right) + \frac{\epsilon^2 z^2}{2}F^2\left(\frac{1}{2}, 2; -z\right)\cos 2\pi p\tau\right.$$
$$+ \frac{z}{2}F^2\left(\frac{1}{2}, 2; -z\right)\rho(\tau) + \frac{1}{4}\rho^2(\tau)\left\{F^2\left(\frac{1}{2}, 1; -z\right) + \left[F\left(\frac{1}{2}, 1; -z\right)\right.\right.$$
$$\left.\left.\left. - F\left(\frac{1}{2}, 2; -z\right)\right]^2\right\}\right) \quad (3)$$

in which the contribution $\sim \epsilon^2$ in the d-c term has still been neglected.

With the help of the general formula [Eq. (7·26)] the audio spectrum of signal and noise can be deduced immediately from Eq. (3). The result is clear; the first two terms give the d-c peak and the signal peak at the frequency p; the third and fourth term give the continuous noise background. It is easy to show that for $W \to 0$ or $z \to \infty$ (3) goes over into

$$R(\tau) \xrightarrow[z \to \infty]{} S_0^2\left(1 + \frac{\epsilon^2}{2}\cos 2\pi pt\right),$$

which is the correlation function for the signal (1), whereas for $z \to 0$

$$R(\tau) \xrightarrow[z \to 0]{} \frac{\pi W}{2} \left[1 + \frac{1}{4} \rho^2(\tau) \right],$$

which is, up to terms $\sim \rho^2$, the correlation function of noise alone.

It should be emphasized that Eq. (3) is only an approximation, since terms of higher order than $\rho^2(\tau)$ and ϵ^2 have been neglected. The term $\sim \epsilon^4$ would give rise, for instance, to a discrete line at the frequency $2p$, so that although the detector is linear in the presence of noise, the harmonics of the signal will appear. It can be shown that the intensities of these harmonics go to zero both for $z \to \infty$ and for $z \to 0$. For our purposes they can be neglected.

The power criterion can now be applied. To be specific, we shall consider the case that the shape of the i-f pass band is rectangular of width B and that the audio spectrum is passed through a square low-pass audio filter of width $b \leqq \frac{1}{2}B$. The signal peak at frequency p has then to compete with the integral of the continuous noise spectrum from zero to b. Putting the ratio of the powers equal to a constant k, we obtain for the minimum detectable modulation $\epsilon_{\min}$ the result

$$(\epsilon_{\min}^2)_{am} = \frac{k}{z^2 F_2^2} \left\{ [F_1^2 + (F_1 - F_2)^2 + 2zF_2] \frac{b}{B} \right.$$
$$\left. - \frac{1}{2} \{F_1^2 + (F_1 - F_2)^2\} \frac{b^2}{B^2} \right\}, \quad (4a)$$

where $F_1 \equiv F(\frac{1}{2}, 1; -z)$, $F_2 \equiv F(\frac{1}{2}, 2; -z)$. The constant k has to be determined by experiment. In Fig. 13·1 $(\epsilon_{\min}^2)_{am}/k$ has been plotted as a function of z for the two cases $b/B = \frac{1}{2}$ and $b/B = \frac{1}{8}$. As is to be expected, $(\epsilon_{\min}^2)_{am}$ is a monotonic decreasing function of z, and it can be easily shown that for small z

$$(\epsilon_{\min}^2)_{am} \xrightarrow[z \to 0]{} \frac{k}{z^2} \frac{b}{B} \left(1 - \frac{b}{2B} \right) \qquad (4b)$$

whereas for large z

$$(\epsilon_{\min}^2)_{am} \xrightarrow[z \to \infty]{} \frac{2k}{z} \frac{b}{B}. \qquad (4c)$$

13·3. The Noise Spectrum for an F-m Receiver.—The calculation of the minimum detectable frequency modulation is more involved because the f-m receiver contains besides the detector a second nonlinear element, the amplitude limiter. We shall consider therefore first the spectrum of noise alone.

The output of the i-f amplifier can be represented by

$$N(t) = x(t) \cos 2\pi f_c t + y(t) \sin 2\pi f_c t$$
$$= \sqrt{x^2 + y^2} \cos \left(2\pi f_c t - \tan^{-1} \frac{y}{x} \right), \qquad (5)$$

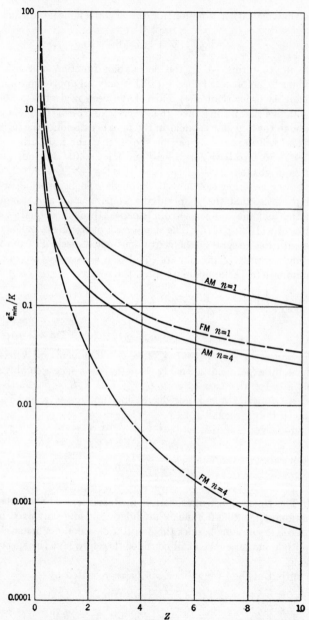

FIG. 13·1.—Minimum detectable modulation as a function of z for a-m and f-m systems and for different values of the deviation ratio $n = B/2b$.

where, when only noise is present, $x(t)$ and $y(t)$ are independent Gaussian random functions, with a spectrum determined by the shape of the i-f pass band (*cf.* Sec. 3·8 or 7·2). The output $N(t)$ enters now the amplitude limiter. Assuming strong amplitude limitation the result will be

$$N_1(t) = \cos\left(2\pi f_c t - \tan^{-1}\frac{y}{x}\right),$$

which is a wave of constant amplitude but with the variable angular frequency

$$\omega_N(t) = \frac{d}{dt}\left(2\pi f_c t - \tan^{-1}\frac{y}{x}\right) = 2\pi f_c + \frac{y\dot{x} - x\dot{y}}{x^2 + y^2}. \tag{6}$$

The slope filter transforms this variation in frequency into a variation in amplitude, so that its output will be a high-frequency wave with an envelope given by (6). With a *linear* second detector the final audio output will therefore be given by $\omega_N(t)$.

To find the audio spectrum one has first to calculate again the correlation function

$$R_N(\tau) = \overline{\omega_N(t)\omega_N(t+\tau)} = 4\pi^2 f_c^2 + 2\pi f_c\left(\overline{\frac{y_1\dot{x}_1 - x_1\dot{y}_1}{x_1^2 + y_1^2}}\right.$$
$$\left. + \overline{\frac{y_2\dot{x}_2 - x_2\dot{y}_2}{x_2^2 + y_2^2}}\right) + \left(\overline{\frac{y_1\dot{x}_1 - x_1\dot{y}_1}{x_1^2 + y_1^2}\frac{y_2\dot{x}_2 - x_2\dot{y}_2}{x_2^2 + y_2^2}}\right), \tag{7}$$

where the indices 1 and 2 refer to the two time points t and $t + \tau$ and where the ensemble averages have to be performed with the joint probability distribution of the eight variables x_1, y_1, $\dot{x}_1$, $\dot{y}_1$, x_2, y_2, $\dot{x}_2$, $\dot{y}_2$. Clearly, this probability distribution will be an eight-dimensional Gaussian distribution, which can be found with the method explained in Sec. 3·7. For the calculation of the averages in Eq. (7), it is best to keep the Gaussian distribution expressed as the Fourier transform of its characteristic function (*cf.* Sec. 3·5). Denoting the eight variables by $z_1, z_2, \ldots, z_8$, one can then write

$$W(z_1, z_2, \cdots, z_8) = \frac{1}{(2\pi)^8}\int\cdots\int_{-\infty}^{+\infty} dt_1\cdots dt_8 \exp$$
$$\left(-\frac{1}{2}\sum_{k,l} b_{kl}t_k t_l + i\sum_j z_j t_j\right), \tag{8}$$

where $b_{kl} = \overline{z_k z_l}$ can easily be calculated from the defining equations for $x(t)$ and $y(t)$ (*cf.* Secs. 3·7 and 3·8). With the same notation as used in Sec. 7·2, the results are

$$b_{11} = b_{22} = b_{55} = b_{66} = \sigma^2 \int_{-\infty}^{+\infty} df A^2(f) \equiv W,$$

$$b_{33} = b_{44} = b_{77} = b_{88} = 4\pi^2\sigma^2 \int_{-\infty}^{+\infty} df f^2 A^2(f) \equiv V,$$

$$b_{15} = b_{26} = \sigma^2 \int_{-\infty}^{+\infty} df A^2(f) \cos 2\pi ft \equiv U(\tau),$$

$$b_{17} = b_{28} = -b_{35} = -b_{46} = \frac{dU}{d\tau} \equiv \dot{U},$$

$$b_{37} = b_{48} = -\frac{d^2U}{d\tau^2} \equiv -\ddot{U}.$$

$$(9)$$

Clearly, the average values in the second and the third term of Eq. (7) are zero, since the functions, which have to be averaged, are odd. To calculate the fourth term of Eq. (7), the following 16-fold integral has to be evaluated:

$$\frac{1}{(2\pi)^8} \int_{-\infty}^{+\infty} \cdots \int dz_1 \cdots dz_8 \, dt_1 \cdots dt_8 \frac{z_1 z_4 - z_2 z_3}{z_1^2 + z_2^2} \frac{z_5 z_8 - z_6 z_7}{z_5^2 + z_6^2}$$

$$\exp\left(-\frac{1}{2}\sum_{k,l} b_{kl} t_k t_l + i \sum_j z_j t_j\right). \quad (10)$$

The integral over the variables $z_1 \ldots z_8$, which will be performed first, can be written as the product of two fourfold integrals of similar form. The first one is

$$\int_{-\infty}^{+\infty}\!\!\!\int\!\int\!\int \frac{z_1 z_4}{z_1^2 + z_2^2} \exp\left(i \sum_{j=1}^{4} z_j t_j\right) dz_1 \, dz_2 \, dz_3 \, dz_4$$

$$= -4\pi^2 i \delta(t_3) \delta'(t_4) \int_{-\infty}^{+\infty}\!\!\!\int \frac{z_1}{z_1^2 + z_2^2} e^{i(z_1 t_1 + z_2 t_2)} \, dz_1 \, dz_2 \quad (11)$$

using the integral representation

$$\delta(t) = \frac{1}{2\pi} \int_{-\infty}^{+\infty} dz \, e^{itz}$$

of the Dirac δ-function. The integrals over z_1 and z_2 can be performed by introducing polar coordinates $z_1 = r \cos\theta$, $z_2 = r \sin\theta$ and by using Eq. (7·61) for the integral over θ, and

$$\int_0^{\infty} dr \, J_1(kr) = \frac{1}{k}$$

for the integral over r.   The result is

$$\int\int\int_{-\infty}^{+\infty}\int \frac{z_1 z_4}{z_1^2 + z_2^2} \exp\left(i\sum_{j=1}^{4} z_j t_j\right) dz_1 \ldots dz_4 = (2\pi)^3 \delta(t_3)\delta'(t_4)\frac{t_1}{t_1^2 + t_2^2}.$$
(12)

The integral over $z_5 \ldots z_8$ is completely similar.   Introducing these results in Eq. (10), one sees that the integrals over t_3, t_4, t_7, and t_8 can be carried out immediately so that one is left with the fourfold integral

$$\frac{1}{4\pi^2}\int\int\int_{-\infty}^{+\infty}\int dt_1\, dt_2\, dt_5\, dt_6\, \frac{\ddot{U}(t_1 t_5 + t_2 t_6) + \dot{U}^2(t_2 t_5 - t_1 t_6)^2}{(t_1^2 + t_2^2)\,(t_5^2 + t_6^2)}$$

$$\exp\left[-\frac{W}{2}(t_1^2 + t_2^2 + t_5^2 + t_6^2) - U(t_1 t_5 + t_2 t_6)\right]. \quad (13)$$

By putting

$$t_1 = r\cos(\eta + \varphi), \qquad t_2 = r\sin(\eta + \varphi),$$
$$t_5 = l\cos\varphi, \qquad t_6 = l\sin\varphi,$$

the integrand becomes independent of φ, so that the integration gives 2π. The η integration can be carried out by means of Eq. (7·61), and the r integration by means of Eq. (7·62).   The hypergeometric functions $F(a, b; x)$ that appear at this stage of the calculation have positive integer values for a and b, so that they can be expressed in exponential functions and polynomials in x.   The last integration over l is elementary.

The final result is

$$R_N(\tau) = 4\pi^2 f_c^2 + \frac{1}{2}\left(\frac{\ddot{\rho}}{\rho} - \frac{\dot{\rho}^2}{\rho^2}\right)\log(1 - \rho^2), \quad (14)$$

where $\rho(\tau) = U(\tau)/W$ is again the normalized correlation function of the noise at the output of the i-f amplifier.   Since $\rho(\tau) \to 1$ when $\tau \to 0$, it follows from Eq. (14) that $R_N(\tau)$ becomes logarithmically infinite when τ approaches zero. The reason for this strange behavior is the fact that in the calculation, the width of the slope filter has not been limited.   At the output of the amplitude limiter, the instantaneous frequency will vary mainly in the i-f range, but occasionally [when $x(t)$ and $y(t)$ become small at the same time], the frequency can become very high.

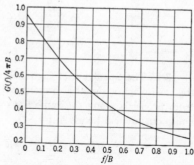

FIG. 13·2.—Noise spectrum for an f-m receiver.

With a slope filter of unlimited width one will therefore get very high peaks, which are responsible for the logarithmic infinity of the correlation function $R_N(\tau)$. In practice, the slope filter will have a finite width so that the peaks will be cut off, which will make the correlation function finite for $\tau = 0$. For small values of τ, Eq. (14) cannot therefore be trusted. However, since this will affect only the h-f part of the spectrum, it is not necessary to consider it for further calculations.

Assuming again the shape of the i-f pass band to be rectangular of width B, so that

$$\rho(\tau) = \frac{\sin \pi B\tau}{\pi B\tau},$$

one obtains from Eq. (14) the spectrum

$$G(f) = 2\pi B \int_0^\infty dx \cos \frac{2fx}{B} \frac{\sin^2 x - x^2}{x^2 \sin^2 x} \log \left(1 - \frac{\sin^2 x}{x^2} \right). \tag{15}$$

This integral has to be done numerically. The results are shown in Table 13·1, and the shape of the spectrum is shown in Fig. 13·2.

TABLE 13·1.—CONTINUOUS NOISE SPECTRUM FOR AN F-M RECEIVER

$\dfrac{f}{B}$	$\dfrac{G(f)}{4\pi B}$
0	0.955
0.1	0.816
0.2	0.698
0.3	0.586
0.4	0.501
0.5	0.428
0.6	0.373
0.7	0.329
0.8	0.295
0.9	0.266
1.0	0.242

13·4. The Spectrum of Signal Plus Noise for an F-m Receiver.—For the case when a signal is present with noise, the calculation of the spectrum proceeds along the same lines as for the case of noise alone. The audio output will be given by

$$\omega_{S+N}(t) = 2\pi f_0 + \frac{Y\dot{X} - X\dot{Y}}{X^2 + Y^2}, \tag{16}$$

where

$$\left. \begin{array}{l} X(t) = \alpha(t) + x(t), \\ Y(t) = \beta(t) + y(t), \end{array} \right\} \tag{17}$$

and

$$\left.\begin{aligned}
\alpha(t) &= S_0 \cos\left(\frac{\epsilon f_c}{p} \sin 2\pi p t\right), \\
\beta(t) &= -S_0 \sin\left(\frac{\epsilon f_c}{p} \sin 2\pi p t\right).
\end{aligned}\right\} \tag{18}$$

Here the assumption of a wide i-f pass band has been made, so that the signal is not deformed by the i-f amplifier and is still represented by Eq. (2) or by

$$S_F(t) = \alpha(t) \cos 2\pi f_c t + \beta(t) \sin 2\pi f_c t,$$

where $\alpha(t)$ and $\beta(t)$ are given by Eq. (18).

For the correlation function $R_{S+N}(\tau)$, one obtains an expression analogous to Eq. (7) except that $x(t)$ and $y(t)$ must be replaced by $X(t)$ and $Y(t)$; and in addition to the ensemble average, a time average over the initial time t has to be performed.

The ensemble averages of the second and third terms in the expression for $R_{S+N}(\tau)$ will not be zero as they were in the case of noise alone. Since the joint probability distribution of $X(t)$, $Y(t)$, $\dot{X}(t)$ and $\dot{Y}(t)$ is given by

$$W(X,Y,\dot{X},\dot{Y}) = \frac{1}{4\pi^2 W V} \exp\left[-\frac{(X-\alpha)^2 + (Y-\beta)^2}{2W}\right.$$
$$\left. -\frac{(\dot{X}-\dot{\alpha})^2 + (\dot{Y}-\dot{\beta})^2}{2V}\right],$$

where V and W have the same meaning as in Eq. (9), it is easily found that

$$\begin{aligned}
\overline{\frac{Y\dot{X} - X\dot{Y}}{X^2 + Y^2}} &= \frac{\beta\dot{\alpha} - \alpha\dot{\beta}}{\alpha^2 + \beta^2}\left(1 - e^{-\frac{\alpha^2+\beta^2}{2W}}\right) \\
&= 2\pi\epsilon f_c \cos 2\pi p t \left(1 - e^{-\frac{S_0^2}{2W}}\right).
\end{aligned} \tag{19}$$

It is clear that the time average of this expression is zero, and therefore, the second and third terms will not contribute to the final result for $R_{S+N}(\tau)$.

There remains the calculation of the term

$$\overline{\frac{Y_1\dot{X}_1 - X_1\dot{Y}_1}{X_1^2 + Y_1^2} \frac{Y_2\dot{X}_2 - X_2\dot{Y}_2}{X_2^2 + Y_2^2}}, \tag{20}$$

which is analogous to the fourth term in Eq. (7). The ensemble average can be carried out in the same way as in the previous section. The probability distribution of X_1, Y_1, $\dot{X}_1$, $\dot{Y}_1$, X_2, Y_2, $\dot{X}_2$, $\dot{Y}_2$ can again be found by the method explained in Sec. 3·7, and the result is similar to Eq. (8) except that in the integral the z_i have to be replaced by $Z_j - \sigma_j$, where the Z_j's denote the eight variables X_1, Y_1, $\dot{X}_1$, $\dot{Y}_1$, X_2, Y_2, $\dot{X}_2$, $\dot{Y}_2$, and the σ_1, σ_2, . . . , σ_8's stand for α_1, β_1, $\dot{\alpha}_1$, $\dot{\beta}_1$, α_2, β_2, $\dot{\alpha}_2$, $\dot{\beta}_2$, respectively. The integrals over Z_1, Z_2, . . . , Z_8 and over t_3, t_4, t_7, and t_8 can be performed in exactly the same way as in the case of noise alone. The remaining fourfold integral (over t_1, t_2, t_5, and t_6) is more complicated than Eq. (13). It is found to be

$$
\frac{1}{4\pi^2} \int\!\!\!\int\limits_{-\infty}^{+\infty}\!\!\!\int\!\!\!\int dt_1\, dt_2\, dt_5\, dt_6
$$

$$
\frac{\exp\left[-\dfrac{W}{2}(t_1^2 + t_2^2 + t_5^2 + t_6^2) - U(t_1 t_5 + t_2 t_6) - i(\alpha_1 t_1 + \beta_1 t_2 + \alpha_2 t_5 + \beta_2 t_6) \right]}{(t_1^2 + t_2^2)(t_5^2 + t_6^2)}
$$

$$
\{(\dot{\alpha}_1 \dot{\beta}_2 t_2 t_5 + \dot{\beta}_1 \dot{\alpha}_2 t_1 t_6 - \dot{\alpha}_1 \dot{\alpha}_2 t_2 t_6 - \dot{\beta}_1 \dot{\beta}_2 t_1 t_5) + [\dot{U}(t_1 t_5 + t_2 t_6)
$$
$$
+ \dot{U}^2(t_2 t_5 - t_1 t_6)^2] + i\dot{U}[\dot{\alpha}_1(t_1 t_2 t_6 - t_2^2 t_5) + \dot{\beta}_1(t_1 t_2 t_5
$$
$$
- t_1^2 t_6) + \dot{\alpha}_2(t_1 t_6^2 - t_2 t_5 t_6) + \dot{\beta}_2(t_2 t_5^2 - t_1 t_5 t_6)]\}. \quad (21)
$$

Since an exact evaluation of this integral does not seem feasible, a few approximations will be made at this stage. It is clear that the first term between the braces is proportional to ϵ^2 and will give rise to the signal peak in the spectrum of signal plus noise. Therefore, in this term we neglect the $U(\tau)$ and obtain

$$
\frac{1}{4\pi^2} \int\!\!\!\int\limits_{-\infty}^{+\infty}\!\!\!\int\!\!\!\int dt_1\, dt_2\, dt_5\, dt_6 \frac{\dot{\alpha}_1 \dot{\beta}_2 t_2 t_5 + \dot{\beta}_1 \dot{\alpha}_2 t_1 t_6 - \dot{\alpha}_1 \dot{\alpha}_2 t_2 t_6 - \dot{\beta}_1 \dot{\beta}_2 t_1 t_5}{(t_1^2 + t_2^2)(t_5^2 + t_6^2)}
$$
$$
\exp\left[-\frac{W}{2}(t_1^2 + t_2^2 + t_5^2 + t_6^2) - i(\alpha_1 t_1 + \beta_1 t_2 + \alpha_2 t_5 + \beta_2 t_6) \right]. \quad (22)
$$

This integral can be written as a linear combination of products of double integrals. Each double integral is of the same form as the one occurring in Eq. (11) and can therefore be evaluated easily. Thus, it is found that the fourfold integral (22) is equal to

$$
4\pi^2 \epsilon^2 f_c^2 (1 - e^{-\frac{S_0^2}{2W}})^2 \cos 2\pi p t \cos 2\pi p(t + \tau). \quad (23)
$$

The remaining terms between the braces in Eq. (21) will give rise to the continuous noise spectrum. In these terms, therefore, we shall neglect the modulation of the signal and put

$$
\alpha_1 = \alpha_2 = S_0, \qquad \beta_1 = \beta_2 = \dot{\alpha}_1 = \dot{\alpha}_2 = \dot{\beta}_1 = \dot{\beta}_2 = 0.
$$

These terms then reduce to the integral

$$\frac{1}{4\pi^2} \int\int\limits_{-\infty}^{+\infty}\int\int dt_1\, dt_2\, dt_5\, dt_6\, \frac{\dot{U}(t_1 t_5 + t_2 t_6) + \dot{U}^2(t_2 t_5 - t_1 t_6)^2}{(t_1^2 + t_2^2)(t_5^2 + t_6^2)}$$

$$\exp\left[-\frac{W}{2}(t_1^2 + t_2^2 + t_5^2 + t_6^2) - U(t_1 t_5 + t_2 t_6) - iS_0(t_1 + t_5)\right]. \quad (24)$$

Substituting in (24),

$$t_1 = R\sin\theta\cos(\eta + \varphi), \qquad t_2 = R\sin\theta\sin(\eta + \varphi),$$
$$t_5 = R\cos\theta\cos\varphi, \qquad t_6 = R\cos\theta\sin\varphi,$$

one sees that the integrations over φ and R can be carried out by means of Eqs. (7·61) and (7·62). The remaining two variables θ and η are then transformed into

$$x = \sin 2\theta\cos\eta, \qquad y = \sin 2\theta\sin\eta.$$

The integration over y is elementary, but the final integration over x can be reduced only to the integral logarithm $Ei(u)$, defined as

$$Ei(u) = \int_{-\infty}^{u} \frac{e^x}{x}\, dx,$$

where for positive u, the principle value of the integral has to be taken. The final result for the integral (24) can be written as

$$R_1(\tau) + R_2(\tau) + R_3(\tau),$$

where

$$R_1(\tau) = \frac{\dot{\rho}^2}{2\rho^2}\left[1 - e^{-\frac{z}{\rho}}\left(\frac{\ddot{\rho}\rho}{\dot{\rho}^2} + \frac{z}{\rho} - 1\right)Ei\left(\frac{z}{\rho}\right)\right], \quad (25a)$$

$$R_2(\tau) = \frac{\dot{\rho}^2}{2\rho^2}\left[-\frac{2e^{-z}}{1 - \rho} + 2e^{-\frac{z}{\rho}}\left(\frac{\ddot{\rho}\rho}{\dot{\rho}^2} + \frac{z}{\rho} - 1\right)Ei\left(\frac{1 - \rho}{\rho}z\right)\right] \quad (25b)$$

$$R_3(\tau) = \frac{\dot{\rho}^2}{2\rho^2}\left[\frac{1 + \rho}{1 - \rho}e^{-\frac{2z}{1+\rho}} - e^{-\frac{z}{\rho}}\left(\frac{\ddot{\rho}\rho}{\dot{\rho}^2} + \frac{z}{\rho} - 1\right)Ei\left(\frac{1 - \rho}{1 + \rho}\frac{z}{\rho}\right)\right] \quad (25c)$$

and $z = S_0^2/2W$.

The average over the time t affects only Eq. (23). With all these approximations, the correlation function for signal plus noise becomes

$$R_{S+N}(\tau) = 4\pi^2 f_c^2 + 2\pi^2\epsilon^2 f_c^2(1 - e^{-z})^2 \cos 2\pi p\tau + R_1(\tau) + R_2(\tau) + R_3(\tau) \quad (26)$$

with R_1, R_2, R_3 given by (25). Equation (26) is the analogue of Eq. (3) for the case of frequency modulation. Since for small u

$$Ei(u) = \log u + C + u + \frac{1}{2}\frac{u^2}{2!} + \cdots,$$

it is easy to show that for $z \to 0$, $R_{s+N}(\tau)$ goes over into $R_N(\tau)$ as given by Eq. (14).   For large u

$$Ei(u) = \frac{e^u}{u}\left(1 + \frac{1!}{u} + \frac{2!}{u^2} + \cdots\right),$$

from which it follows that for large z

$$R_1(\tau) \cong -\frac{1}{2}\frac{\ddot{\rho}}{z} + (\dot{\rho}^2 + \ddot{\rho}\rho)\frac{1}{2z^2} + \cdots . \qquad (27)$$

whereas $R_2(\tau)$ and $R_3(\tau)$ go to zero for $z \to \infty$ as $\exp(-z)$ and $\exp(-2z/(1 + \rho))$, respectively, so that they will be negligible compared with $R_1(\tau)$ The first two terms in (26) become, of course, for $z \to \infty$ the correlation function for the signal alone.

The spectrum $G_{s+N}(f)$ follows from (26) by a numerical integration. Again we have assumed a rectangular i-f pass band of width B and have calculated the spectrum for $z = 1.5$ and for $z = 10$.   The results are presented in Tables 13·2 and 13·3 and are shown in Figs. 13·3 and 13·4.

TABLE 13·2.—PARTIAL SPECTRA AND TOTAL CONTINUOUS SPECTRUM OF SIGNAL PLUS NOISE FOR $z = 1.5$

$\dfrac{f}{B}$	$\dfrac{G_1(f)}{4\pi B}$	$\dfrac{G_2(f)}{4\pi B}$	$\dfrac{G_3(f)}{4\pi B}$	$\dfrac{G_{s+N}(f)}{4\pi B}$
0	−0.001	−0.001	0.136	0.134
0.2	0.108	−0.051	0.125	0.182
0.3	0.236	−0.106	0.113	0.243
0.4	0.405	−0.149	0.092	0.348
0.6	0.081	0.021	0.014	0.116
0.8	0.037	0.130	−0.071	0.096
0.85	0.015	0.166	−0.089	0.092
1.0	−0.083	0.291	−0.132	0.076

TABLE 13·3.—PARTIAL SPECTRA OF SIGNAL PLUS NOISE FOR $z = 10$

$\dfrac{f}{B}$	$\dfrac{G_1(f)}{4\pi B}$		$\dfrac{G_2(f)}{4\pi B} \times 10^3$	$\dfrac{G_3(f)}{4\pi B} \times 10^3$
0	0		−0.0013	0.0151
0.1	0.0033			
0.2	0.0132		−0.0034	0.0146
0.3	0.0294			
0.4	0.0520		−0.0078	0.0138
0.5	0.0809	0.0023		
0.6		0.0027	−0.0112	0.0109
0.7		0.0028		
0.8		0.0025	−0.0108	0.0078
0.9		0.0017		
1.0		0.0004	−0.0070	0.0043

The quantities $G_1(f)$, $G_2(f)$, $G_3(f)$ are the spectra corresponding to $R_1(\tau)$, $R_2(\tau)$, and $R_3(\tau)$, respectively. For large z, only $G_1(f)$ is of importance; for $z = 10$, it has a discontinuity at $f/B = 0.5$. For small z, all three spectra contribute in a rather erratic fashion. The total continuous spectrum (represented by Curve 4 in Fig. 13·3) clearly has a shape intermediate between the shape of the pure noise spectrum (Fig. 13·2) and the shape of the spectrum for $z = 10$ (represented by Curve 1 in Fig. 13·4,

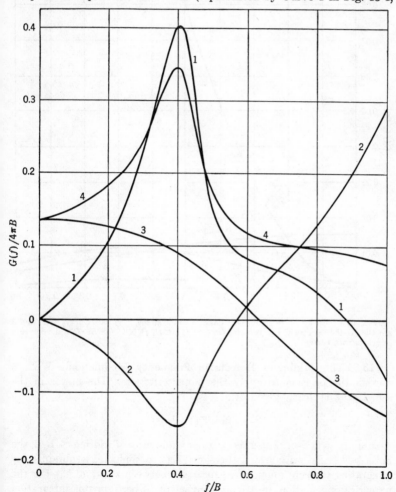

FIG. 13·3.—Spectrum of signal plus noise in f-m systems; $z = 1.5$. Curves 1, 2, and 3 are the partial spectra $G_1(f)/4\pi B$, $G_2(f)/4\pi B$, and $G_3(f)/4\pi B$. Curve 4 is the total spectrum $G(f)/4\pi B$.

since the contributions of $G_2(f)$ and $G_3(f)$ are negligible). In addition to these continuous spectra, there are, of course, the d-c peak and the signal peak at frequency p, which follow from the first two terms in Eq. (26).

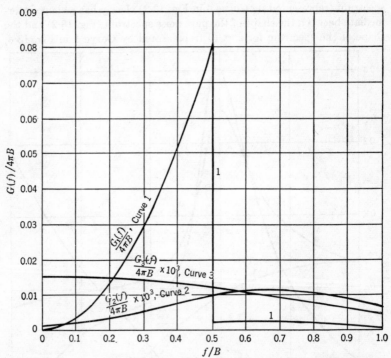

Fig. 13·4.—Spectrum of signal plus noise in f-m systems, $z = 10$. Curves 1, 2, and 3 are the partial spectra $G_1(f)/4\pi B$, $G_2(f) \times 10^3/4\pi B$, $G_3(f) \times 10^3/4\pi B$. Total spectrum coincides with Curve 1.

13·5. The Minimum Detectable Frequency Modulation.

We are now in the position to apply the power criterion. The power in the signal peak is clearly given by

$$P_S = 2\pi^2 \epsilon^2 f_c^2 (1 - e^{-z})^2. \tag{28}$$

Assuming, as in Sec. 13·2, a rectangular audio filter of width $b \leqq B/2$, the noise power P_N, with which the signal has to compete, is obtained by integrating the continuous noise spectrum between zero and b. For the numerical calculation, it is more convenient to perform this integration before carrying out the Fourier transformation of the correlation function (26). The noise power can then be written as the single integral

$$P_N = 2\pi B^2 \int_0^\infty dx \; \frac{\sin \dfrac{x}{n}}{x} \left\{ \frac{\dot{\rho}^2}{2\rho^2} \left(\frac{1+\rho}{1-\rho} e^{-\frac{2z}{1+\rho}} - \frac{2e^{-z}}{1-\rho} + 1 \right) \right.$$

$$\left. + \frac{e^{-\frac{z}{\rho}}}{2\rho^3} (\ddot{\rho}\rho^2 - \dot{\rho}^2\rho + \dot{\rho}^2 z) \left[2Ei\left(\frac{1-\rho}{\rho} z\right) - Ei\left(\frac{z}{\rho}\right) - Ei\left(\frac{1-\rho}{1+\rho}\frac{z}{\rho}\right) \right] \right\},$$

$$\tag{29}$$

where $\rho(x) = \sin x / x$ and the dots denote differentiations with respect to x. The symbol $n = B/2b$; in the paper by Crosby, this is referred to as the deviation ratio.

In order to make a fair comparison between the a-m and the f-m systems, it is better to replace ϵ in Eq. (28) by

$$\epsilon_{fm} = \frac{2\epsilon f_c}{B}. \tag{30}$$

Putting the ratio of P_S to P_N equal to a constant k, it is then found that

$$(\epsilon_{\min}^2)_{fm} = \frac{2kP_N}{\pi^2 B^2 (1 - e^{-z})^2}, \tag{31a}$$

TABLE 13·4.—MINIMUM DETECTABLE MODULATION FOR A-M AND F-M SYSTEMS FOR DIFFERENT VALUES OF $z = S_0^2/2W$ AND OF $n = B/2b$

z	$\dfrac{\epsilon_{\min}^2}{k}$			
	A-m, $n = 1$	F-m, $n = 1$	A-m, $n = 4$	F-m, $n = 4$
$\to 0$	$3/8z^2$	$1/1.2z^2$	$15/128z^2$	$1/3.62z^2$
0.1	37.5	83.4	11.7	27.6
0.2	13.5	20.8	3.89	6.9
0.3	6.96	9.71	1.97	2.83
1.5	0.769	0.433	0.199	0.072
3.0	0.352	0.124	0.090	0.011
8.0	0.125	....	0.031	
10	0.10	0.033	0.025	0.00052
$\to \infty$	$1/z$	$1/3z$	$1/4z$	$1/192z$

which must be compared with Eq. (4). The noise power P_N has been calculated numerically for $n = 1$ and $n = 4$ and for different values of z. The corresponding results for $(\epsilon_{\min}^2)_{fm}$ are presented in Table 13·4, where the values of $(\epsilon_{\min}^2)_{am}$ computed from Eq. (4) are also recorded, and both are shown in Fig. 13·1. It is clear that for large z, the f-m system is better than the a-m system. The factor is $3n^2$, which can be seen as follows: For large z, $R_2(\tau)$ and $R_3(\tau)$ can be neglected in Eq. (26), whereas the first term in the asymptotic series (27) can be used for $R_1(\tau)$. This gives for P_N

$$P_N \cong -\frac{\pi B^2}{z}\int_0^\infty dx\,\ddot\rho(x)\,\frac{\sin\dfrac{x}{n}}{x} = \frac{\pi^2 B^2}{6n^3 z}$$

since $\rho(x) = \sin x/x$. Substitution in Eq. (31) leads to

$$(\epsilon^2_{\min})_{fm} \xrightarrow[z\to\infty]{} \frac{k}{3n^3 z}, \tag{31b}$$

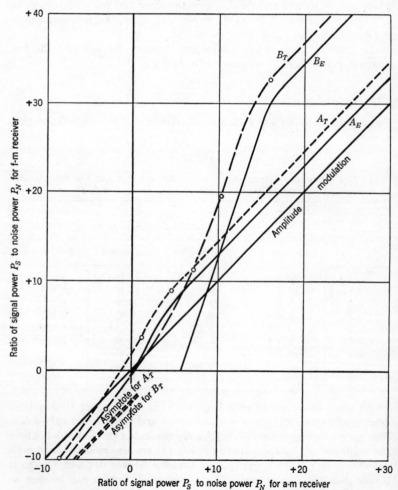

Fig. 13·5.—Comparison of a-m systems with f-m systems for different values of the deviation ratio $n = B/2b$; A_E and A_T are the experimental and theoretical curves for $n = 1$; B_E and B_T are the same for $n = 4$.

which has to be compared with Eq. (4c). This shows that for large z, the f-m system is better by the factor $3n^2$ or by 4.76 db for $n = 1$ and by 16.8 db for $n = 4$. This is in agreement with the theoretical results of Crosby.

For small z, the correlation function $R_N(\tau)$ for noise alone can be used in the calculation of P_N. Since P_N will now be only a function of n, it follows from Eq. (31a) that $(\epsilon_{\min}^2)_{fm}$ will become inversely proportional to z^2. The proportionality factor, however, has to be calculated numerically for the different values of n. Thus, it is found that for $z \to 0$

$$(\epsilon_{\min}^2)_{fm} \xrightarrow[z \to 0]{} \begin{cases} \dfrac{k}{1.2z^2} & \text{for } n = 1, \\[2mm] \dfrac{k}{3.62z^2} & \text{for } n = 4, \end{cases} \tag{31c}$$

which has to be compared with Eq. (4b). For small z, therefore, the a-m system is better than the f-m system by the factor 2.22 (or 3.46 db) for $n = 1$ and by the factor 2.36 (or 3.73 db) for $n = 4$.

TABLE 13·5.—SIGNAL-TO-NOISE RATIO FOR F-M AND A-M SYSTEMS FOR DIFFERENT VALUES OF z

z	Deviation ratio $n = 1$		Deviation ratio $n = 4$	
	Abscissa a-m system	Ordinate f-m system	Abscissa a-m system	Ordinate f-m system
$\to \infty$	......	4.76 db above a-m	......	16.8 db above a-m
10	......	......	15.92	32.6
3	4.54	9.08	10.45	19.6
1.5	1.14	3.64	7.02	11.4
0.3	−8.43	−9.87	− 2.94	− 4.51
$\to 0$	......	3.46 db below a-m	......	3.72 db below a-m

The results are presented in another way in Fig. 13·5 (based on Table 13·5), where the ratio of the signal power P_S to the noise power P_N for frequency modulation is plotted against the same ratio for amplitude modulation. Both abscissa and ordinate are expressed in decibels. The unmodulated signal-to-noise ratio z is (in Fig. 13·5) simply a parameter. It is clear that the a-m system gives a 45° line. The two dotted curves, marked A_T and B_T, are the theoretical curves for the f-m system for $n = 1$ and $n = 4$. The two solid curves, marked A_E and B_E, represent the experimental results found by Crosby.[1]

[1] "Frequency Modulation Noise Characteristics," *Proc. IRE*, **25**, 803 (1937), Fig. 10.

Index